马小跳的身上寄予了我的教育理想、对家庭教育和学校教育及当今教育现状的思考，有对童年的理解，对孩子天性的理解，还有做老师、做母亲的亲身体验。我希望让孩子们感到马小跳是他们中间的伙伴，能活在孩子们的心中。

给小读者阅读和写作的贴心指导

杨红樱

作品精选导读

杨红樱/著

王泉根/主编

乔世华/导读

淘气包马小跳系列

浙江出版联合集团
浙江少年儿童出版社

杨红樱

和她的淘气包马小跳

"马小跳一直是我想写的一个儿童形象，可以说，他是我的理想，我在他的身上，寄予了太多的东西：比如我的教育理想，我对当今教育的思考，我对童年的理解，对孩子天性的理解，这里还包括我做老师、做母亲的体验。我笔下的马小跳是一个真正的孩子，我想通过这个真正的孩子，呈现出一个完整的童心世界。"正是因为理想的投射和爱意的凝结，杨红樱笔下的马小跳，自2003年诞生以来，已然成为一个家喻户晓的儿童形象，一个被一代又一代孩子视为同龄人的心灵伙伴。

马小跳是一个快乐的孩子，他拥有着快乐的能力，在生活中遭遇各种各样的问题他都能保持健康快乐的心态。

马小跳是一个真正的孩子，他爱玩爱闹，爱哭爱笑，闯祸不止，成绩一般，但是却有情有义、真诚动人，小读者在他的身上能找到成长的力量。

"淘气包马小跳系列"展示了这样一个孩子完整的成长过程。凡是孩子在成长中必须受到的教育，其中包括生活的理念、人生的追求、做人的品质、社会的责任感等等，杨红樱都通过马小跳的童心世界淋漓尽致地展现了出来。

跟着马小跳，让我们一起触摸童心，回归童年。

珍藏相册

杨红樱

记录如歌岁月

Wanghongying

放飞儿童的精神与梦想 »»»

——序"杨红樱作品精选导读"丛书

王泉根

　　杨红樱的名字已成为新世纪中国儿童文学的一根标杆、一个符号、一道风景。她的作品发行量累计超过 4000 万册，多部作品签约全球多语种版权，创下中国当代儿童文学走向世界的奇迹；她所创造的"马小跳"、"笑猫"等形象，受到孩子们发自内心的广泛喜爱，杨红樱本人也因此受到孩子们明星一般的追捧。在少儿出版、发行界，杨红樱则被视为"救市"的财神。前不久在江西南昌举行的全国少儿图书交易会上，有一位书店总经理忧心忡忡地这样说："杨红樱三年不写书，我们卖什么？"一语哗然，让无数少儿出版人为之心悸。

　　人们不禁要问：杨红樱究竟靠什么掀起了一场新世纪中国原创儿童文学看不见的风暴？靠什么拉动了中国少儿出版业的杠杆？对此，人们可以从不同角度加以探讨。作为一名职业儿童文学教学研究工作者，我愿从儿童文学自身的规律，从儿童阅读那些最基本、最核心的层面，来加以剖析。

　　我认为杨红樱之所以能获得成功，其秘诀就是一句话：

全心全意为儿童服务，具体地说就是认准"为小学生年龄段服务的童年文学"不动摇。

一

儿童阅读有一条黄金定律："什么年龄段的孩子看什么书。"虽然大家都在为儿童写作，为儿童出版，为儿童服务，但如果没有具体、明确的服务对象，则会事倍功半，甚至吃力不讨好，适得其反。什么是儿童？对"儿童"最权威最科学的界说是1989年联合国大会通过的《儿童权利公约》的规定："儿童系指十八岁以下的任何人。"但十八岁以下的儿童是一个由不同年龄段的孩子组成的综合体，因此，儿童文学的具体接受对象实际上是包括了从三至六岁的学龄前的幼儿和到十六七岁的"准青年"。

由于各个年龄段孩子的身心特征、思维特征、社会化特征存在着极大的差异，对各自所需的文学在题材内容、艺术形式、表现手法乃至语言运用等方面都有着不同的要求，因此儿童文学必须适应不同年龄阶段的少年儿童主体结构的同化机能，必须在各个方面契合"阶段性"读者对象的接受心理与领悟能力，这就是"什么年龄段的孩子看什么书"。深了，孩子看不懂，对阅读产生排斥、畏惧心理，逃避阅读，讨厌读书；浅了，孩子则会产生逆反心理。"我都这么大了，还看这些？"认为是把自己当成弱智、低能儿。所以，儿童文学的"度"最难把握。茅盾曾不无感慨地说："儿童文学最难写，试看自古至今，全世界有名的作家有多少，其中儿童文学作家却只有寥寥可数的几个。"原因就在这里。

据此，儿童文学审美创造也有一条自身的黄金定律，这就是根据不同年龄段少年儿童年龄特征的差异性，将广义的儿童文学细分为三个层次：为幼儿园小朋友服务的"幼年文学"，为小学生年龄段服务的"童年文学"，为中学生年龄段服务的"少年文学"。对此，杨红樱有着相当清醒的理解与把握，她说："小孩子一天一个样，五岁和四岁、六岁和五岁都不一样，小孩子的认知程度也就不一样。"这就要求儿童文学作家必须"具备一定的儿童心理学和儿童教育学的专业素养，才能顾及不同年龄特征孩子的认知程度、接受程度。"

三个层次构成了儿童文学的统一性与完整性，缺一不可，各有其充分的美学价值与艺术地位。但三个层次中的核心层次、主体文学则是为小学生年龄段服务的童年文学。这不仅因为从六七岁到十二三岁的小学生年龄段的孩子是构成"儿童"的主体，而且他们实质上是儿童文学、儿童读物潜在的主体读者群与最大的少儿图书消费群体。

第一，与中学生相比，应试教学的压力对他们还不大，他们还有大量的课余时间可以自由阅读；第二，当今中小学语文教学改革与"新课标"的实施，要求小学生要有数百万字的课外阅读量，由此敞开了儿童文学直接进入校园的渠道；第三，小学生比之幼儿园小朋友，他们已经长大，可以自己选择、自己购买喜欢的图书；第四，更重要的是，小学生年龄段的孩子正处于长知识、长身体的黄金时期，是记忆力最强、想象力最丰富、求知欲最旺盛、精力最充沛的时期，是人生"多梦的时期"，是一生中最佳的读书时期。

因此，如何做好做大做强为小学生年龄段服务的童年文学，自然成了儿童文学原创生产与图书出版的重中之重。实

品藏版

际上，当下一些牛气冲天的少儿出版社的畅销品牌无一不是冲着小学生、做着童年文学的，如浙江少年儿童出版社的"冒险小虎队系列"，二十一世纪出版社的"郑渊洁童话系列"，安徽少年儿童出版社的"虹猫蓝兔七侠传系列"，明天出版社的"笑猫日记系列"、接力出版社的"淘气包马小跳系列"，等等。人民文学出版社的"哈利·波特系列"的主要读者也多为小学生。童年文学应当居于整个少儿文学创作与出版的核心地位，这是符合儿童文学供需关系与生态特征的。

杨红樱的可敬之处、聪明之处就在于此。虽然杨红樱从十九岁就开始发表作品，写过幼儿文学、科幻读物，但她最投入、最忘我、最花精力与智慧的就是童年文学。这一方面既与她曾经担任过七年小学语文教师、七年少儿读物编辑，对孩子们精神成长的需求有着刻骨铭心的了解有关；另一方面更与她认准的儿童文学观、儿童文学创作理念密切相关。她所创作的校园小说"淘气包马小跳系列"、人文童话"笑猫日记系列"，以及《男生日记》、《女生日记》、《漂亮老师和坏小子》等成长小说系列，《寻找美人鱼》等科学童话系列，其核心读者就是面向小学生。

杨红樱是全心全意地而不是半心半意、三心二意地为小学生年龄段的孩子们服务的，她深情地说："我对儿童心理学和儿童教育学有深入研究，我懂得孩子的心理特征。孩子阅读时，几乎会把自己放进一个角色中，好的儿童书就是要满足他们的想象力，满足他们的求知欲，满足他们心灵成长的需要。要让孩子们爱上阅读，这是童书作家的责任。我写马小跳其实就是写给小学生看的。""我最大的愿望就是破解童心。有小读者来信说：这个愿望，你已经实现了。我将小读者的这些话视为对我的最高褒奖。"

二

或许有人会说，童年文学的重要性与出版价值这是显而易见的，圈内人谁不想这么做？但为什么似乎只有杨红樱做大做强了呢？这其中的奥秘又是什么？我认为，如果要说杨红樱在童年文学方面已经积累了成功经验的话，倒不如说她是迎难而上，在重重困难甚至是在嘲笑与蔑视中走出了一条属于她自己的路。因为，事实是：在儿童文学三个层次的审美创造中，童年文学最难写，而且在以往最少有人愿意写。

我们先来看幼年文学。幼年文学表面上是为了幼儿，实际上是写给大人（家长、教师）看的。由于幼儿处于启蒙时期，还没有形成独立阅读能力，因而幼年文学主要是通过"亲子共读"的方式由家长和老师讲读给幼儿听，这是一种以"听"为特色的听赏文学。幼年文学首先是由大人阅读接受，再经由大人的挑选、理解、过滤之后，转述给幼儿。从这个角度说，幼年文学的"度"是比较容易把握的。

同样，少年文学的"度"也比较容易把握。少年文学以中学生为主体接受对象，中学生已有相当程度的文学阅读鉴赏能力，他们正在快速地成长与成熟，他们的关注兴趣、阅读兴趣正在向成人社会与成人文学靠拢。事实上，已有不少中学生的书包里放的是成人文学作品了。因而少年文学的审美创造整体上已与成人文学相互融通。作家主体意识的诉求、创作手法的多样化、人物形象的典型化，使少年文学最易在儿童文学三个层次中呈现出"纯文学"与"深度文学"的特色。

比较而言，童年文学的"度"最难把握，最难写。因为这是提供给已有一定文学阅读能力但又处于"初级阶段"的小学生接受的文学。小学生接受文学的最大特点是"自主性"——自己选择、自己阅读、自己理解。与幼儿园小朋友相比，他们已不需要大人在一旁陪读，已有自我阅读的能力与读完一部长篇作品后的成就感。但与中学生相比，他们的文学修养与阅读理解能力毕竟还很有限，他们的思维特征还处于对现实和幻想不是分得很清楚的阶段，社会化程度还相当低。他们的可塑性最大，也是最淘气、最需要大人操心的时期，正如四川民间俗语所说，"七（岁）嫌八不爱九臭十难闻"。

小学生年龄段孩子的这些特点决定了童年文学写作的难度：深了不行，浅了更不行；完全是虚构幻想，不靠谱，完全是现实生活的投影，又不易理解。同时，在儿童文学圈内，又长期存在着视童年文学为"平庸"、"肤浅"的偏见，认为难以呈现作家的深度主体意识。然而，童年文学对于小学生的意义又非同一般，如果这一时期的孩子不喜欢文学阅读，从不看童话，那就会讨厌读书，害怕作文，甚至终生排斥阅读。

杨红樱深谙童年文学的个中三昧及其所承载的巨大的文化价值与教育意义，她是以一种彻底的奉献精神来对待小学生的文学需求的。她对童年文学创作有着极高的要求："我对于自己的要求是：如果有下一本的话，一定要比前一本写得好，绝不硬写，所以写作的时候我常有如履薄冰的感觉。"

"我写的书是给孩子看的，书中塑造的人物形象或者动物形象，比如马小跳，比如笑猫，还有书中的故事，能成为他们童年的记忆，书中的内涵能成为他们成长的力量，对我而言，这就是一部成功的作品。"

经过多年探索，杨红樱已积累起了童年文学创作的新鲜经验，她说："我是一个坚持'儿童本位'的作者，我努力想要追求的是在我的作品里能够把对儿童的性情培养、知识传递、有趣的故事有机融合在一起，兼容情商、智商、玩商这三方面的元素，其实这是一种高难度的写作。""好的儿童文学作品，必须具备在读者心中立得起来的形象和引人入胜的故事。""让读者品味出丰富的内涵，这是我一直坚持的观点。"集中起来就是三点：一是要有好看的故事；二是要有记得住的人物形象；三是看了能感动。这些朴素实在的体验，远胜于那些《文学理论教程》的滔滔宏论。

我们的文学作品，如果真有引人入胜、欲罢不能的情节，读之难忘、鲜活丰满的形象，感动人、感染人、感悟人的内涵，怎么会不受读者的欢迎？怎么会不产生文学的精神灯火与生命营养的作用？问题是我们的文学似乎已经丢弃了文学之所以为文学的那些最基本最常态的东西，文学的滑坡乃至"死亡"也就难免了。

从整体上看，杨红樱童年文学的创作基调阳光、健朗、向上，作品风格明亮、幽默、晓畅，在引人入胜的故事情节中机智地恰到好处地融入一些易于为孩子们理解接受的立人、做事、为学的人生道理，启人思悟，引人向上，导人向善。事实证明，这实在是童年文学创作的高明手法。

比如"淘气包马小跳系列"中的《巨人的城堡》，在极

具童话氛围、悬念迭出的精彩故事中，演绎了孩子们与有着严重心理障碍的"巨人"之间的沟通、同情与友谊，使人一读难忘。杨红樱自己说："《巨人的城堡》其实就写到了后工业时代出现的问题是人的心理问题，而不是生理、生存问题。我写东西，是要滋养孩子的心灵成长，要展现一个孩子完整的成长过程。凡是孩子成长中必须要接受的教育，我都要通过马小跳的童心世界来展示出来。"

又比如"笑猫日记系列"中的《塔顶上的猫》：因为嫉妒塔顶上虎皮猫的成功，众猫使尽了坏招："我们上不去，别的猫也休想上去！就算有谁上去了，我们也要把她灭掉！"嫉妒产生的摩擦甚至仇恨，实在令人心悸。但塔顶上那只高贵的、优雅的虎皮猫，在疗救好自己的伤痛以后却悄然地离开了塔顶，她不愿成为被无数的花鹭围绕着的耀眼人物，而对嫉妒她的同类，表现出了超然物外的极大宽容。"笑猫日记系列"所要表达与倡扬的正是这一类的精神：与人为善，人与人之间应有的理解、同情、友善、帮助、责任、道义，以诚相待，以心换心，建构起温情脉脉的人性谱系，让人性的光辉战胜邪恶，照彻四方。

儿童文学的终极目标是要通过艺术的形象化途径，在下一代心里打下坚实的人之为人的人性基础。杨红樱的童年文学正是努力践行这一美学目的的精彩之作，或者说这正是杨红樱童年文学具有强大艺术魅力、令无数小读者和他们身边的大读者爱不释手的深层次的美学因素。

三

由于多种原因，长期以来我国儿童文学原创生产存在着"两头大、中间小"的局面，即服务中学生年龄段的"少年文学"与服务幼儿园小朋友的"幼年文学"，作家队伍强大，作品产量质量可喜可观，但服务小学生年龄段的"童年文学"，则是势单力薄、佳作寥寥。使人欣慰的是，进入新世纪以来，一个多元共生、百花齐放、百鸟和鸣的儿童文学和谐格局正在形成。以杨红樱为代表的童年文学创作的异军突起，有力而有效地改变了我国儿童文学"两头大、中间小"的艺术格局，童年文学原创生产与出版传播正在日益做强做大，并极有希望成为我国少儿出版业的核心产品。但同时，我们也必须清醒地看到：当前童年文学创作出现了跟风、一窝风、同质化、脸谱化，甚至为利所驱胡编乱造的现象，更有甚者还有大量盗印杨红樱名字的伪书，这不仅是对杨红樱本人更是对童年文学的伤害，对此我们必须予以高度警觉。

我也注意到，有的评论文章不问青红皂白，将这种低俗倾向归咎于杨红樱，说杨红樱是这些平庸之作的始作俑者，起了不好的领头作用。这对杨红樱显然是极大的不公与污辱。《水浒传》中的李鬼假冒李逵拦路抢劫，该打击的应当是李鬼，口水显然不应吐向李逵。在这里我要呼吁：有关出版管理部门应当加大打击盗版、伪书的力度，还儿童文学一个干干净净的身份。

现代中国儿童文学已经走过了百年历史，作品可谓汗牛充栋，但容易被孩子们记得住的、为大人耳熟能详的人物形

象大概只有十多个,如稻草人、大林和小林、神笔马良、宝葫芦和王宝、小兵张嘎。杨红樱出手不凡,短短数年间,就将"马小跳"和"笑猫"这两个形象牢牢地矗立在了中国儿童文学的艺术版图、中国孩子们的精神世界中,而且漂洋过海,被英国哈珀·柯林斯集团购走了全球出版发行的英文、法文版权。我们完全可以这样说:"马小跳"和"笑猫"已成为中国儿童文学与少儿出版的民族品牌,我们应当像保护知识产权那样,维护好我们民族自己的具有原创意义的儿童文学品牌与形象。

前不久,我写了一篇题为《我心目中的新世纪十位中国儿童文学作家》的文章,这十位活跃在新世纪少儿文坛的作家按年岁排序是:孙幼军、金波、张之路、高洪波、曹文轩、秦文君、沈石溪、黄蓓佳、郑春华、杨红樱。杨红樱最为年轻,她正处于文学创作的盛年,中国儿童文学无疑应对她提出更高的期待,她的童年文学创作还有很大的艺术发展空间与审美张力。

我在这篇文章中对杨红樱有过下面百余字的评价,现在把它转录过来,作为本文的总结:"杨红樱是中国儿童文学三个层次(少年文学/童年文学/幼年文学)中童年文学创作的杰出代表。坚守'儿童本位'的写作立场,选择'儿童视角'的叙事方式,倾注'儿童情结'的诗性关怀,践行'儿童话语'的审美追求,向往'儿童教育'的理想形态,使杨红樱的作品水乳大地般地浸透到孩子们的心田,她所创造的'马小跳'与'笑猫'已成为新世纪中国儿童文学的品牌。一个儿童文学作家,难道还有比受孩子们衷心欢迎和喜爱更为荣耀、幸福的事吗?现代中国儿童文学的历史,由于杨红樱的出现，已被重新改写。杨红樱的创作证明：真正儿童本位的儿童文学不但是属于中国儿童的，也是属于世界儿童的。"

　　一贯注重打造文学精品与读者接受意识的浙江少年儿童出版社经过精心设计、精心选择、精心编制，出版了"杨红樱作品精选导读"丛书，同时邀请国内一批熟谙杨红樱作品的文学博士撰写导读。目前，这套书又将进一步优化、升级为"品藏版"，更令人期待。这是一套真正意义上的经典性、可读性、时代性兼具的新世纪儿童文学原创佳作，我由衷地祝贺这套丛书的出版！祝福千百万少年儿童拥有美好的感动人的文学精品！

■**王泉根**　北京师范大学文学院二级教授、博士生导师，中国儿童文学研究中心主任。中国作家协会儿童文学委员会副主任，亚洲儿童文学学会副会长，中国儿童文学研究会副会长，国家社会科学基金评审专家，终生享受政府特殊津贴专家。

目录 MULU

《侦探小组在行动》

杨红樱
Yanghongying

作品精选导读

帮儿子做作业被罚写一百遍

马天笑先生从小玩到大，现在更好玩了，做了玩具厂的厂长，工厂里到处是玩具，各种各样的玩具，随时随地随便他玩。

马天笑先生白天在厂里玩，回到家里就想跟他儿子玩，但马小跳不跟他玩，因为他没时间玩。

马小跳每天放学回家，没时间踢足球，没时间看动画片，没时间喂金鱼，放下书包就做作业。做呀做呀，总也做不完。

马天笑先生一直在等马小跳做完作业，想和他玩飞镖。

"马小跳，完了没有?"

马天笑先生不知这样问了多少遍。

"快了。"

马小跳不知这样回答了多少遍。

马天笑先生十分同情马小跳："这么小的孩子，做这么多的作业，你们老师怎么忍心?"

马小跳问他爸爸："你小时候作业多不多?"

马天笑先生说："不多，二十分钟，全部搞定。"

"哇，才二十分钟!"马小跳羡慕得……"还有那么多时间，用来干什么呢？"

"玩呀！"马天笑先生说起玩，浑身是劲，他扳着手指头，"滚铁环，放风筝，打水枪，打泥巴仗，捉迷藏，捉'特务'，做标本，做模型……"

作业那么少，玩得那么多，老爸长大了还不是一样当厂长。马小跳真后悔，后悔没能生在那个时代，跟他老爸一块儿玩。

"傻儿子，如果你生在那个时代，就只有马小跳，没有马天笑了。"

是啊，没有爸爸，哪有儿子呢？

墙上的钟敲了十下，已经是晚上十点钟了。

马天笑先生问："马小跳，完了吗？"

这次马小跳没有回答他，原来他已经趴在作业本上睡着了。

马天笑先生把他儿子抱上床，见马小跳的生字还没抄完，便接着帮他抄。一边抄，一边心里沾沾自喜：他模仿儿子的笔迹还挺像的。

第二天下午放学的时候，语文老师把马小跳叫到办公室去，翻开他的作业本："昨天抄写的生字，你写错了一个字，拿去重写一百遍。"

秦老师教学经验丰富，她最好的经验，便是学生写错一个字，让学生重写一百遍。

"你怎么会把'认真'的'真'字写错？"语文老师用手指点着马小跳的脑门儿，一副恨铁不成钢的样子，"我在课堂上一再强调，'真'字里面是三横，千万不要写成两横，可是你还是写成两横了。马小跳，你的耳朵长到哪里去了？"

"这里。"

马小跳扯着他的耳朵，送过去给语文老师看。办公室里，其他的老师都笑起来，可秦老师没有笑，她得在学生面前保持她的威严。

"快去写，写完了才准回家。"

"我不写。"马小跳已经看出这个错字不是他写的，"又不是我写错的。"

秦老师奇怪了："不是你写错的，难道是我写错的？"

"也不是你写错的，你又没到我家里来。"

秦老师哭笑不得，问："马小跳，这是不是你的本子？"

"是我的本子。"马小跳振振有词，"可是，我刚写到这一页的第一行，就睡着了。下面这些字，根本不是我写的。"

秦老师仔细地辨认着字迹，马小跳也凑过去看。

"奇怪了。"秦老师左看右看，"这字跟你的字差不多呀。"

马小跳说："是模仿得很像。"

"马小跳，你认为这是谁干的呢？"

马小跳皱着眉头，认真地想了一会儿，然后十分肯定地说："我爸爸，肯定是我爸爸。"

秦老师还有点不相信："你爸爸一个大厂长，还会写错字？"

马小跳为了让秦老师相信他没有撒谎，马上给马天笑先生打电话，让他火速赶到学校。

马天笑先生真的火速赶到了学校。他一进办公室，秦老师就给他来了个措手不及："马小跳爸爸，你模仿你儿子的字，模仿得真像啊！"

"过奖！过奖！"马天笑先生点头哈腰，"主要是时间晚了

点，不然还可以模仿得更像一点。"

办公室里，其他老师都轻声地笑起来，秦老师没有笑，她很生气，生马小跳的气，更生他爸爸的气。

马天笑先生浑然不知，马小跳悄悄地踩了他爸爸一脚，又向他挤眉弄眼，马天笑先生终于反应过来。刚才走得太急，他暂时神经短路，听不出秦老师的话中有话。

马天笑先生赶紧向秦老师承认错误，又向她解释，帮儿子做作业是迫不得已的事，作业太多，儿子太累，所以……

秦老师不听他解释。她扔个铅笔头给马天笑先生，然后在一张白纸上，一笔一画写了个大大的"真"字，告诉他里面是三横，不是两横。

马天笑先生说他知道是三横，只是昨晚写着写着，眼睛就写花了，把三横写成了两横。

秦老师脸上一点表情都没有。她像对马小跳说话一样对他爸爸说："写错了就要受罚！"

在这样的老师面前，再大的大厂长也只是一名小学生。

可怜的马天笑先生，握着铅笔头，把那个"认真"的"真"，认认真真地抄写了一百遍。

不对称的情境 ·

　　意大利作家亚米契斯所著的《爱的教育》中有个小学生裘里亚，他在夜间模仿父亲的笔迹偷偷抄写订单，以帮助父亲养活一家人。这个故事让人为之感动，恒久难忘。而在杨红樱的这篇作品里，却有一个不愁吃穿的厂长父亲在夜间偷偷模仿儿子的笔迹抄写生字以减轻其课业负担，就太耐人寻味，令人感慨万千了。

　　小学生课业负担重，是一个常见的事实，出现家长为子女代劳的情形也不足为奇。把一个人们习以为常的事件写得一波三折、妙趣横生，作者杨红樱靠的是两个关键词：认真，不对称。

　　马小跳和秦老师都是很认真的角色。杨红樱抓住了他们的这个特征而大做文章。按理，秦老师发现马小跳的错别字而罚他写一百遍，马小跳老老实实地认罚，也就万事大吉了，可马小跳的认真劲儿却令事态有了扩大的可能：他只对自己做的事情负责，矢口否认那个少了一横的"真"

字是自己写的，还认真地帮助秦老师分析、寻找写错别字的"罪魁祸首"。

同样的，秦老师也太认真了。知道真相，批评马小跳两句，让他补写上没做的作业就行了，顶多再告诫马天笑先生以后不可以这样做，就足够了。可她还非得请来马天笑先生"夸奖"他一通，而且认准了一条死理——"写错了就要受罚"，害得偌大一位厂长、著名玩具设计师马天笑先生乖乖地在秦老师面前再做一回小学生。

按常规，应该是马小跳急三火四地一遍遍询问正忙着的父亲"完了没有"能不能陪自己玩，应该是马天笑先生漫不经心地回答"快了"来搪塞敷衍儿子。现实情况却恰好相反：父亲比儿子"玩心"还要重，儿子比父亲还要"稳当"。这是多么不对称不和谐的事情啊！

还有说者和听者的"不对称"呢。当秦老师问马小跳"你的耳朵长到哪里去了"，这是在指责马小跳不用心，而马小跳偏就从字面上理解，当真"扯着他的耳朵，送过去给语文老师看"；当秦老师说"马小跳爸爸，你模仿你儿子的字，模仿得真像啊"，这是在讽刺马天笑，而马天笑先生偏就一时没听出弦外之音，竟会点头哈腰感谢秦老师的赏识："过奖！过奖！主要是时间晚了点，不然还可以模仿得更像一点。"发送信息的说话人和接受信息的听话人思路上"拧"，于是，幽默的效果出来了。

话都说不清楚的张达当了总经理，像猴子一样坐不住的毛超当上副总经理，一打架就输的马小跳偏偏去当保镖——这几个孩子的理想都是与他们的能力大相径庭的职业。这种"不对称"当然要引得跟屁虫唐飞为这样的想象而笑得"打跌"了(《四个调皮蛋》)。同样的,一个堂堂正正的大厂长要握着铅笔头在严厉的秦老师面前认认真真地抄写一百遍认真的"真"字,我们也该会为看到这样滑稽的场景而笑得打嗝。

《贪玩老爸》

乌龟也有脾气

不知从什么时候起，每天下午放学，学校附近的一棵大树下，会出现一个卖乌龟的歪嘴男人。他把十几只乌龟放在一个木盆里，手里拿一根小棍，不停地敲打着乌龟的背，好让乌龟伸出头来，吸引那些放学的孩子来买他的乌龟。

马小跳好不容易挤到最前边，蹲在木盆边看乌龟。

有一只背上有三块黄斑的小乌龟，无论歪嘴男人怎样抽打它，它也不伸出头来。

这是一只犟乌龟，它把歪嘴男人彻底激怒了。

"打死你！打死你！"

马小跳看不下去了，站起身来大喝一声："不许你打乌龟！"

"我打我的乌龟，关你什么事？"

"怎么不关我的事？"马小跳振振有词，"保护动物，人人有责。"

歪嘴男人说不过马小跳，继续用木棍去折腾那只坚决不伸头的犟乌龟。

马小跳见歪嘴男人用木棍捣那只乌龟的脖子窝，便顺手捡起地上的一根树枝，伸进歪嘴男人的衣领窝里捣起来。

"你……你干什么？"

歪嘴男人和马小跳吵起来。他的嘴本来就歪，吵起架来嘴就更歪了，简直把马小跳笑死了。

为了挽救那只不伸头的犟乌龟的命运，马小跳很想把那只乌龟买下来，可是他身上没有那么多钱。

他对那个歪嘴男人说："你把这只乌龟给我留着，我明天带了钱来买。"

歪嘴男人的气不打一处来："我偏不卖给你！我偏不卖给你！"

"我偏买！我偏买！"

马小跳和歪嘴男人头顶头，像两头牛互不相让。

就在这时候，那只不伸头的小乌龟伸出头来，张嘴衔住了马小跳的裤脚，马小跳没有发现，那个歪嘴男人也没有发现。

这只乌龟衔住马小跳的裤脚就不松口，跟着马小跳回到了家里。

马小跳还是没有发现，因为一到家里，乌龟就松开了马小跳的裤脚，默默地爬到一个角落里去了。

乌龟不吃不喝不拉不叫，就像一块石头，所以马小跳全家人都不知道他们家里来了一只乌龟。

直到有一天，马小跳的爸爸马天笑先生买了一张新饭桌回来。这张饭桌有四条腿，有一条腿比其他三条腿短了一截，所以桌面像滑梯一样是斜的，如果把碗和盘子放在上面，就会滑到地上摔得粉碎。

"怎么会这样子呢？"

这个问题，马天笑先生已经想了很久了："买的时候我还摇了摇，平平的嘛，怎么拿回家里，一条腿就短了一截呢？"

这个问题太简单了，不用一秒钟，马小跳就想出来了。

"老爸，你买的时候，那条短了一截的桌腿的下面，垫了一块东西。"

"嘿，我怎么就没有想到呢？"马天笑先生一拍桌子，那张跛腿桌子差点倒下来，"儿子，你说老爸是不是很笨？"

其实，马天笑先生不笨。一般说来，他考虑特别复杂、特别深奥的问题容易一点；而考虑特别简单的问题，对他来讲，却反而有些困难。

马天笑先生跑下楼去，捡了一块砖上来，垫在那张桌子的短腿下面，一摇，高了点。

马小跳又去把装糖的铁盒子拿来垫，一摇，矮了点。

马天笑先生开始搓手了。想不出办法的时候，他就搓手。

马小跳一拍手，他想出了办法。他书包里有那么多课本，有薄有厚，拿来垫桌子最合适。

马天笑先生坚决不同意，他说马小跳"糟蹋圣贤"。

还得再去找东西来垫。马天笑先生和马小跳又分头去找，当他们又回到桌子跟前时，歪斜的桌子已经垫平了，一摇，四平八稳。

是什么东西，这么合适？

马天笑先生和马小跳蹲下去一看，垫在短桌腿下面的，居然是一只小乌龟。

"奇怪，哪儿来的乌龟？我们家没有乌龟啊！"

"我认识这只小乌龟！"

是什么东西，
这么合适？
马天笑先生和马小跳蹲下去一看，
垫在短桌腿下面的，
居然是一只小乌龟。

马小跳看到这乌龟背上有三块黄斑，他认出这就是那只不伸头的犟乌龟。

"我救过这只小乌龟。"马小跳添油加醋地讲道，"那天下午放学，我见一个歪嘴男人在残酷地折磨这只小乌龟，我路见不平一声吼，该出手时就出手，冒着可能被这凶恶的歪嘴男人打得遍体鳞伤的危险，挺身而出，制止了歪嘴男人对它的非人虐待。"

"马小跳，不是非人虐待，是非龟虐待！"

马天笑先生及时纠正马小跳的用词不当，接着，再及时地给予表扬："马小跳，好样的，不愧是我马天笑先生的儿子，见义勇为，舍己救人……"

"老爸，是'舍己救龟'。"

这次，是马小跳及时纠正马天笑先生的用词不当。

"对，是舍己救龟。所以，好人有好报，你看，现在乌龟来报答你了。"

"可是——"马小跳想不通，"乌龟是怎么找到我们家来的？"

这个问题属于比较复杂、比较深奥的问题，对于马天笑先生来说，却非常容易想清楚。

"乌龟又叫神龟，是有灵性的动物。如果它想报答你，就是你到了天涯海角，它也能够找到你。"

马小跳觉得老爸说得合情合理，可他心里还有一点顾虑。

"用乌龟来垫桌子，是不是太……太'那个'了？"

"你是不是想说太残忍了？可这是它自愿的呀！是乌龟自己爬来垫桌子的，也许这是它报答你的一种方式。"

品藏版

这也合情合理。

每天，马小跳一家都在这张四平八稳的饭桌上吃饭。想到乌龟垫桌子很辛苦，开始几天，他们一家三口还不忘给乌龟一点吃的，以表示全家人对它的感激之情。后来，随着日子一天一天地过去，他们渐渐地忘记了桌子下面的乌龟，也渐渐忘记了吃饭的桌子有一条腿短了一截，好像这张桌子买回来就是这么好好的，四平八稳的。

终于有一天，沉默的乌龟造反了。

那天，马小跳的妈妈把那么多好吃的饭菜摆上桌，其中有马小跳爱吃的京酱肉丝，马天笑先生爱啃的糖醋排骨……一家三口刚拿起筷子，只见桌子一斜，哗啦一声，桌上的饭菜都滑到了地上，碗呀盘子呀通通摔得粉碎。

马小跳的妈妈和马天笑先生大惊失色，他们以为世界末日到了。只有马小跳还算平静，他说："哦，我忘记告诉你们了，这是一只有脾气的犟乌龟。"

错落有致的对比

这个富有童话气息的故事带有早期"淘气包马小跳系列"的"超写实"风格。故事主角无疑应该是这只有脾气的乌龟，因为马小跳对它有救助和知遇之恩，它也涌泉相报甘做垫脚石。这个情节简单的故事因为作者杨红樱的善于"造势"，自始至终都带着巨大的磁力吸引着读者，让人不时哑然失笑。

在这里，杨红樱"造势"的主要方式是运用对比手法。比如，这里有歪嘴男人和马小跳亦即恶与善的对比：前者抽打乌龟，马小跳挺身制止；"歪嘴男人用木棍捣那只乌龟的脖子窝"，马小跳即以其人之道还治其人之身，捡起树枝"伸进歪嘴男人的衣领窝里捣起来"；歪嘴男人口口声声"我偏不卖给你！我偏不卖给你"，马小跳毫不相让"我偏买！我偏买"。两人在肢体与语言的冲突当中表现出来的"犟"，与这只乌龟的"犟"相映成趣，令人忍俊不禁。

再如，这里还有着马小跳父子之间的对比：对于桌腿缘何短一截的简单问题，马天笑搞不懂，为此"已经想了很久了"，而马小跳"不用一秒钟"就想出来怎么回事了；马天笑下楼捡砖头垫在桌腿下面，"一摇，高了点"，马小跳在家里找来铁盒子垫在下面，"一摇，矮了点"；马天笑"搓手"，因为"想不出办法"，马小跳"拍手"，"他想出了办法"；当发现乌龟，追述"前尘影事"时，马天笑"及时纠正"马小跳的"用词不当"，马天笑对马小跳给予表扬时，马小跳又反过来"及时纠正"马天笑的"用词不当"；对于乌龟怎么找到自己家里的深奥问题，轮到马小跳"想不通"了，马天笑又能"非常容易想清楚"；当初马小跳要用课本垫桌腿，马天笑认为"糟蹋圣贤"，现在马天笑认可乌龟垫桌子，马小跳又于心不忍……这爷俩如同表演相声的逗哏和捧哏，但又并不一演到底，而是轮换着"逗"与"捧"，时而你是红花，时而他是绿叶，相互在"主"与"次"的角色间游弋。

全家人对待乌龟的态度前后对比鲜明：起始是心存感激，到后来则置若罔闻。乌龟"造反"后，全家人的反应也不一样："马小跳的妈妈和马天笑先生大惊失色，他们以为世界末日到了"，马小跳"还算平静"，还能恰到好处地幽上一默，为这个趣味盎然的故事画上一个圆满的句号。

还有时机上的对比呢：乌龟"造反"之时，正值全家人眼福大饱、胃口大开跃跃欲试之时，"那么多好吃的饭菜摆上桌"，却出其不意出现了"烟消云散"的戏剧性场面，全家人的心理落差有多大，爆笑的效果就该有多好。因为时机之"弓"被拉得最圆满，幽默之"箭"当然也最能中"的"，牢牢地穿透人心。

正是张弛有度的叙述节奏、错落有致的人物、情节与时机的对照，令这个故事结构参差互补，造成了有意味、有美感的形式，也强力地渲染了诙谐风格。

值得提及的是，在杨红樱此前的童话和此后的"笑猫日记系列"中也都出现过类似可爱的乌龟形象。从寂寂无闻到举足轻重，我们见识了乌龟这一形象在杨红樱笔下是怎样一步步丰富和成长起来的。至于故事中见利忘义、虐待小动物的歪嘴男人，我们在后续的"淘气包马小跳系列"和"笑猫日记系列"中也不难发现他的同类。

《轰隆隆老师》

三种颜色的心情卡

有一天，有一家儿童报纸的记者到马小跳他们班来调查，调查他们的童年是不是快乐，结果，从交上去的调查表上统计出，全班有近一半的学生不快乐。

"怎么会呢？怎么会有这么多的孩子不快乐？"

这样的调查结果，显然出乎秦老师的预料之外。她有点震惊，也有点内疚，有那么多孩子感到不快乐，她作为老师，是有责任的。

秦老师很着急，她想让所有的孩子都快乐，首先她得知道，哪些孩子是快乐的，哪些孩子是不快乐的。

秦老师总是有办法的。她发给每个学生三张卡片，一张红色的，一张绿色的，一张黄色的。

"这是心情卡。"秦老师说，"如果你今天心情是快乐的，你就别上这张红色的心情卡；如果你今天的心情是不快乐的，你就别上这张绿色的心情卡；如果你今天的心情一般，你就别上这张黄色的心情卡。"

开始几天，马小跳每天都别着红色的心情卡，他没有一天是不快乐的。班上的同学，大多数别着黄色的心情卡，也有几个同学别着绿色的心情卡，秦老师就会把这些同学留下来，反反复复地问他们为什么不快乐，她要他们把不快乐的事情讲出来！

这些本来不快乐的同学，很怕把自己不快乐的事情讲出来，更怕秦老师把他们留下来，所以都违心地别上红色的快乐心情卡。

后来，全班同学都别上了清一色的红色心情卡。看到全班同学都快乐起来了，秦老师自然比谁都高兴，她想她搞的这个心情卡的活动还真灵，那么多不快乐的孩子，一下子都快乐起来了。

马小跳应该是所有的人中最快乐的一个。但他不知怎么搞的，偏偏把红色心情卡搞丢了，他只有把代表一般心情的黄色心情卡别在胸前。

马小跳一到学校，就引起了秦老师的注意。全班同学都别着红色的心情卡，全班同学都快乐，就只有马小跳别着黄色的心情卡，就只有马小跳的心情一般，秦老师一定要搞清楚一直都很快乐的马小跳，为什么会心情一般。

下午放学，本来要急着回去看动画片的马小跳被秦老师留下来了。

"马小跳，在秦老师的心目中，你一直是很快乐的孩子，怎么……"

马小跳想，如果他告诉秦老师说他把红色心情卡搞丢了，秦老师一定会批评他，所以马小跳这样说："人是会变的，昨天跟今天不一样，今天跟明天不一样……"

"你的意思是说，昨天你是快乐的，今天你就变了，变得心情一般？"

"是这样的。"马小跳想快点回家，"秦老师，我可不可以回家了？"

秦老师不同意："你还没有跟我说，为什么昨天你是快乐的，今天就有了变化。"

"这……"

"你讲出来吧！有什么问题，咱们就解决什么问题，秦老师会帮助你快乐起来的。"

"谢谢秦老师。"马小跳给秦老师鞠了一躬，"如果你现在放我回家看少儿剧场的动画片，我马上就会快乐起来。"

秦老师问："就这么简单？"

对于马小跳来说，快乐是一件简单的事情，不快乐也是一件简单的事情，只有大人才会把简单的事情搞得很复杂。

秦老师终于放马小跳回家了。但是马小跳回到家里，打开电视，调到少儿频道，他喜欢看的动画片刚好演完，正在显示片尾的字幕。

马小跳啪的一声关了电视，坐在沙发上生起气来。

"马小跳！"

马小跳的爸爸马天笑先生下班回来了，一进门，他就叫马小跳。

马小跳猛一转身，用背对着他的爸爸："别理我，我烦！"

马天笑先生不相信他的儿子会烦，在他的心目中，他儿子总是欢天喜地的。

"有什么烦的，讲给老爸听听。"

马小跳真的很烦，他烦秦老师，他烦马天笑先生，这些大人真够烦的。本来他不烦，就是被他们惹烦的。

第二天，想起昨天没看成动画片，马小跳一早起来就不快乐，他别着绿色的心情卡，去了学校。

全班同学的心情卡红成一片，马小跳的绿色心情卡格外引人注目。

马小跳又被秦老师叫了去。

"马小跳，你今天的心情又变了？"

马小跳心里烦得很。

"说吧，马小跳，把你不快乐的事情都说出来！"

马小跳豁出去了，豁出去就是什么话都敢讲了。

"昨天，你把我留下了，讲了半天快乐不快乐的问题，结果我回家后没有看到动画片，所以我今天不快乐。"

秦老师拉下脸来："这么说，你的不快乐是我造成的？"

马小跳没吭声，但他心里在说："的确如此。"

也不知是不是马小跳的话对秦老师有些触动，从此以后，秦老师不再规定同学们每天都别心情卡。而心情卡的三种颜色，更没有任何意义了。

导 读

·快乐其实很简单

　　"人是会变的，昨天跟今天不一样，今天跟明天不一样……"这是马小跳对付秦老师问询的话，却有几分道理。孩子的心情就写在脸上，"娃娃脸"是说变就变的。对于孩子来说，快乐的道理很简单。一盘大虾、一部动画片，都能给他们带来快乐。可大人偏偏喜欢把简单的事情搞得很复杂。就像马小跳喜欢跟夏林果同桌，"动机"非常单纯，但是大人神经兮兮的，又是挖思想，又是发"鸡毛信"，又是请家长的，思想太复杂了。

　　秦老师这类的教育者很敬业，很关心学生，可是他们的教育方法却并不可取。他们自认为很懂得孩子的心理，用心良苦地发明出心情卡来，要孩子们给自己的心情贴上标签，这是在把"本质"（复杂）的事情"表面"（简单）化；而要通过与孩子反反复复谈话帮助他们快乐起来，又等同于无视孩子的情感领地而任意进入，又把"简单"的事情"复杂"化了。结果呢？孩子们学会了伪装，事实真相被掩藏了。所以，心情卡看着很新颖，但是它的实际功用并不大。当教育者为自己的创举、为全班同学都别上清一色的红色心情卡而沾沾自喜时，有没有考虑到孩子的真实感受？当教育者自以为是地与孩子亲密接触时，有没有发现自己离孩子越来越远了呢？

"适得其反"，是杨红樱经营这个故事的方式。这一手法，在"淘气包马小跳"中屡屡被用到，常令故事趣味盎然、一波三折。马小跳本来是快乐的，因为不想说真话，免不了秦老师的反复追问，以致错过了动画片的时间，终于变得不快乐了；秦老师一心一意要帮助马小跳快乐起来，结果委屈了马小跳不说，自己也被马小跳的真话弄得"拉下脸来"。可以说，不光这个故事本身，就连故事的经营方式，都在诉说着心情卡的"弄巧成拙"。

"马小跳豁出去了，豁出去就是什么话都敢讲了"，不要这后一句行不行呢？也能表达意思，但是就缺少了好多韵味。这里，"豁出去就是什么话都敢讲了"是对"豁出去"的进一步的申说，是对它潜藏着的韵味的深一层的发掘。

归根结底，小说乃至一切以情动人的文章，都是讲"废话"的艺术。在杨红樱的作品中，就颇多看上去可有可无的语句，但缺少了这些"废话"，文章就分明显得干巴乏味。废话大王毛超讲过很多没用的废话，可是有一句对唐飞说过的话倒是能见出作文的真谛："故事要讲得精彩，必须要有铺垫。你不懂铺垫，所以你的故事讲得干巴巴的。"所以，写作时，要考虑如何讲好"废话"，讲得让人爱读，还真得费尽思量。

《轰隆隆老师》

马小跳的日记

秦老师在课堂上说："日记就是记你一天所看的、所做的、所说的、所想的。日记必须是很真实的，写作文还允许虚构，写日记是绝对不允许虚构的，所以，日记又是一个人的隐私，别人是不可以看的。"

马小跳不知道什么是"隐私"，但他记住了这样一个意思：你写的日记，别人是不可以看的。

有一天，秦老师布置的家庭作业，就是写一篇日记。

吃过晚饭，马小跳开始写日记。今天有一件事情，一直令他耿耿于怀，一直让他不开心。虽然吃晚饭的时候，那一盘水煮大虾让他开心了一会儿，但吃完晚饭后，他又想起这件事情，真的没法开心起来。

今天的日记，马小跳要把这件事情记下来：

今天上美术课，我用削笔刀削了两支彩色笔。路曼曼看见我削笔，她也要削，就找我借削笔刀，她说如果我不借给她，她一辈子都不理我。后来，我还是把削笔刀借给了她。她一连削了四五支彩色铅笔，把铅笔屑都削到我的椅子下面。结果，秦老师批评我破坏班上的清洁卫生，要罚我今天一个人打扫教室。我说路曼曼也削了，要罚就应该罚我们两个人打扫教室。没想到路曼曼竟会撒谎，她坚决不承认她削了笔，她说她根本就没削笔刀。秦老师相信了她，说像路曼曼这样的好学生，绝不可能把铅笔屑削在地上。

真是气死我了。还是毛超、唐飞和张达够哥们，为了等我去踢足球，他们偷偷地帮我做了清洁，还劝我不要生气。张达说秦老师本来就是个偏心眼。毛超说爱撒谎的女孩子会变成丑八怪。唐飞说，他好像听人说，秦老师是路曼曼的亲戚，所以对她才那么偏心眼。

我真的很生气，生路曼曼的气，生秦老师的气。后来，回到家里吃了妈妈做的大虾，才不那么生气了。

马小跳刚要把写好的日记收起来，他爸爸就走过来要检查作业。

"你不可以看！"马小跳用双手护住他的日记，"日记是不可以拿给别人看的。"

"你有没有搞错？"马天笑先生指着他自己的额头，"我是别人吗？我是你老爸！"

"是我老爸也不能看。"

马小跳牢牢记着秦老师的话：别人是不可以看你的日记的。

"好好好！"马天笑先生知道怎么对付马小跳，"你不给我看，我也知道你写的是什么。"

马小跳果然上当："写的是什么？"

"跟路曼曼有关。"

"你怎么知道的？"

马天笑先生仰天大笑："我是谁呀？你小子尾巴一翘，你老爸就知道你是拉屎还是撒尿。"

其实，马天笑先生也是胡蒙马小跳的。不过是有一次，马小跳赔路曼曼一条裙子，马小跳想让马天笑先生买好一点的裙子赔给路曼曼，就跟他讲路曼曼长得如何如何漂亮。从此以后，马天笑先生就经常拿路曼曼来打趣马小跳。

第二天上学，路曼曼要马小跳交日记。

"为什么要交日记？"马小跳对路曼曼很凶，"你想看我的日记吗？"

"谁稀罕看你的破日记？"路曼曼对马小跳更凶，"你交不交？"

"不交。"

"我去告诉秦老师。"

马小跳才不怕呢！他想这是秦老师亲口说的：不可以看别人的日记。

很快，路曼曼就把秦老师搬来了。

"马小跳，为什么不交日记？"

马小跳说："你不是说，不可以看别人的日记……"

"我是说过这样的话。但是——"秦老师语气一转，"我这是布置作业，你不交上来给我看，我怎么知道你会不会写日记？"

马小跳想到他日记的内容，心有点虚："我……不知道要交……"

秦老师厉声问道:"马小跳,你是不是没写?"

"写了的。"

"既然写了,为什么不交?"

马小跳没有退路了,只好把他昨晚写的日记交出来。他有一种预感:大祸要临头了。

果然,中午放学的铃声刚响,秦老师就堵在教室门口,叫马小跳、张达、唐飞和毛超到办公室去。

马小跳心知肚明,但张达、唐飞和毛超三个却丈二和尚——摸不着头脑。

张达说:"我今天没犯什么事呀!"

唐飞说:"我今天也没怎么着呀!"

毛超问马小跳:"马小跳,你呢?"

马小跳说:"去了不就知道了!"

四个人一排,端端正正地站在秦老师的面前。

"知道你们为什么站在这里吗?"

除了马小跳,其他三个都摇头。

秦老师拿起马小跳的日记本:"马小跳的日记,暴露了这么几个问题:第一,昨天我罚他一个人扫地,你们几个是不是都去帮他了?"

三个人狠狠地瞪了马小跳一眼,然后都点头。

"第二个问题:张达,你昨天是不是说了我偏心眼?"

张达从后面狠狠踢了马小跳一脚。

"第三个问题:毛超,你昨天是不是说过路曼曼爱撒谎,会变成丑八怪一类的话?"

毛超的手，悄悄伸到马小跳的身后，揪住他屁股上的一块肉，狠狠一拧。

"哎哟……"

马小跳叫起来。

"干什么？站在办公室还不老实！"

四个人都老实起来，听秦老师往下说。

"第四个问题——"这个问题好像最严重，秦老师的脸色变得非常不好看，"唐飞，你是听谁讲的，我是路曼曼的亲戚？"

秦老师的两只火眼金睛，死死地盯着唐飞。唐飞像一堆奶油，快被这火眼金睛射化了。

"我……没听谁说，我胡编的……"

唐飞的鼻涕眼泪都出来了。

幸好秦老师要开会。她让他们四个都回去写检查，明天再来处理。

四个人做出低头认罪的样子。

刚一走出秦老师的视线，马小跳便像逃命的兔子，飞奔起来。张达、毛超和唐飞，在后面紧追不舍，他们饶不了马小跳。

从"芝麻"到"西瓜"

　　只知其一、不知其二，这是马小跳小错不断的原因之一。马小跳对于日记的认识就只记住了"写日记是绝对不允许虚构的"，"日记又是一个人的隐私，别人是不可以看的"，但却没弄清：写日记是老师布置的家庭作业，老师可是要检查日记的。所以，当他毫无保留地把他的不公平遭遇写到日记中尽情发泄的时候，就无意中"出卖"了自己的三个好朋友，"大祸"可就临头了。

　　我们生活中可能遭遇的都是一些芝麻小事，微不足道，可小事件却是可以生长成大故事的。围绕着马小跳的日记，相关的人、事都被作者杨红樱网罗在一起。马小跳日记写成后，马天笑要看，路曼曼要收，秦老师要检查，马小跳的反应各不相同：或理直气壮，或凶蛮强悍，或心虚胆怯。他能抵御住贪玩老爸和同桌冤家，坚持不交日记，却无法抗拒循规蹈矩的秦老师的威严。

　　秦老师在处理张达、毛超、唐飞三个"同案犯"时的程序是由轻到重、由一般到特殊，先是处理三个人偷偷帮助马小跳做清洁的共同问题，接下来再各个突破单个人的"这一个"。这个处理程序也是作品的写作顺序。

三个孩子在被质询时反应也都各有不同：练跆拳道、当头霸王的张达对马小跳公开打击，"狠狠踢了马小跳一脚"；坐不住的毛超则采取偷袭方式，悄悄拧马小跳的屁股；胖胖的唐飞就不得不老实多了，因为已经有老师的威严震慑，更有老师的火眼金睛盯着，加上自己"罪行"最重，他不仅前言不搭后语，而且"鼻涕眼泪都出来了"。

作品充分描述了他们四个调皮蛋被请到办公室前与后的反应、在办公室内与外的不同表现，几个人的不同动作非常吻合他们各自的性格。一起事件的方方面面都注意到了，于是，一篇小说也就枝繁叶茂地生长出来，"芝麻"也就变成了"西瓜"。

《马小跳的日记》还同时揭示出这样的问题：教育者偏向自己喜欢的好学生，不相信他们会做出不道德的事情，而将一切过错均视为"问题"学生惹的祸。而且，教育者不能正确对待学生日记中的心声表达，没有对自己的教育方式加以必要的反省；长此以往，学生就都会给自己的日记"违心地别上红色的快乐心情卡"了，日记也就会和作文一样充满着水分，学生也都会被"格式"成清一色的"懂事"的"小大人"。

小说中，马小跳情绪能够变得好一些，是靠了妈妈水煮大虾的魔力。其实，他用日记形式记录下自己白天在学校的"不幸"遭遇，对于调节自己的心理、排解不良情绪很有帮助。

　　写日记是很好的宣泄情感、释放压力的方式。所以，我们在遇到快乐或者忧伤的事情的时候，既可以选择向师长好友诉说，也可以选择一个人在日记中静静地自我倾诉。只是要记住：日记有写给别人看的和写给自己读的两种哟。

《笨女孩安琪儿》

众所周知的密码

从小到大，安琪儿的压岁钱都是她妈妈管的，管着管着，安妈妈就把她的钱混着安琪儿的压岁钱一块儿用了。安琪儿呢，也早忘了她还有笔压岁钱在她妈妈那里。

看见马小跳把压岁钱存进银行，得到一张卡，只要把这张卡喂进提款机里，提款机马上就可以吐出钱来，安琪儿就从她妈妈那里要出她的压岁钱来，也想存进银行，得到一张可以变出钱的卡。

是马小跳带着安琪儿到银行去的。

当银行的工作人员叫安琪儿输密码时，安琪儿说她没有密码，她问马小跳有没有密码。

"真笨！"马小跳指指柜台上的密码器，"你摁六个数字，不就有密码了吗?"

"马小跳，你帮我摁吧！"

马小跳说，密码只能自己摁。

安琪儿又问马小跳："你的密码是什么?"

"不能告诉你。"

"为什么不能告诉我?"

"密码能告诉别人还叫密码吗? 你连这个都不懂!"

马小跳很生安琪儿的气, 如果换了别的女生, 比如路曼曼或者夏林果, 虽然马小跳有时很讨厌她们, 但她们绝不会像安琪儿有那么多愚蠢的问题。

看安琪儿还是不会输密码, 银行的工作人员脸上有了不耐烦的表情, 马小跳觉得他很没面子, 毕竟, 安琪儿是他带去的嘛。

马小跳不得不教安琪儿, 教她把她的生日输进去。

"原来我的生日就是我的密码!"

安琪儿怪马小跳不早告诉她。

安琪儿拿着卡, 欢天喜地地回到家里。

"爸爸妈妈, 你们看——"安琪儿扬起手中的卡, "我的变钱卡!"

安爸爸和安妈妈有些吃惊, 他们的笨女儿居然也知道把钱存进银行。

安琪儿还在兴高采烈地讲个不停:"只要我把这张变钱卡喂进提款机里, 哗哗哗, 就会吐出好多钱来。"

"哦?"

安琪儿很高兴看她爸爸妈妈目瞪口呆的样子。

"这张卡是有密码的哦! 可是, 我不能把我的密码告诉你们。马小跳说, 密码是不可以告诉别人的。"

安妈妈说:"安琪儿, 你可千万不要忘记了你的密码, 忘了密码, 你的变钱卡就变不出钱来了。有一次, 我忘记了我的密码……"

安琪儿迫不及待地打断她妈妈的话:"难道你会忘记你的生

日吗？"

"生日？"安妈妈听不明白，"怎么又扯上生日了？"

"你的生日就是你的密码呀！"

安爸爸、安妈妈相视一笑，他们都知道了：安琪儿的银行信用卡的密码是她的生日。

过完正月十五就开学了。

马小跳和安琪儿不约而同都将自己的银行信用卡带到学校去，马小跳在男生中显摆，安琪儿在女生中显摆。

张达、毛超和唐飞围着马小跳，轮流看那张会变钱的卡，看了正面看背面，看了背面又看正面。

"看吧看吧！"马小跳十分慷慨的样子，"我就是把这张卡送给你们，你们也变不出钱来。"

唐飞傻呵呵地问："为什么你能变出钱来，我们就变不出钱来？"

"因为我有密码呀！"

"什么密码？"

马小跳不耐烦地说："密码就是密码。"

"我知道——"毛超自作聪明，"密码就是开保险箱的。"

马小跳赶紧声明："我的密码不是开保险箱的，我的密码是——"

"你的密码是什么？"

三个脑袋凑拢了过来。

"我的密码是——"马小跳差一点就脱口而出了，但他还是及时地管住了自己的嘴巴，"我凭什么要告诉你们？"

毛超理直气壮地问："难道你不是我们的好朋友吗？"

唐飞也在一旁附和："连密码都不告诉我们，还算什么好朋友？"

"密码是不可以告诉别人的。"马小跳立场坚定，"就是好朋友，也不能告诉。"

"你就是要告诉我们，我们还不听呢！"

一脑袋鬼主意的毛超跟张达和唐飞眨眼睛，然后又朝安琪儿努努嘴。张达和唐飞会意，他们三个撇下马小跳，到安琪儿那边去了。

安琪儿正在跟几个女生讲，她的银行卡是怎样哗哗哗地变出钱来的。

毛超开始下套了："安琪儿，人家马小跳都有密码，你有没有密码？"

"我当然有密码。"安琪儿一本正经地回答毛超，"没有密码是变不出钱来的。"

"你和马小跳的密码是一样的吗？"

"我跟马小跳又不是一天生的，怎么会是一样的呢？"安琪儿今天才发现毛超有点傻，"马小跳的密码是他的生日，我的密码是我的生日。"

轻而易举，毛超他们几个不仅知道了马小跳的密码，还知道了安琪儿的密码。

道高一尺，魔高一丈，马小跳亡羊补牢，有办法对付他们。一放学，马小跳就拖着安琪儿去银行改密码。

一路上，安琪儿有无穷多的问题问马小跳。

"为什么要改密码？"

"因为全世界的人都知道了我们的密码。"

"密码可以改，是不是我们的生日也可以改？"

"密码跟生日没有关系。"

"马小跳，你说密码怎么改？"

安琪儿没完没了的问题，彻底地激怒了马小跳："你想怎么改就怎么改！"

"我把我的密码改成你的生日，好不好？"

马小跳快被安琪儿气死了。

结果，马小跳在改密码时，不知是被安琪儿气的，还是一时神经短路，摁的六个数字，居然就是安琪儿的生日。安琪儿呢？她本来就打算把她的密码改成马小跳的生日。

这回，只要安琪儿不再改密码，无论是安琪儿的爸爸妈妈，还是像猴子一样精的毛超，他们就是把脑瓜儿想出水来，也想不到安琪儿的密码是马小跳的生日，马小跳的密码是安琪儿的生日。

导读

简单与不简单·

　　用成人的眼光来打量安琪儿，她确实是个笨女孩，有过很多傻念头，干过很多笨事情：她让马小跳给自己浇水而异想天开自己会由此长高；在调皮蛋的忽悠下，把爸爸的宝贝足球拿给他们踢，结果把球上的球星签名弄"飞"了；还会因为把别人的捉弄当真而憧憬着长大了到意大利去见达·芬奇……之所以如此搞笑，那是因为她的头脑过于简单。可是她在回答让所有聪明人都伤透脑筋的脑筋急转弯的问题时，却能够应付自如，处处见出她的"机警"来；她能如此不简单，却是因为她想得简单。

　　其实，安琪儿的"笨"很大程度上是因为她童心完好，心理不设防，成人的世故老辣未能侵袭到她的心灵。因为绝无虚假、不懂得计算利害，在"精明"面前，她自然就显出"笨"来了。

　　这一回呢，安琪儿好不容易懂得理财了，从爸爸妈妈那里讨回自己压岁钱的支配权，并由马小跳带着去银行存钱办卡，却又不明白为什么要设立密码。这实在是笨得可爱，而且她还再次犯下"简单"的错误，简单到在别人的诱哄下很轻易地就把自己的银行密码弄得人尽皆知，而且连带着把马小跳的密码也爆了料。

可是笨女孩也有不笨的时候。在她发出"密码可以改，是不是我们的生日也可以改"等一类无穷多的"傻"问题而把马小跳气得够呛的时候，却也有"神机妙算"（这其实也是作者杨红樱的神来之笔），与马小跳的密码来了个简单的对调。这一回，再不简单的人就是把脑瓜想出水来，也无法破译安琪儿"神秘的微笑"了。简单与不简单、智与愚之间辩证统一的关系，在她身上竟能体现得如此完美。

英国教育家夏洛特·梅森说过："除了令人同情的白痴，无论其父母有无文化，从未有一个诞生在这个世界上的孩子生而不带天赋，并且没有发展的可能性。"安琪儿就是一个拥有着无限发展可能性的可爱的小天使。我们还有什么理由像马小跳那样小觑她呢？

《笨女孩安琪儿》

小孩子为什么不像小孩子

　　那天下午，同学们正在收拾书包，准备放学，校长突然闯进教室，后面还跟着一个报社的记者。这个记者很年轻，如果她不戴一副眼镜，也许还算得上是一个美女。马小跳的审美观是，再美的美女，只要一戴上眼镜，就算不上什么美女了。

　　"同学们——"校长一讲话就是作报告的腔调，"这位记者要在咱们班作一个调查，调查什么呢？过一会儿她会给每个同学发一份调查表，同学们一定要严肃认真地对待，想好了再填。我的话你们听明白了吗？"

　　"听明白了。"

　　校长很不满意这种稀稀拉拉、拖腔拖调的回答，他提高声音又问了一遍："听明白了吗？"

　　"听明白了！"

　　这次的回答很整齐、很响亮。校长满意了，十分绅士地向年轻的女记者做了个"请"的动作，然后退到教室门边。

　　"非常抱歉，我只占用同学们一点点时间。"这位女记者非常客气，她并没有把同学们当小孩子对待，"我的调查内容非常简单，现在有三种选择摆在你们的面前：聪明、漂亮、有钱，你只能选择其中的一样，在下面打一个钩就可以了。听明白了吗？"

马小跳把手高高地举起来。

女记者和颜悦色地走到马小跳的座位前："这位同学，你有什么问题？"

"可不可以三样都选？"

"马小跳，你老毛病又犯了？"

秦老师不知什么时候进了教室，马小跳被她逮个正着。人家说话的时候，马小跳不长耳朵听，人家说完了，他又来问，这确实是马小跳的老毛病。一年级就有这毛病，现在读三年级了，这毛病还没改。

女记者在发调查表，秦老师赶紧给大家敲警钟："同学们一定要严肃认真地对待这张调查表。这三种选择不是只画一个钩那么简单，这个钩可以反映出你们的思想品质，反映出你们有没有高尚的情操，反映出你们是不是有理想、有抱负……"

马小跳的老毛病又犯了，秦老师在说什么，他一句都没有听进去。他的眼睛一直盯着女记者，盼望着她快点把调查表发到他手上。

调查表终于发到了马小跳的手上，马小跳毫不犹豫地在"有钱"下面画了个大大的钩。马小跳画完了，就去看他的同桌路曼曼画的什么。

路曼曼在"聪明"下面画了一个大大的钩。

"哇，你都那么聪明了，还想聪明，你是不是想成人精啊？"

"马小跳，你在说什么？"

秦老师又逮住了马小跳。

路曼曼向秦老师报告："我选择的是'聪明'，马小跳说我想成人精。"

"马小跳，放了学不许走，到我办公室来。"

马小跳无所谓，他经常放学后被秦老师留下来。他转身去看坐在他后面的夏林果画的是什么，他想路曼曼是班上最聪明的女生，她还想要聪明，夏林果是班上最漂亮的女生，她是不是还想要漂亮呢？

结果，马小跳看见夏林果也在"聪明"的下面画了一个大大的钩。

马小跳转身看唐飞的，居然唐飞也在"聪明"下面画了一个大大的钩。

"唐飞，你不想有钱啊？"

"去！"

"你那天还说，你长大了要当百万富翁。"

唐飞说："从现在起，我要做有理想、有抱负的人。"

马小跳突然发现唐飞很假。他前面是毛超，他扑在毛超的肩膀上，看他选的是什么。

毛超选的是"聪明"，坐在他旁边的女生也选的是"聪明"。

女记者把调查表收起来，跟秦老师到了办公室。马小跳也来到办公室。

秦老师迫切地想知道调查表的结果，她已经忘了是她叫马小跳到办公室来的。

"你来这里干什么？"

"是你刚才叫我来的。"

女记者一张一张地在整理调查表，校长和秦老师都在等着看她的调查结果。

"全班同学，除了一个男同学选择'有钱'，一个女同学选择'漂亮'外，其余都选择的是'聪明'。"

马小跳看见校长和秦老师都很高兴的样子。可那位女记者，看不出她是高兴，还是不高兴。

第二天，秦老师在班上说："昨天的调查结果，我还是比较满意的，全班同学，除了一个男同学选'有钱'，一个女同学选'漂亮'，其余都选的是'聪明'，这充分说明了我们班除了极个别同学，大多数同学都是有理想、有抱负，有健康的人生追求……"

下课后，同学们都在猜测：这个选"有钱"的男同学是谁？选"漂亮"的女同学又是谁？

"你们不用猜，这个人就是我。"马小跳一副敢作敢为的样子，"我就是想有钱，有钱可以开公司，有钱可以给我妈妈买漂亮别墅，有钱可以周游全世界，有钱可以……"

有钱的好处太多了，马小跳说都说不完。

那个选"漂亮"的女同学是谁呢？同学们猜来猜去，猜到上课铃响，也没猜出来。

隐隐约约的，马小跳有一种预感：这个选"漂亮"的人应该是安琪儿。因为他常常有一种遗憾：安琪儿性格还可以，就是太不漂亮。如果她有夏林果的一半漂亮就好了。如果，如果他是安琪儿，他会毫不犹豫地选择"漂亮"。

"安琪儿，我知道那个选'漂亮'的女同学就是你。"

安琪儿一下子就招了："马小跳，你怎么知道的？"

马小跳好不得意，他甚至以为他将来可以去做那种靠推理破案的超级侦探。

　　当马小跳和安琪儿差不多都要忘记有个年轻的女记者在他们班搞调查这件事情时，这个女记者写了一篇题为《一次调查活动引发出来的思考》的文章，并在社会上引起了轰动，许多人都在思考这个女记者提出的一个问题：现在的小孩子为什么不像小孩子？

导 读

童心是怎样遗失的

　　父亲问孩子人生有什么追求，孩子回答金钱和美女，父亲凶狠地打了孩子的脸；当孩子改口追求事业与爱情时，父亲赞赏地摸了孩子的头。是啊，从什么时候开始，孩子们都学会了用冠冕堂皇的话语来给自己涂脂抹粉？这篇故事就让我们看到了孩子是怎样在成人的训导下一步步进入了成人设计好的套子中的。

　　当孩子只能在"聪明"、"漂亮"和"有钱"这三项中选择一样时，校长、老师就都紧张兮兮的，再三郑重其事地发出"预警"："一定要严肃认真地对待，想好了再填。我的话你们听明白了吗？""这三种选择不是只画一个钩那么简单……"于是，孩子都变得不简单了：原本长大了要当百万富翁的唐飞要改做"有理想、有抱负的人"了，本来最漂亮的女生也不爱漂亮而是爱聪明了，本来就够聪明的路曼曼都要想成"人精"了。不过，还是有例外，那就是童心完好的马小跳和安琪儿。

小孩子是感性的、直觉的，金钱的好处触目可见，漂亮的外表人见人爱。当从孩子嘴里说出成人才能讲的话，当孩子都变成了丁文涛式的小大人时，我们真能高兴起来吗？被社会激素催熟的果子会像自然成熟的果子那样润泽芬芳吗？

杨红樱曾借马小跳最喜欢的林老师之口一语中的："这不是孩子本身的问题，这是一个社会问题，也是教育制度的问题。"连丁克舅舅这样的新新人类都渴望无忧无虑，希望再做一次小孩子，我们有什么理由过早地把成人的理念强加给孩子呢？当校长和秦老师为绝大多数孩子们的"正确"选择而感到满意时，他们有没有意识到自己做法的后果？为什么一律要按照成人既定的标准来塑造孩子呢？那可是对孩子自身感受、自尊和天性的极大冷落、忽视和扭曲啊！

许多小书迷喜欢杨红樱笔下的夏林果这个人物，我想，这不仅仅是因为夏林果会跳芭蕾舞，背挺得笔直、眼睛平视前方而表现出高雅的气质来，恐怕还在于夏林果的"前缀"，她可是个"漂亮女孩"啊！

《四个调皮蛋》

用牙嚼钢珠

身材胖得像企鹅一样的唐飞，喜欢吃，特别喜欢带零食到学校里来。他的上衣兜里、裤子兜里，几乎每个兜里都装着不同的零食。一个兜里装着各种颜色的朱古力豆，一个兜里装着鸡味薯条，一个兜里装着棒棒娃牛肉粒，一个兜里装着小乖乖奶油米果……只要他从你身边走过，就会有一股糖果店的味道。

唐飞特别喜欢在上课的时候吃东西，技巧很高，几乎没有被上课的老师发现过。老师在黑板上板书时，是唐飞吃东西的最佳时刻，他从来不会放过；老师在念书时，他也埋下头来看书，这时候吃东西，老师也不会发现；老师讲课时，目光在每个同学的脸上扫来扫去，唐飞也有办法吃东西：他把橡皮或铅笔弄到地上，然后装作去捡的样子，就把吃的东西塞进了嘴里；或者，就在老师眨眼睛的那一刹那，唐飞把东西塞进嘴里，装模作样地像听懂似的微微点头，老师还以为他听课听得认真呢！

唐飞在上课时吃的东西，一般都是好东西：像奶油米果，像鸡味薯条，像朱古力豆……因为上课吃，他可以一个人独吃，没有人向他要，更没有人抢他的。他的同桌夏林果，知道他在不停地吃东西，但她从来不向他要东西吃，她在练芭蕾，特别怕胖，而唐飞吃的东西，都是特别容易使人发胖的东西。

唐飞在下课时吃的东西，一般是不太好的东西：比如那种很便宜的水果硬糖，比如那种像木柴一样干的牛肉干，比如那种吃了就要放屁的糖豌豆……马小跳、张达和毛超他们几个，只要一见到他的嘴巴在动，就会向他要东西吃；如果他不给他们，他们就把他按在地上，抢！幸好唐飞还藏有好东西，这些不太好的东西，抢就让他们抢吧。

有一种好东西，是唐飞的姨妈从日本带回来的，唐飞下课的时候也敢吃，他不怕别人来要，也不怕别人来抢，因为别人都不敢吃。

"唐飞，你在吃什么？"

"钢珠。"

"你敢吃钢珠？"

马小跳他们几个不信。

唐飞从裤兜里掏出一把钢珠来："你们好好看看，这是不是钢珠？"

真是钢珠耶！几粒像豌豆一样大小的钢珠，在唐飞肉乎乎的手心里，闪烁着冰冷的金属光泽。

唐飞很潇洒地扔了几颗钢珠在嘴里，嘎嘣嘎嘣地嚼起来，还问张达敢不敢吃钢珠。

张达不敢吃钢珠，虽然他的嘴巴很大，但是牙齿没有钢珠硬，嚼不动钢珠。

唐飞问毛超敢不敢吃钢珠。

毛超更不敢吃钢珠，他的几颗大牙都是蛀牙，补过的，哪里敢嚼钢珠？

唐飞又问马小跳敢不敢吃钢珠。

马小跳却问唐飞："钢珠是什么味道的？"

唐飞很不耐烦地回答他："钢珠就是钢珠的味道。"

马小跳还有一个问题："你为什么要吃钢珠？"

"为什么？为什么？"唐飞不耐烦极了，"我就是要让你们瞧瞧，我的牙齿比钢珠还硬。"

唐飞一咧嘴，露出几颗东倒西歪的大板牙来。

马小跳对唐飞刮目相看了，甚至开始崇拜他了，就像他崇拜张达可以在脑门上敲鸡蛋一样，他崇拜唐飞可以用牙嚼钢珠。

河马张达和猿猴毛超也不敢小看唐飞了。平时，唐飞总像跟屁虫似的跟在他们三个后面，被他们呼唤来使唤去：他们踢足球，他给他们扛书包；他们打水仗，他给他们看衣服……如果现在谁要使唤唐飞，他会扔几颗钢珠在嘴里，嚼得嘎嘣嘎嘣响，然后，斜起眼睛，抬高了下巴看着你："谁敢嚼钢珠，我就听谁的。"

他们谁都不敢嚼钢珠，所以唐飞可以谁的话都不听。

如果不是唐飞太得意忘形，把天机泄露给了夏林果，也许，马小跳他们几个会对唐飞永远地崇拜下去。

唐飞知道他的同桌，就是班上长得最漂亮的女生夏林果，曾经崇拜过河马张达在脑门上敲鸡蛋，便故意对夏林果说："张达在脑门上敲鸡蛋根本不算什么，还有人可以用牙嚼钢珠呢!"

夏林果问:"谁可以用牙嚼钢珠?"

唐飞故意卖关子:"这个人远在天边,近在眼前。"

"到底是谁?你再不说,我就不听了。"

唐飞赶紧说:"这个人就是我。"

"你?"

唐飞摸出几颗钢珠来:"你看这是什么?"

夏林果仔细看了,确实是钢珠。

唐飞一把扔进嘴里,嘎嘣嘎嘣嚼起来。

"啊——"

夏林果发出一声尖叫。

唐飞想听的就是这一声尖叫,他以为这一声尖叫过后,夏林果就会崇拜他的。

可是,唐飞太得意了。嚼完钢珠吞下肚,他居然张开嘴巴,向夏林果哈出一口气,向她证明他真的把钢珠都吃下去了。

就在唐飞哈气的一刹那,夏林果闻到一股很浓的果香味。

钢珠怎么会有果香味?

夏林果多了一个心眼:"我再看看你刚才吃的钢珠。"

唐飞毫无防备,他摸出一粒钢珠来,放在夏林果的手心里。

夏林果看了又看,真的是钢珠。趁唐飞不注意,她悄悄地把钢珠放进嘴里,开始只有冰凉的感觉,慢慢地,有了一点甜味,慢慢地,有了果香味。果香味越来越浓,越来越浓,夏林果一嚼,嘎嘣一声,满嘴都是果香味。

原来是糖豆!

很快，马小跳、张达和毛超都知道了唐飞嚼的不是钢珠，嚼的是做得像钢珠一样的糖豆。他们从他的书包里搜出一个漂亮的玻璃瓶来，上面有一些日本文字，这是日本的"钢珠糖豆"。

还剩半瓶子的钢珠糖豆，被马小跳他们几个瓜分了，一把一把地扔进嘴里，嘎嘣嘎嘣！嘎嘣嘎嘣！

唐飞的"小"与"大"

在塑造唐飞这个形象时，作者杨红樱注重到了他的最大特征：对于吃的东西特别热情。在这篇故事中，对他爱吃的描写，也是从概括到具体、由静到动的。先是静态的造像："身材胖得像企鹅一样"，这可是他爱吃的一个体征和后果；口袋里装着各种零食，身上散发出糖果店的味道——这也是他对吃孜孜不倦的表现形式。

接下来就都是动态的描写了，唐飞的性格也在动态描写中表露无遗——上课的时候瞅准一切时机恰到好处地吃东西，而不被老师发现，真可谓聪明过人，当然，这是在耍小聪明；而且，上课时与下课时吃的东西有着质量的高下之分，以防好东西被好朋友抢走——除了有小聪明之外，还是一个不折不扣的小气鬼。这些概括性的描写，让我们看到了唐飞的"小"。

不过，当作者杨红樱全力具体描写唐飞"嚼钢珠"这一件事情的时候，却让我们领教了唐飞在"小"之外的东西。

那就是他还是有"大气磅礴"之处的。他敢于当众潇洒地吃好东西——钢珠，以致震慑住了对他的食品虎视眈眈的好朋友们。唐飞咧嘴露出的几颗东倒西歪的大板牙，可是他的牙齿比钢珠还要硬的铁证啊！

拿嚼钢珠作为自己不听别人使唤的资本，这就颇有点诸葛亮唱空城计吓退敌兵的风采了。你看，"真是钢珠耶！几粒像豌豆一样大小的钢珠，在唐飞肉乎乎的手心里，闪烁着冰冷的金属光泽"，表面上是在写钢珠，其实作者杨红樱是在通过这一细节活灵活现地投射出马小跳们的内心世界来。短短一句口语化的"真是钢珠耶"，尤其是语气助词"耶"的使用，把调皮蛋们惊讶、害怕的心理活生生表现了出来。那"冰冷的金属光泽"不仅仅是钢珠在闪烁，分明是马小跳们胆在战心在寒哪！

而唐飞嚼钢珠时一再发出的"嘎嘣嘎嘣"声，更壮大了他牙齿比钢珠还硬的声威。要知道，"嘎嘣嘎嘣"这个拟声词在小说中多次出现，它不仅仅是模拟唐飞们吃东西时发出的声音，还增强了作品的节奏感。特别是结尾的"嘎嘣嘎嘣！嘎嘣嘎嘣"，把马小跳们窥见真相后瓜分钢珠时的快意情态和得意心理淋漓尽致地传递出来了。而且就像这"嘎嘣嘎嘣"传递出来的"干脆"一样，故事到这里戛然而止，让人在"绕梁"的余音中来到现场，同时感受着杨红樱作品的神韵——那一贯的干净、利落、不拖泥带水的结尾方式，以及其中透出的无穷意味。

《四个调皮蛋》

最后的大赢家

  毛超的那个"四全其美"的计划，就是淘气包马小跳、猿猴毛超、河马张达、企鹅唐飞四个人，他们计划这样选三好学生：你选我，我选你；他选你，你选他。这样不是四个人都被选上了吗？这就是"四全其美"的计划。结果，毛超选了张达，张达选了毛超，马小跳选了唐飞，唐飞却没有选马小跳。

  "四全其美"成了"三全其美"，那种被朋友欺骗、被朋友背叛的滋味，在马小跳这样小小的年纪，他就已经尝到过了。

  马小跳不是那种躲在卫生间里哭一会儿就算了的人，他才不会善罢甘休呢！

  在操场上，马小跳堵住了那三个勾肩搭背的人，他们都神气得很，因为他们的名字都写在黑板上了，都以为大功告成。

  "你为什么不选我？"马小跳质问唐飞，"难道你忘了我们那个'四全其美'的计划吗？"

  唐飞倒满有理由："我们那个计划都快被秦老师识破了，我怎么敢选你?"

马小跳又质问张达和毛超:"你们为什么不选我?"

张达振振有词:"你又没有选我们,我们凭什么选你?"

毛超也振振有词:"'四全其美'的计划中,又没有计划我们选你。"

听听他们都说了些什么? 马小跳气得差点一头栽倒在地上。

"你们是不是我的朋友?"

"是呀!"

三个人都点头。

"我们是不是击过掌、拉过钩、宣过誓?"

"是呀!"

"是呀!"

"是呀!"

三个人都承认这一切都是事实。

"那你们怎么可以这么不讲信用呢?"马小跳一声怒吼,"从此以后,你们不再是我的朋友,我也不再是你们的朋友。大路朝天,各走半边。"

马小跳十分悲壮地说完这些话,头也不回地走了。

马小跳说到做到,说不理他们三个,就不理他们三个。他们三个也无所谓,马小跳不理他们,地球还不是一样地转。

到了下一个星期,马小跳还是不理他们三个。唐飞觉得毕竟是他对不起马小跳,就对张达和毛超说:"马小跳好像真的生气了。"

"换了我也要生气。"毛超很理解马小跳的样子,"我们三个都当三好学生了，就他没当上，你们说他能不生气吗?"

其实这时候，他们都还没有当上三好学生，秦老师只不过把他们的名字写在了黑板上，他们就以为自己都已经当上了三好学生。

张达说这件事情都怪唐飞。

"马小跳选……选了你，你……却不选马小跳，他肯定是生你……的气。你给他道……道……"

张达结巴，他们都知道他要说的是"道歉"。

毛超说:"马小跳这次生的气特别大，你光是道歉还不行，还得……"

唐飞一下子明白了毛超的意思:"马小跳喜欢漫画书，我送一本漫画书给他吧。"

唐飞当天就跑到报刊亭里，买了一本最新出版的漫画书，送给马小跳。

马小跳接受了唐飞的漫画书，又重新开始和唐飞说话，但他还是不理张达和毛超。

唐飞得意了:"看见没有? 马小跳不是生我的气，是生你们两个的气。你们都宣过誓的，怎么能不守信用呢?"

不管张达和毛超承不承认自己是"不守信用的人"，他们都有跟马小跳和解的愿望，他们心里是这样想的: 他们当上了三好学生，马小跳没有当上三好学生，他们不能跟马小跳一般见识。

唐飞告诉张达，马小跳还喜欢自动铅笔。张达就把那支存了很久、自己都舍不得用的自动铅笔送给了马小跳。

马小跳接受了张达那支自己都舍不得用的自动铅笔，又重新开始和张达说话，但还是不理毛超。

毛超知道如果他不送东西给马小跳，马小跳是不会理他的。唉，谁叫他当上了三好学生，马小跳没有当上呢？

马小跳一直喜欢毛超的双面乒乓球拍，毛超就把那个乒乓球拍送给了马小跳。

马小跳接受了毛超的乒乓球拍，又重新开始和毛超说话。

马小跳、毛超、张达、唐飞四个人重归于好，又成了形影不离的好朋友。

马小跳很快就忘记了选三好学生这件事。

又到了星期三下午最后一节的班队活动课，秦老师又重新提起选三好学生这件事。上次选出来的那些同学要举手表决，票数过一半的才能当选为三好学生。

路曼曼、丁文涛、夏林果的票数都过了半数。

"同意张达同学当三好学生的同学请举手。"

除了选张达的毛超，没有一个同学举手。连崇拜张达、曾经为张达系过鞋带的夏林果也没有举手。

张达满脸通红，连耳根子都红了，恨不得地上有条缝钻进去。

马小跳笑死了。

"同意毛超同学当三好学生的同学请举手！"

没有一个同学举手，连选毛超的张达都忘了举手。

秦老师提醒张达："张达，不是你选的毛超吗？"

"哦，我忘了。"

班上的同学都笑起来。毛超狠狠地瞪着张达，可是张达没看见。他在找地上有没有缝，他好钻进去。

马小跳笑死了。

"同意唐飞同学当三好学生的同学请举手！"

马小跳只顾笑，哪里还想得起唐飞是他选的？

"马小跳，快举手！"

唐飞急得在后面戳他的背。

马小跳在心里充满了对唐飞的感激，幸好唐飞那天没有选他，不然的话，他今天也会像他们那样丢人现眼。

导 读

逆转的情势

八字还没一撇，只不过是被自己人提了个名，张达、毛超和唐飞就都认为自己已经是名副其实的三好学生了，这种好笑的心理让人想到那个捡了个鸡蛋就开始梦想蛋生鸡、鸡生蛋最终"鸡飞蛋打"的痴人，三个"三好生"的结果也可想而知。这种"种瓜得豆"甚至连"豆"也没得到的情势逆转手法，在杨红樱作品中经常出现，是其故事喜剧效果产生的一个重要原因，也算得上是杨红樱创作的一个艺术特色了。

以本篇故事来说，先后出现两次情势的逆转。一次是马小跳和三个好朋友友谊的破裂和修复。原本确定好的"四全其美"计划，因为朋友们的临阵背叛，变成了"三全其美"；气愤已极的马小跳理直气壮也是十分悲壮地与好朋友分道扬镳，发誓"大路朝天，各走半边"。

不过，在好朋友们相继投其所好奉上心中最爱之后，势难挽回的事情立时出现了转机，调皮蛋们重又勾肩搭背起来。说分就分，说合就合，这就是小孩子间大起大落的友谊。能不让人捧腹？

再一次情势的逆转，则是围绕着三好学生的举手表决。张达、毛超和唐飞原以为能"三全其美"，不承想却逢上同学们表决时的"三缄其口"，就是在自己人内部，也先后要么遭遇"孤掌难鸣"而丢人现眼，要么遭遇无人喝彩而抓心挠肝。满以为登上了三好学生最高峰的三个调皮蛋一下子跌入了谷底，洋相百出；而马小跳却因祸得福，先前未获提名而生的阴霾一扫而光，心中充满了对唐飞背叛自己的感激。一场在四个调皮蛋心目中早就想当然决出胜负的结局最终却完全出乎他们的意料，来了个彻底的命运大"翻盘"，最后的大赢家竟是笑到最后的马小跳。能不让人大跌眼镜？

"播下的是龙种，收获的是跳蚤。"用这句西方谚语来形容唐飞们的心理落差，是再恰当不过的了。

《同桌冤家》

羊肉串都白请了

虽然张达、毛超、唐飞一人吃了马小跳五串羊肉串，但他们还是没有选路曼曼当大队委。

那天选大队委，采用的是无记名投票的方式，就是在选票上，写上三个候选人的名字：路曼曼、丁文涛、夏林果，每个同学只能在这三个候选人中选一个，在这个名字前边画一个圈，不能在选票上写任何字，更不能写自己的名字，否则，就不叫无记名投票了。

秦老师说，人民代表就是用这样的方式选出来的，国家主席和国务院总理也是用这样的方式选出来的。每个同学都要严肃认真地对待自己手中的选票。

听秦老师这么一说，张达、毛超和唐飞都觉得应该严肃认真地对待自己手中的选票。他们想选的人是夏林果，总不能因为吃了马小跳几串羊肉串，就违心地去选路曼曼吧？这样做，也太不严肃、太不认真了。再说在选票上又不写名字，马小跳怎么知道他们选的是谁？

张达在夏林果的名字前边画了个圈。

毛超在夏林果的名字前边画了个圈。

唐飞在夏林果的名字前边画了个圈。

马小跳拉了一阵选票，结果只有安琪儿和他自己在路曼曼的名字前边画了圈。马小跳的那个圈，画得特别大，特别圆。

把选票收上来，秦老师说要选一个同学上台来唱票，选一个同学上台来监票。

唱票的人，声音一定要洪亮，这非毛超莫属；监票的人只要会写"正"字就行，秦老师选了一个女同学上来监票。

毛超用唱歌的声调，拖声拖气地唱着选票上的名字。

"路—曼—曼！"

"夏—林—果！"

"夏—林—果！"

"毛超，谁叫你这么唱票的？"

毛超以为唱票就是把选票上画了圈的名字，用唱歌的声调唱出来。他一脸茫然地看着秦老师："不这样唱，应该怎样唱？"

秦老师说："你清清楚楚地把名字念出来就行了。"

唱票不唱，何必又要叫唱票呢？

毛超念一个名字，那个监票的女生就在黑板上画一笔。

没有几个人选丁文涛，他才一个"正"字，路曼曼和夏林果已各有四个"正"字。

"夏林果！"

"路曼曼！"

路曼曼的得票和夏林果的得票不相上下。路曼曼十分紧张，手指冰凉。马小跳比路曼曼还紧张，他头顶冒汗，拼命地向毛超挤眉弄眼，巴不得从他嘴巴里念出来的都是路曼曼的名字。

还剩最后一张选票了。

"夏林果!"

就这么一票，便一锤定音：夏林果就比路曼曼多一票，当选为大队委。

路曼曼是中队长，还得继续管马小跳。

"马小跳，下课不许去玩，把课文背三遍。"

下课的时候，马小跳带着乒乓球拍正要冲下楼去占乒乓球桌，路曼曼从他手中夺下乒乓球拍，命令他背课文。

马小跳跟路曼曼套近乎："看在我帮你拉选票的分上，求你放我一马。"

路曼曼根本不买他的账："谁让你帮我拉选票了？"

"我真的帮你拉了选票。"马小跳说，"我还请张达、毛超、唐飞他们三个，每人吃了五串羊肉串。"

"你请他们吃羊肉串，跟我有何相干？"

马小跳真是哪壶不开提哪壶，路曼曼为没被选上大队委已哭了好几场，现在马小跳又提起她的伤心事，路曼曼正好拿他出气。

马小跳已经背了课文，可路曼曼就是不让他走，鸡蛋里面挑骨头，让他背了一遍又一遍。等到她同意放马小跳走，上课铃却响了。

就因为马小跳又提起选大队委的事，路曼曼根本没有办法集中精力来听课。

秦老师请一位同学归纳课文的中心思想，秦老师不太满意。又请了一位同学来归纳，秦老师有点满意了，但还不是十分满意。要使秦老师十分满意，只有请路曼曼来回答。

"路曼曼！"

路曼曼站了起来。刚才她一直心猿意马，不知道秦老师要她干什么。

马小跳悄声告诉她："背诵课文。"

路曼曼松了口气，清了清喉咙，便流利地背诵起来。

课文背到一半，教室里就有笑声。秦老师那张一见到路曼曼就有喜色的脸，也变得难看起来。

"停！"秦老师走到路曼曼的跟前，"路曼曼，你上课没有听讲，思想开小差了？"

哈，路曼曼也有挨批评的时候！

马小跳向秦老师揭发路曼曼："她没有被选上大队委，她就不好好上课。"

秦老师的脸色更难看了："路曼曼，是这样吗？"

路曼曼的心里恨死马小跳了。

"我没有。"路曼曼不是那么容易被马小跳打倒的。她反戈一击："马小跳故意让我出丑。是他叫我背课文的。"

秦老师的目光从路曼曼的身上转移到马小跳的身上，看得马小跳心里发虚。

"马小跳，下了课到我办公室去。"

下了课，路曼曼拿着马小跳的乒乓球拍打乒乓球去了，马小跳却不能去，他得到秦老师的办公室去。

马小跳想不通：路曼曼上课思想开小差，却要他马小跳去站办公室，还讲不讲理呀？！

导 读

·快慢相济的叙事节奏

一般说来，孩子是喜欢快节奏阅读的，但这并不意味着孩子就不需要慢阅读。

本篇的前一个故事《帮冤家拉选票》已经告诉我们，为了不再让路曼曼管自己，甚至还想入非非夏林果能被派来管自己，马小跳暂时与路曼曼结成了"统一战线"，全力为她拉选票。所以，孩子们迫切地想知道唐飞们在吃了马小跳的羊肉串后有没有"嘴软"。本篇开门见山地就满足了孩子们的"求知欲"："虽然张达、毛超、唐飞一人吃了马小跳五串羊肉串，但他们还是没有选路曼曼当大队委"；在说出结局的同时也吊起了孩子们的阅读胃口——他们为什么没有选路曼曼？

至此，作者杨红樱开始放慢叙事节奏，回溯投票选举过程，将个中原委细细道来。杨红樱对小读者的接受心理把握得很好，节奏快慢相济，该加速时绝不拖沓，该停顿时尽管饶舌。所以，虽然张达、毛超、唐飞都是以"在夏林果的名字前边画了个圈"的方式不约而同地"背叛"了马小跳，但杨红樱并没有把他们的行为放在一起说，而是分开来一个一个地描述。这种复沓的叙述方式强化了叙事力度，增加了阅读的机趣；更重要的是，他们每个人的画圈就像是依序给正做白日梦的马小跳一记又一记闷棍似的。同样是画圈，马小跳画给路曼曼的那个圈，"画得特别大，特别圆"，这里的潜台词有多丰富！马小跳的全部希望、憧憬都寄托在这又大又圆的圈上了。因此，不难理解，力挺路曼曼的马小跳在整个唱票过程中"比路曼曼还紧张，他头顶冒汗，拼命地向毛超挤眉弄眼"，这段描写非常生动恰当地表现了马小跳微妙的心理。

在选举结果出来后，故事出现了一个大幅的跳跃。"路曼曼是中队长，还得继续管马小跳"。它既是对夏林果当选为大队委事实的肯定与强调，也诉说了路曼曼落选大队委后的心有不甘，一面又暗示着马小跳与路曼曼的"战争"还将继续。这句话在整篇故事中起着承上启下的作用——选举已告结束，"战争"行将开始。

"马小跳，下课不许去玩，把课文背三遍"，这不仅仅是路曼曼"继续管马小跳"的形象说明，还有如电影的切换镜头，"战争"取代了之前的"和平"。路曼曼处处找马小跳的茬儿，拿他当出气筒，马小跳也伺机反扑，在路曼曼心猿意马之时捉弄了她一回，还不失时机地告了她一状。眼看着要大获全胜了，可是峰回路转，偏心的秦老师还是做不到"好而知其恶，恶而知其美"，最终将批评的

矛头对准了马小跳。于是出现了令人啼笑皆非的场面：路曼曼不需为自己上课的思想溜号"买单"，"下了课，拿着马小跳的乒乓球拍打乒乓球去了"，欲打乒乓球而不得的马小跳却得为路曼曼的上课思想开小差负责，去站办公室了。

结尾一段"马小跳想不通"可不是可有可无的，它是对这哭笑不得的结果包含的无奈意味的深度发掘。

路曼曼病了

路曼曼从来不迟到。可是今天，都打上课铃了，路曼曼还没来。

哈，中队长也会迟到！

路曼曼的优点太多，要找出她身上的缺点，像登天那么难。每当马小跳发现了她的一个缺点，就会高兴得手舞足蹈，这时候，他的心里就会很平衡：中队长还不是跟他马小跳一样有缺点。

上完一节课，路曼曼还没来。

哈，中队长也会旷课！

旷课比迟到还严重。马小跳觉得应该把这个严重的情况，立即报告给秦老师。

"秦老师！秦老师！"就像报火警，马小跳一路大呼小叫，来到秦老师的办公室，"路曼曼旷课了！"

"什么旷课了？"秦老师白了一眼马小跳，"人家路曼曼生病了，请了病假。"

"哦，路曼曼生病了？"

路曼曼和马小跳的恩恩怨怨、是是非非、疙疙瘩瘩，刹那间都在马小跳的心中荡然无存。马小跳的心中，现在牵挂的是路曼曼的病：她是发烧了？还是拉肚子了？因为他自己生病，不是发烧，就是拉肚子。

"秦老师，我能不能去看路曼曼？"

"可以。"秦老师答应得很爽快，"下午放学，你和夏林果、丁文涛一块儿去。夏林果代表学校大队委，丁文涛代表班上中队委，你呢，就代表全班同学……"

秦老师还说了些什么，马小跳已经听不见了，他只听得见他的心咚咚地跳着，快从喉咙里跳出来了。马小跳长这么大，还是第一次做全班同学的代表。

下午放学，马小跳看见夏林果和丁文涛走在一起，便抛下张达、毛超和唐飞，追了过去。

"还有我！还有我！"

夏林果莫名其妙，不知道马小跳说的"还有我"是什么意思。

"秦老师说，让我代表全班同学，和你们一道去看路曼曼。"

"让你代表全班同学？"丁文涛用了很夸张的腔调，表示怀疑。

"不信，你们去问秦老师。"

"我是担心——"丁文涛吞吞吐吐，"你去了会不会加重路曼曼的病情？"

"为什么我去会加重路曼曼的病情？"

"因为路曼曼看见你就会生气。"

眼看着马小跳就要和丁文涛打起来，夏林果赶紧横在两个人中间。

三个人一起向路曼曼家走去。

丁文涛还在肚皮里跟马小跳打官司，马小跳早就没事了。

"我们总不能这样空着手去看路曼曼吧？"

马小跳很调皮、很淘气，但也很有人情味。

丁文涛说："我身上可没带钱。"

其实，丁文涛身上有钱，在内裤的内袋里，他妈妈给他的每一条内裤都缝了一个秘密的内袋，那就是装钱的地方。

夏林果说："我有三元钱。"

马小跳说："我有六元钱。"

马小跳的这六元钱，是准备买这个月新出来的漫画书的。

夏林果说："把我俩的钱合起来，我们去买束鲜花送给路曼曼。"

"买花没意思。"马小跳不同意，"花只能看，不能吃。要买就给路曼曼买吃的。"

马小跳是这样想的：如果他生病了，他才不希望别人送花给他，他希望别人送吃的给他。

夏林果是这样想的：如果她生病了，她才不希望别人送吃的给她，她希望别人送花给她。

夏林果要送花，马小跳要送吃的，两个人互不相让。结果，夏林果去花店买了一小束蓝色的小菊花；马小跳去一家西饼屋，买了一袋刚烤好的巧克力核桃小西饼。

来到路曼曼的病床边，夏林果献上那束蓝色的小菊花，路曼曼夸张地惊叫道："哇，好漂亮好漂亮的花！"

马小跳紧接着献上那袋香喷喷的巧克力核桃小西饼，路曼曼只说了声："谢谢，放在桌上吧！"

品藏版

　　夏林果朝马小跳得意地一笑：看，路曼曼喜欢她送的小菊花，不喜欢他送的小西饼。

　　其实，路曼曼是喜欢小西饼的，她已经闻到了小西饼的巧克力香，她现在就想吃，可是当着他们的面，特别是当着丁文涛的面，她得装着不想吃的样子。等他们走了再吃。

　　"马小跳，你怎么也想起来看我了？"

　　"我是代表全班同学来看你的。"

　　如果换一个人代表全班同学，路曼曼还能接受。可马小跳代表全班同学，路曼曼心里就有点不舒服。

　　马小跳看出了路曼曼心里有点不舒服，便高声声明道："是秦老师让我代表全班同学，让丁文涛代表中队委，让夏林果代表大队委……"

　　路曼曼一看见马小跳，就想管他。

　　"马小跳，古诗二首你背了没有？"

　　马小跳以为今天路曼曼生病了，他可以不背古诗二首。

　　"路曼曼，你看你都生病了，还管我背古诗二首？"

　　"你背不背？"

　　不知怎么的，刚才路曼曼还像个病人，现在管起马小跳来，一点都不像病人。

　　难道马小跳比给路曼曼治病的药还灵？

　　马小跳后悔了，后悔他来看路曼曼。这不是自己找上门来让路曼曼管吗？

　　路曼曼见马小跳不服她管的样子，就叫夏林果把她的书包拿来。

　　"你都生病了，还拿书包做什么？"

来到路曼曼的病床边，
夏林果献上那束蓝色的小菊花，
路曼曼夸张地惊叫道：
"哇，好漂亮好漂亮的花！"

"我要拿小本子，记马小跳不背古诗二首。"

马小跳见路曼曼已经把小本子从书包里拿出来，赶紧拦住她："我背！我背！"

马小跳背了一遍，路曼曼说他背错了两个字的音。

马小跳背第二遍，路曼曼说他背得没有感情。

马小跳又声情并茂地背第三遍，感情丰富得过了头，还加了动作，夏林果和丁文涛都偷着笑。路曼曼实在忍不住，也笑了。

马小跳不想再在路曼曼家待下去了，想走。路曼曼的奶奶却拦住马小跳，不让他走，说他医好了路曼曼的病，一定要留他吃晚饭。

真是的，在马小跳来之前，路曼曼好像还病得很厉害；马小跳来了以后，她整个心思都扑在马小跳身上，病一下子就好了，人也精神了许多。

路曼曼奶奶的意思是，马小跳简直就是一剂医病的药。为了快点把路曼曼的病医好，马小跳只好留下来了。

品藏版

导 读

·开掘丰富的心理内涵

台湾知名作家林良先生在《浅语的艺术》一书中如是说:"每一个儿童文学作家,都要具备运用'浅语'来写文学作品的能力。这也就是说,他必须懂得把他所知道的种种文学技巧用在浅语的写作上。"杨红樱就能够用很简洁浅白的语言准确、传神且富有张力地为人物心理"把脉",把人物性格特征"和盘托出"。

马小跳与路曼曼是同桌冤家,两个人的"战争"一直不断。所以,一旦抓住了路曼曼的缺点和把柄,马小跳能不高兴吗?"哈,中队长也会迟到","哈,中队长也会旷课",马小跳幸灾乐祸的心理,还有那将心比心的"攀比"心理同时跃然纸上。总算能够有机会学着路曼曼那样向秦老师打小报告,"反攻倒算"一把,既解恨又快意。

小说是这样写马小跳去报告路曼曼旷课的严重情况的:"'秦老师!秦老师!'就像报火警,马小跳一路大呼小叫,来到秦老师的办公室。'路曼曼旷课了!'"杨红樱以同时具有视觉效果和听觉效果的略带夸张的语言，极力渲染了马小跳迫不及待的心情。

但接下来，马小跳幸灾乐祸的心理消退，惺惺相惜的悲悯心理上升。那是在他获悉了路曼曼生病之后，他开始推己及人地牵挂着路曼曼可能得了什么病，并主动提出去看路曼曼。秦老师随口让他代表全班同学，又使得他飘飘然忘乎所以。所以，放学后那让人丈二和尚摸不着头脑的"还有我！还有我"，以及"让我代表全班同学"的再三声明，却又是再恰当不过地把马小跳受宠若惊、显摆炫耀的心理勾画出来了。

当然，马小跳后来的情绪又急转直下，因为在路曼曼家里受管制而生悔意，因为路曼曼要记名而生畏惧而强作"欢颜"，因为要快点把路曼曼的病医好而委曲求全地留下来……从"幸灾乐祸"到"忍辱负重"，马小跳这一天当中丰富的心理内涵又岂是那三种颜色的心情卡所能代表得了的呢？

正是因为儿童绵密细微的心理变化都被杨红樱敏锐细致地捕捉到了，所以小读者在阅读杨红樱的作品时才会产生"深得我意"的快感。而在这"意"的开掘中，杨红樱并没有用什么艰深华丽的语言，而是以其运用得烂熟于心的浅语就达到了出神入化的境地，这种驾驭语言的能力实在令人叹服。

《暑假奇遇》

奶奶家的猪呀狗呀猫呀

马小跳还是在五岁那年回过他奶奶家。

那时的记忆已经变得很模糊。马小跳只记得下了车还要走很长很长的山路，走着走着，他就睡着了，也不知是他的爸爸，还是来接他们的三表叔，把他背到奶奶家的。

奶奶家在山脚下。天一黑，奶奶就要关上院门，她说山上有许多野兽，夜里会下山来叼小孩吃。

马小跳一直以为奶奶是吓唬他的，他从来没有看见过有什么野兽从山上下来。

几年过去了，那里还真成了野生动物保护区。现在的人啊，都喜欢跟动物交朋友。于是，这野生动物保护区就成了风景旅游区，城里的人没事就往山上跑，如果能跟山上的猴子合影，那肯定是一件值得炫耀的事情。

马小跳要到他奶奶家去过一个暑假。

现在去不用再爬山路。马天笑先生开着汽车，一直开到奶奶的家门口。

汽车刚停下来，就有一只老白鹅摇摇摆摆地走过来，对着汽车嘎嘎地叫。

马小跳和马天笑先生从汽车里出来，就听见不知是谁在高声叫唤："贵客驾到！贵客驾到！"

爷爷和奶奶赶忙迎出来。

"什么贵客呀！"奶奶一手拉着马天笑先生，一手拉着马小跳，"这是我的儿子，这是我的孙子。"

马小跳不知奶奶在跟谁讲话，见她的眼睛是朝上看的，他也朝上看。原来，屋檐上挂着一只鸟笼，鸟笼里有一只褐色的黄嘴鸟，奶奶说："它叫鹩哥，见人说人话，说得比鹦鹉还好呢！"

"谢谢夸奖！谢谢夸奖！"

鹩哥在笼子里不停地向奶奶点头。

他们都往院子里走，老白鹅摇摇摆摆地跟在后面。

"去！"爷爷拍了拍老白鹅的脑袋，"你不去看门，跟进来干什么？"

马小跳觉得很奇怪：奶奶家不是有条大黄狗吗？怎么狗不去看门，倒叫鹅去看门？

"奶奶，咱们家的大黄狗呢？"

"大黄狗在睡觉。昨天夜里，它辛苦了，捉了好几只大老鼠呢！"

狗捉老鼠，真是多管闲事！狗把猫的事都干了，那猫又干什么呢？马小跳记得，奶奶家还养着一只大黑猫。

"奶奶，那……那只大黑猫呢？"

"你问大黑猫呀？唉，说起它我就伤心。"

奶奶真的抹起眼泪来。

"它死了吗？"

"它死了，我还没有这么伤心。"奶奶又重重地叹了一口气，

"它上树了。"

"猫上树有什么好伤心的？猫就喜欢上树玩。"

"它在树上不下来，风吹雨淋的，已经有三个月了。"

"三个月不下树，那还不被饿死？"

"我们每天给它送饭，一天三顿，一顿也不少。"爷爷看看墙上的挂钟，"再过一小时，就到送饭的时间了。"

马天笑先生坐着说了一会儿话，就开车走了，他还要上班呢！这次他是专门把马小跳送到爷爷奶奶家过暑假的。

马小跳要跟着爷爷去给大黑猫送饭。

爷爷把一碗猪肝拌饭放进篮子里，篮子里还有一根很长的绳子。

那棵树离奶奶家不远，几分钟就走到了。

马小跳看见了大黑猫，它趴在树杈上，眼睛死死地盯住一个地方，脸上的表情十分忧伤。

"大黑猫，快下来吃饭！"

"它才不会下来吃呢！得给它送上去。"

马小跳一看那树很高，难道爷爷要爬上去吗？

只见爷爷把篮子里的那根长绳子拿出来，一头系在篮子的提把上，一头挽成团儿，向树上一扔，绳子就挂在了大黑猫身旁的树枝上。

爷爷一拉绳子，篮子就升起来了，升到大黑猫的身边，大黑猫轻轻跳进篮子里。

过了一会儿，大黑猫从篮子里跳出来，跳到它刚才趴的树杈上，眼睛又死死盯住它刚才盯住的地方，脸上的表情比刚才还忧伤。

"爷爷，大黑猫怎么会这样？"

爷爷指着那棵树正对着的一个院落："大黑猫喜欢这家里的一只大白猫，可是大白猫的主人不喜欢它，就把大白猫拴在家里，不准它出来。大黑猫想念大白猫，就爬到这棵树上来，天天在上面看着大白猫。"

"难道那只大白猫永远被拴在家里，大黑猫就永远不下树吗？"

"我们什么办法都想了，对它都不管用。"爷爷说，"有一次，大雨下了一天一夜，大黑猫在树上冻得直打哆嗦，可它就是不下来。"

这猫好有脾气！马小跳也有脾气，他就不相信他没有办法让大黑猫从树上下来。

"我们快回去吧！"爷爷催促道，"黑旋风也该回家吃饭了。"

"黑旋风是谁？"

"是一头猪。"

"为什么叫黑旋风？"

"因为它是一头黑猪，跑起来像风一样快，所以叫它黑旋风。"

这就怪了，猪会跑得像风一样快？马小跳恨不得马上就回家去见见这头非凡的猪。

"它不在家里，到外面野去了。"

"那我们去找它吧！"

"找不到它的。它从来不让人知道它在什么地方。"

"那怎么办？"

爷爷哈哈一笑："我有的是办法。"

回到家里，爷爷拿出一把小号来，站在院子门口，滴滴答答地吹起来。

吹了好一会儿，也不见有什么黑猪跑回来。

"回家等着吧，它会回来的。"

马小跳刚回到屋里，就看见站在院子门口的老白鹅，扑闪着翅膀，弯着脖子，把脑袋藏在翅膀里。

"黑旋风回来了！"奶奶笑眯眯地说，"每次黑旋风回来，老白鹅都会这样。"

真的像一股黑旋风旋进门来，黑猪回来了！

马小跳走近了去看那头黑猪，黑猪的肚子很小，眼睛很大。马小跳还发现，在这头猪身上，最与众不同的是它的两只耳朵。别的猪耳朵都是耷拉下来的，可这头猪的耳朵却是竖着的。

马小跳去按它的耳朵，按下去，它又竖起来。再按下去，它再竖起来。

奇了怪了，爷爷奶奶家养的动物，怎么都是奇奇怪怪的？

小说中的童话元素 ■

最近，有国内科学家研究发现，十岁左右的儿童观看卡通片中的虚拟人造角色时，其大脑内侧前额叶可以被自动激活。这与成人的神经活动方式不同，成人对卡通片表现的虚拟场景中的人物角色或非人物角色没有类似的自动加工，大脑内侧前额叶不会被激活，该是所谓"脑残"了。这一研究结果让我们懂得，儿童与成年人在自动地区分真实与虚拟角色的认知与神经机制方面存在明显的差异；换言之，十岁左右的儿童还无法很好地区分开现实与幻想。

其实，杨红樱很早就已经敏锐地注意到了孩子的这种生理特征和由此产生的心理取向，所以在创作中并不完全为现实所束缚，而是放飞心灵，让想象成分弥漫于作品中。于是，现实与想象交织，造成了小说真真幻幻、扑朔迷离的艺术效果。

这种效果的获得，得益于杨红樱过去童话创作的经验。杨红樱曾明确表示过："没有以前的童话创作做底，就没有现在的小说风格。"这种介乎现实与幻想之间的状态在展示了她丰沛想象力的同时，也将小读者的心带到了幽邈辽远的魔幻境界，让他们在阅读的时候有了"飞"的感觉。

这篇小说就有着许多童话元素。你看，奶奶家的动物都奇奇怪怪的，它们各自都有着让人匪夷所思的本领，从事着与同类、与"本职"不同的"事业"：比鹦鹉说话说得还好的鹩哥，能够发出"预警"，与人对话；老白鹅看守大门，迎来送往；大黄狗多管闲事，捉拿耗子；大黑猫因为喜欢邻家的大白猫而上树守望，无论风吹雨打，三个月不肯下树；就连黑猪也与众不同，两只耳朵竖起来，每天旋风般地奔跑，有着让人捉摸不透的理想。杨红樱对于这些人们生活中比较熟悉的动物品性的书写，恰好改写了人们对于它们在认知上的日常生活经验，让人觉得不可思议，但一切又在情理之中。

作为《暑假奇遇》的开篇，本篇故事给整本小说定下了"奇"的基调，就是在这种亦真亦幻的境地中，马小跳开始了他重新"发现"动物的神奇旅程；这其实也是杨红樱引领着我们"发现"这些动物身上被人的偏见遮掩了的"美"的过程。当这些动物多姿多彩的另一面向我们打开的时候，杨红樱对于动物的关爱之情也在字里行间映射出来。

可以说，《暑假奇遇》是一本生态小说，它令读者重新打量身边的世界，重新思考人与动物、人与自然应该怎样和谐共处这一既古老又现代的话题。

是谁过节日

即使是周末，宝贝儿妈妈也从来不睡懒觉，睡懒觉容易发胖，宝贝儿妈妈怕胖。何况，她还要做三个人的早餐，而这三个人的早餐还不一样：马小跳要吃加牛奶的麦片粥；马天笑先生要喝很浓的豆浆；而她自己吃水果色拉。把水果色拉当早餐吃，既有营养，又不会长胖，对皮肤也很好。

进了厨房，宝贝儿妈妈的第一件事就是开冰箱。可是这天早晨，她刚走到冰箱那里，就哭了。因为她看见了冰箱门上的一张画："祝母亲节快乐！"这是她亲爱的儿子马小跳画给她的。

马天笑先生经常说，宝贝儿妈妈是个永远长不大的小女孩，她爱哭——生气时哭，高兴时也哭，而且哭起来就没个完。

宝贝儿妈妈只顾哭，一直到马小跳穿着拖鞋，吧嗒吧嗒走进厨房，她才想起做早餐。

"宝贝儿妈妈，不用做了，我带你出去吃。"马小跳一副男人气概，"今天，我要带你出去过母亲节。快去换衣服吧，穿我最喜欢的那件。"

马小跳最喜欢宝贝儿妈妈穿那件桃红色的、高领无袖的羊毛衫，这件衣服把宝贝儿妈妈的脸色衬托得非常好看。

宝贝儿妈妈跟着马小跳出了门，她也不问马小跳去哪儿，反正今天她把自己都交给马小跳了。

马小跳要到取款机那里去取钱。宝贝儿妈妈说不用取了，她带着钱。

"哪能用你的钱！"马小跳说，"今天是我给你过母亲节，当然是用我的钱。"

马小跳跑到取款机那里，取了三百元钱。身上有了钱，走起路来都是理直气壮的样子。

走过了几家卖早点的餐馆，马小跳都视而不见。快到一家肯德基店，马小跳开口问道："宝贝儿妈妈，你早餐想吃什么？"

"我……"

宝贝儿妈妈想吃水果色拉。

"想吃什么大胆说。"马小跳拍拍他衣服的口袋，"我有的是钱！"

"我想吃肯德基。"

宝贝儿妈妈说的，其实是马小跳想的。

"好，我就带你去吃肯德基。"

这家肯德基店刚开门，还没有顾客。马小跳和宝贝儿妈妈是最早的顾客，所以受到了全体服务员的热情接待。

"宝贝儿妈妈，你想吃什么就点什么。"马小跳拍拍他衣服的口袋，"我有的是钱。"

宝贝儿妈妈只点了一杯柠檬茶，马小跳却点了一大堆：香辣鸡腿汉堡、巧克力奶昔、小份的薯条，外加一大杯冰可乐。

从肯德基店里出来，马小跳对宝贝儿妈妈说："我带你去步行街逛商店吧！"

这正是宝贝儿妈妈想去的地方。

步行街的两旁全部都是商店。宝贝儿妈妈不去看商店里面的东西，只看商店外面的橱窗。

这里，有好几家大商店的橱窗都是宝贝儿妈妈设计的，很豪华、很气派。那些名牌专卖店的橱窗，虽然不大，但布置得很别致、很有味道，宝贝儿妈妈看得特别仔细。如果要在平时，马小跳早就不耐烦了，可是今天，马小跳显得格外有耐心，他对宝贝儿妈妈说："没事，你随便看，想看多久就看多久。"

该吃午饭了，路过许多中餐厅、西餐厅、火锅店，马小跳都视而不见，一直走到一家比萨饼屋，马小跳才停住脚步。

"宝贝儿妈妈，你想吃什么？"

宝贝儿妈妈心里想吃的是那配有许多野山菌的火锅，嘴上却说："我想吃比萨饼。"

马小跳要了一个中份的比萨饼。结果，宝贝儿妈妈连一小块都没有吃完。

从比萨饼屋出来，马小跳问宝贝儿妈妈："还想去哪儿？"

宝贝儿妈妈还想看橱窗，可是她却说想去游乐园。

马小跳欣然同意："过母亲节嘛，就应该去游乐园！"

马小跳进了游乐园便如鱼得水。他最喜欢坐翻滚列车，又惊险又刺激。

"宝贝儿妈妈，我陪你去坐翻滚列车。"

马小跳硬拉着宝贝儿妈妈去坐了翻滚列车，把宝贝儿妈妈弄得晕头转向，整个下午，她都坐在游乐场的长椅上发晕。

天色暗下来，宝贝儿妈妈的头不那么晕了，马小跳把该玩

的都玩了个够，这才回到宝贝儿妈妈的身边。

出了游乐园的门，就看见麦当劳店。

"宝贝儿妈妈，你晚上想吃什么?"

这时候，宝贝儿妈妈最想回家熬点稀饭，就酸辣泡菜吃。可她说出来的，又是马小跳想吃的。

"我想吃麦当劳。"

宝贝儿妈妈什么都没吃，马小跳心里很过意不去。他摸摸口袋里还有一些钱，就一定要送一样礼物给宝贝儿妈妈。

"宝贝儿妈妈，你想要什么样的礼物? 大胆说，我给你买。"

宝贝儿妈妈在心里笑死了，可她却不敢笑出来，她怕伤了马小跳那"男人"的自尊心。

看路边有个卖头饰的专卖店，宝贝儿妈妈说她想要一个别头发的发卡。

宝贝儿妈妈一眼就看中了一个双鱼木发卡，因为她的星座就是双鱼座。

"这个多少钱?"

"三十块。"

"太贵了。"

宝贝儿妈妈嫌贵，不想要。

"喜欢就买。"马小跳男人气十足，"小姐，这个我要了，请包起来。"

马小跳付了三十块，口袋里就只剩下两个钢镚儿了。

这一天，过得很圆满，钱也刚好用完，秦老师布置的作文《难忘的母亲节》也有内容可写:

早晨，带妈妈去吃肯德基。

上午，带妈妈逛街。

中午，带妈妈去吃比萨饼。

下午，带妈妈去游乐园。

晚上，带妈妈去吃麦当劳。

这些内容，马小跳津津乐道。而一个最重要、最有美感的内容，马小跳却只字未提，那就是在母亲节这一天，马小跳送了一个双鱼木发卡给妈妈，因为她的星座是双鱼星座。

马小跳不是忘记了这个内容，而是他对那个双鱼木发卡不感兴趣。

结果，马小跳的这篇作文交上去，秦老师的批语是："是你过节日，还是你妈妈过节日？"

母爱无边

"下笔千言，离题万里。"本来是马小跳一心一意要给宝贝儿妈妈过母亲节，结果宝贝儿妈妈实实在在让儿子过了把儿童节的瘾。马小跳的"作文"整个儿写跑了题，秦老师当然要批评"是你过节日，还是你妈妈过节日"了。

作文跑题的原因不是马小跳不体贴妈妈，而是因为他的心就是那么大，所能想到的会令妈妈感到最圆满的事情就是那些能令自己开心的事情。譬如这一天的内容安排——吃肯德基、吃比萨饼、去游乐园、吃麦当劳，这都是马小跳津津乐道且流连忘返的，推己及人，自然觉得妈妈也该像他一样喜欢，同时也就会对妈妈的"真爱""视而不见"了。

而妈妈的心永远是那么大，儿子送的一幅祝福母亲节快乐的画就足够让她感动不已。她把自己的需要压缩到最低的限度，所做所想的一切就都是为着迁就和满足儿子的需要与感受。所以，母亲节这天，出现了妈妈与孩子对调位置过节的可笑情形：孩子处处以能挡风遮雨的大人自居，妈妈则时时表现得像一个需要受呵护的孩子。

马小跳明明是小孩，说话、行为却处处"装腔作势"，俨然大人。比如语言方面的——"我带你出去吃"，"想吃什么大胆说"，"你想吃什么就点什么"，"我有的是钱"，"你想要什么样的礼物，大胆说，我给你买"；再如行为上的——走起路来时的理直气壮，为显示自己有钱而拍拍衣服口袋，买礼物时的男人气十足……一个一夜之间"长大"的孩子如此一本正经的言行，当然跟他的实际年龄、身份和心智是背道而驰的，这其间的反差当然会引人发笑了。

马小跳的的确确就是一个孩子，所以，在为妈妈做的所有事情当中，能进入到他作文中的事情只是他的兴趣点；而像为妈妈做的最有美感的内容——买双鱼木发卡，他却视而不见了。成人与儿童两种审美观的"歧异"就是这样微妙。

按理来说，成人和孩子该会因为迥然有异的兴趣发生"冲突"的，但在这里却没有。那是因为他们彼此都考虑到了对方，尤其是妈妈，以她博大的胸襟包容了一切，甚至小心翼翼地维护着儿子的"男人"自尊心不要受到伤害。如此的宝贝儿妈妈，多么可敬！

这篇故事在轻松幽默中让我们感受到了融融的亲情、无边的母爱。表现母爱，杨红樱从母亲节母子"换位"这样一个别出心裁的角度入手，避免了平铺直叙，令人击节叹赏。

《天真妈妈》

十二层的三明治

　　破天荒地，马小跳那篇给宝贝儿妈妈洗脚的作文得了一个九十分；破天荒地，秦老师在班上念了那篇作文。念完了作文，秦老师问大家："这篇作文好在哪里？"

　　毛超说："这篇作文把洗脚的过程写得很清楚。"

　　马小跳低着头，他自己心里明白，他并没有真实地写出给妈妈洗脚的全部过程，比如把妈妈的脚烫伤了，他就没写。

　　夏林果说："这篇作文写得很优美，还有真情实感。"

　　夏林果指的是马小跳说"长大了，要给妈妈买水晶鞋"的那段话。凡是有梦想的女孩子，都会对这段话着迷的。

　　因为这篇作文，秦老师对马小跳的印象还有了一些改变。马小跳能写出这样感人的作文，说明他还是一个有情有义的孩子，说明他对他妈妈爱得很深很深。

　　下课了，秦老师把马小跳叫到办公室。秦老师经常把马小跳叫到办公室，每一次都是叫去批评的。破天荒地，这一次，秦老师没有批评马小跳，而是慈爱地拉着马小跳的手。马小跳习惯了秦老师对他凶，像今天这样，马小跳反而不自在。

马小跳把手缩了回来。

秦老师也不介意，她用慈爱的语气说："马小跳，从你的作文里可以看出你是一个有孝心的孩子。孝敬父母，不是一天两天，是一辈子都要做的事情，我希望你能坚持下去。"

是的，马小跳要坚持下去，他要继续做孝敬宝贝儿妈妈的事情，但是，不能再给她洗脚了。秦老师不是说过吗，给父母做一顿饭，也是孝敬父母。

马小跳要给宝贝儿妈妈做一顿饭。

无论做什么事情，马小跳都喜欢跟别人做得不一样。他要给宝贝儿妈妈做的这顿饭，一定是宝贝儿妈妈从来没有吃过的一顿饭，一定是她这一辈子都忘不了的一顿饭。

马小跳他们家的冰箱又高又大，从来都是塞得满满的，水果、蔬菜、肉，应有尽有。

马小跳已经想好他要做什么了。他十分从容地从冰箱里拿出一包还没开封过的全麦面包片，又从消毒柜里拿出一个宝贝儿妈妈最喜欢的蓝花边大盘子。一包全麦面包片有十二片，马小跳要给宝贝儿妈妈做一个十二层的三明治。

第一层，夹芒果片；第二层，夹牛肉松；第三层，夹番茄片；第四层，夹鸡腿肉；第五层，夹花生酱；第六层，夹草莓酱；第七层，夹五香鱼片；第八层，夹香蕉片；第九层，夹色拉酱和黄瓜片；第十层，夹奇异果片；第十一层，夹生菜叶；在最高一层上，马小跳做了一个蛋黄酱的堆儿，在蛋黄酱堆儿上放了一颗鲜红的樱桃。

十二层的三明治有一尺多高，色彩缤纷，看着就让人垂涎欲滴。别说宝贝儿妈妈没吃过这样的三明治，就是美国的总统、

英国的女王，恐怕都没吃过这样的三明治。

这是马小跳的杰作，马小跳越看越爱。

马小跳小心翼翼地把十二层的三明治从厨房端到饭厅里。他见餐桌上的花瓶里插着几朵鲜红的玫瑰花，就用剪刀一朵一朵地剪下来，放在盘子边上，把十二层的三明治围在中间。

在玫瑰花的衬托下，这个本来就不同凡响的三明治更加不同凡响。

宝贝儿妈妈回来了。她一进门就看见了那个不同凡响的三明治。

"哇，好漂亮的三明治！"宝贝儿妈妈的脸上有像小女孩一样惊喜的表情，"马小跳，你要请女同学来玩吗？"

只有请女同学，马小跳才会这么郑重其事。

"宝贝儿妈妈，这是我为你做的。"

马小跳小心翼翼地把十二层的三明治给宝贝儿妈妈端过来。

宝贝儿妈妈又被感动得一塌糊涂，她一感动就会哭。

马小跳不能理解，宝贝儿妈妈为他做的事情数都数不清，而他就为她做了一个三明治，只不过这个三明治特别了一点，她就感动成这样子。

"宝贝儿妈妈，你别哭啊！"马小跳送过去一张擦眼泪的纸巾，"你快尝尝这三明治，看好吃不好吃。"

这么高的一个三明治，宝贝儿妈妈不知道从什么地方下口。

"我不吃！"宝贝儿妈妈说，"我要把它摆起来，让大家都来参观我儿子给我做的三明治。"

"宝贝儿妈妈你吃吧，只要你喜欢，我天天给你做，我一辈子给你做。"

听了马小跳的话，宝贝儿妈妈已经泣不成声，哪里还吃得下这三明治？

客厅里有个陈列柜，里面展示的都是马小跳的爸爸马天笑先生的奖杯、奖状。马天笑先生是著名的玩具设计师，他设计的很多玩具都获过奖，特别是那个根据马小跳的形象设计的"跳跳娃"，更是在世界玩具博览会上获得过金奖。马天笑先生专门为这个一尺多高的金奖杯做了一个精致的玻璃匣子，装起来放在陈列柜的中间。

宝贝儿妈妈把玻璃匣子里的金奖杯取出来，把马小跳做的十二层三明治放进去。这个精致的玻璃匣子，就像是专门为这个十二层三明治定做的，不高不矮，不宽不窄，刚合适。

宝贝儿妈妈把装着十二层三明治的玻璃匣子放在客厅最显眼的地方。果然，马天笑先生一进门就看见了这个玻璃匣子。

"这是什么？我的金奖杯呢？"

当马天笑先生看见他视若命根子的金奖杯被随随便便地扔在一边，他以为是马小跳干的。

"马小跳……"

马天笑先生暴跳如雷。

"你那么凶干什么？"宝贝儿妈妈一脸幸福无比的表情，"咱们儿子给我做的三明治，是我放进去的。"

"是三明治重要，还是我的金奖杯重要？"

"当然是三明治重要。"宝贝儿妈妈理直气壮，"这是我儿子给我做的。"

马天笑先生哭笑不得："你儿子给你做的，你就吃了吧。你把它放进玻璃匣子里干什么？"

"我不吃，我要天天看着它。"

"我看你是吃不了它。"看着这个有一尺多高的十二层的三明治，马天笑先生笑起来，"除非你有一张河马的嘴巴或者鳄鱼的嘴巴。"

马天笑先生说得没错，只有像河马或鳄鱼那样的超级大嘴巴，才可能把这么高、这么多层的三明治一口咬下去。

宝贝儿妈妈才不管那么多，她压根儿就没打算去吃那个三明治。她每天都往家里带人，带这些人来参观那个玻璃匣子里的十二层三明治。当那些人发出啧啧的赞叹声，这时候的宝贝儿妈妈是世界上最幸福的妈妈。

层次分明的"三明治"

　　当过半天"爸爸"的马小跳曾经这样教"儿子"马天笑写"我当爸爸"的作文："为什么我要当爸爸呢？这就是开头；我是怎样当爸爸的呢？这就是经过；我当爸爸的感受是什么呢？这就是结尾。"（《贪玩老爸》）本篇故事也正像三明治一样，开头、经过、结尾都很清晰，层次分明：马小跳为什么要做十二层的三明治？他是怎样做的？做完之后，大家特别是宝贝儿妈妈的感受如何？如果把古人总结的"凤头、猪肚、豹尾"的写作方法搬用过来解说，不免要削足适履，也容易让人如堕云雾之中，反倒是马小跳的作文"三段法"恰切地说明了这篇故事的写作策略。

　　马小跳为什么会想着做十二层的三明治？这实在是跟秦老师的三次"破天荒"之举和同学的积极评价有着直接的关系。破天荒地得到秦老师的鼓励和称赏，马小跳当然要做一件破天荒的事情了。作为孝敬父母表现的"给父母做一顿饭"也就成为题中应有之意了。于是，充满瑰丽想象力的十二层三明治出现了。这可是和杜真子做的"三色饭"、张达外婆摆设过的"鲜桃宴"一样能长时间鲜活地留存在人们记忆中的事情。本来很物质的东西，却成为很精神的享受，普通实在的"米"在杨红樱非凡想象的酵母作用下最终变成了浓香扑鼻的"酒"。

结尾部分是三明治"落成"后宝贝儿妈妈"被感动得一塌糊涂"的感受，这可是杨红樱浓墨重彩地写到的。宝贝儿妈妈平日里为马小跳做过的事情数都数不清，马小跳只不过做了一个稍微特别点的三明治，她就被感动得不得了，会把玻璃匣子里马天笑先生视若命根子的金奖杯随便摆在一边，而把十二层三明治放进去，要天天看着它。

适时出现的马天笑的评价是理智的，从"实用"的角度提醒宝贝儿妈妈、也是在提醒被牵引到五彩斑斓想象世界的读者注意，这样一个大型三明治中看不中吃，要对付它可得有河马或者鳄鱼的嘴巴！可"宝贝儿妈妈才不管那么多"，继续沉浸在幸福的洪水中，每天都往家里带人参观三明治，在别人啧啧的赞叹声中感受幸福。

孩子为母亲做的一点点事情居然会把母亲感动得一塌糊涂，母亲完全是从审美的、超越功利的角度来品评咂摸孩子的言行，母亲的心就是这样容易得到满足与慰藉。宝贝儿妈妈天真的个性、未泯的童心由是毕现。"谁言寸草心，报得三春晖"啊！

不用胶卷的数码相机

　　六一儿童节到了，学校要在阶梯礼堂里举行一个盛大的庆祝会，每个班都要表演节目。马小跳他们班的节目，就是夏林果跳的芭蕾舞《天鹅湖》。

　　每次表演，夏林果都要找人给她拍照片。她有一本厚厚的影集，里面放的全是她的舞台表演照。

　　夏林果想找张达给她拍照片，她比较喜欢话少的男生。而在这个班上，咋咋呼呼的男生特别多，像毛超、马小跳、丁文涛，都属于咋咋呼呼一类的。只有两个男生不属于那一类，一个是唐飞，他爱吃东西，因为嘴巴忙不过来，所以话自然而然就少了；另一个是张达，他说话有点结巴，他知道扬长避短，特别知道在女生面前怎样扬长避短，他的长处是行动敏捷。所以张达基本上是只行动，不说话，越不说话越显得酷。在夏林果的心目中，张达就是一个很酷的男生。

　　夏林果抬着下巴，迈着跳芭蕾舞的外八字步，朝张达走去。那时候，张达正在打乒乓球，跟他在一起的，还有马小跳、唐飞和毛超。

"张达，你会拍照吗？"夏林果直奔主题，漂亮女生不用转弯抹角，"我明天表演时想请你帮我拍照。"

张达还没来得及开口，马小跳和毛超就咋呼开了。

"他连焦距都对不准。"

"摁快门的时候，他的手会发抖。"

连嘴巴没有空闲的唐飞也停止了咀嚼，插了一句："他们家的傻瓜相机，闪光灯都是坏的。"

"我……我……"

张达本来就结巴，一急，就更说不出话来。马小跳乘虚而入："夏林果，我们家有部高级相机，我老爸从日本买回来的名牌，明天我给你拍。"

唐飞把马小跳推到一边："夏林果，我们家有部摄像机，明天，我从头到尾，全给你拍下来。"

在他们旁边还有一个丁文涛，他们的话他都听见了，但他不动声色，他知道该怎么办。

马小跳回到家里，就像报喜一样对马天笑先生说："老爸，你终于可以见到夏林果了。"

马天笑先生正为中国娃娃的形象没搞定而发愁，所以他立刻追问："夏林果什么时候到咱们家来？"

"夏林果明天要在我们学校的礼堂表演芭蕾舞，我可以把我们家的相机带去，把她拍下来，再把她的相片带回来。"

其实，马天笑先生是很不情愿把家里那部从日本带回来的高档相机让马小跳带到学校里去的，可他得尽快地把中国娃娃的形象定下来，所以只好同意马小跳把高级相机带到学校里去。

"老爸，相机里装胶卷了没有？"

马天笑先生平时会买许多胶卷，都存在冰箱里。他从冰箱里取出一卷胶卷来，正要装进相机里，马小跳又在喊了。

"老爸，三角架是怎么用的？"

马天笑先生忙得满头大汗。胶卷还没装好，他又去教马小跳捣鼓三角架。

"其实你不用三角架也可以。"

"要用的，"马小跳说，"如果我给夏林果照相时，手抖了怎么办？"

第二天，马小跳是脖子上挎着相机、肩膀上扛着三角架去学校开庆祝会的。

"马小跳，你这是干什么？"

秦老师皱着眉头。

"一会儿夏林果上台表演的时候，我给她拍照。"

"谁让你拍的？"

"是夏林果让我拍的。不信，你问唐飞。"

唐飞今天也带了摄像机来，不等秦老师问他，他就抢着回答，而且还添油加醋地说："夏林果说，有人给她拍照，她才跳得好；没人给她拍照，她就跳不好。"

秦老师想，夏林果是代表全班表演节目，是为班上争光，就让他们给她拍吧。再说一年才过一次儿童节，何必让他们不高兴呢？

秦老师没有再追究下去，等于是默认了。

马小跳趾高气扬，就怕别人看不见他脖子上挎着一部照相机。

丁文涛凑到马小跳的胸前，看了半天，才说了一句话："你这部相机真大啊！"

"等我把镜头伸出来，那才叫大呢！"

马小跳把照相机端起来，摁了一下什么机关，只听味的一声，黑洞洞的镜头伸出来，足有半尺多长。

"哇噻！"

马小跳的周围响起一片赞叹声。

"看清楚了没有？"马小跳问丁文涛，"这才是高级相机！"

丁文涛笑了一笑，但他是皮笑肉不笑。

庆祝会开始了。校长讲完话就是文艺演出。夏林果是最后一个节目，最后的节目就是最好的节目。马小跳根本不知道前面演了些什么节目，他一心等待的是夏林果的节目。

终于等到了最后一个节目。

当报幕员还没有报出最后一个节目是什么，马小跳已经冲到舞台上去了。

"马小跳，你干什么？"秦老师拉住了马小跳，"下来！快下来！"

"我上去给夏林果拍照！"

"只准你在下面拍！"

下面拍就下面拍。马小跳手忙脚乱地捣鼓着三角架，还没支起来，夏林果已经开始跳了。

有闪光灯在不停地闪。

除了他马小跳，还有谁带了相机来给夏林果拍照？

马小跳找到闪光灯后面的人，原来是丁文涛。他手里捏着一部巴掌大的相机，在那里猛闪。

这家伙就会玩阴的。

马小跳不会输给丁文涛。三角架也不支了，他举着相机，在舞台下面跑来跑去，镜头追随着舞台上的夏林果，一阵猛闪。

夏林果的节目比较长，丁文涛说给夏林果照了一百多张。

马小跳说，他起码给夏林果照了两百多张。本来嘛，他的照相机比丁文涛那巴掌大的照相机高级多了，当然会照得比他的多。

"什么牌子的胶卷可以照两百多张呀？"

丁文涛怪里怪气地问了这么一句。

马小跳有点心虚了，他知道他相机里面的胶卷是三十六张的，最多能照到三十八张。

"难道你相机里的胶卷可以照一百多张吗？"马小跳问。

"我告诉你，我的是数码相机，根本就不用胶卷，只用一张卡，就可以照到四百张。你懂不懂？"

马小跳傻了。丁文涛那部不起眼的、巴掌大的相机，居然是数码相机，不用装胶卷，就可以照四百张。

"我还怀疑你的相机里根本就没有胶卷。"丁文涛指指马小跳脖子上的相机，"你最好把它打开看看。"

马小跳真的心虚了，他老爸完全有可能做出这样的事情。

"怎么，不敢打开？"

丁文涛咄咄逼人，把马小跳的肺都气炸了。

"打开就打开！"

哗的一声，马小跳打开了相机。这时候的马小跳，差点昏死过去——相机里真的没有胶卷！

想起马小跳刚才忙得不可开交的样子，班上的男生女生都笑起来，连秦老师都笑了。

马小跳呀马小跳，你真是白忙了。

导 读

欲抑先扬

　　这则故事够幽默的了，它把马小跳争强好胜的心理刻画得淋漓尽致。作者杨红樱了解小读者的阅读心理，所以在表现马小跳的这一心理时，并没有做太多的静态描写，而主要是通过一系列生动形象的语言、动作描写来表现他是如何咋咋呼呼的。

　　杨红樱在这里采取了先扬后抑的写作方式，为此，做了足够的铺垫，让马小跳出尽风头：起始，马小跳与唐飞咋咋呼呼地对笨嘴拙舌的张达进行了一番人身攻击，把为夏林果照相的"美差"抢了过来；回到家里，马小跳又咋咋呼呼忙东忙西指挥马天笑干这干那，乃至让马天笑忙中出错忘记了装胶卷；来到学校，他趾高气扬地向别人展示自己家的高级相机，一时还真就"镇"住了丁文涛；拍照时，在舞台下面很专业地跑来跑去一阵猛闪、处处不让劲敌……

　　跟丁文涛的同台"竞技"也同样显出他的不服输来：

你丁文涛巴掌大小的相机就照了一百多张，我就要和你抬杠——我日本带回来的大大的高档相机起码照了两百多张；你丁文涛咄咄逼人满腹狐疑，我马小跳就当仁不让打开"天窗"。可马小跳太不知道天外有天了，牛皮吹大了，也就该吹爆了，少不了当众出丑、大爆冷门。相形之下，同样咋咋呼呼的男生丁文涛却更有城府，他能不动声色，不显山不露水，该出手时就出手。马小跳的"浮"无形中就被突出了。

　　小说中有些语言不免夸张，但夸张得恰到好处，属于前人说的那种"夸而有节，饰而不诬"，像"把马小跳的肺都气炸了"、"差点昏死过去"等，不但渲染了马小跳的心情，还凸现了小说的喜剧效果。这与马小跳早先咋咋呼呼的表现是多么的相得益彰啊！

《漂亮女孩夏林果》

只请一个男生的生日会

夏林果的生日快到了，她妈妈准备在家里为她举办一个小型的生日会，说是请的人不要太多，有那么两三个就行了。

夏林果是一定要请路曼曼的，因为上个星期，路曼曼过生日时刚请了她。夏林果还想请张达，但她不好意思亲自去请，她让路曼曼帮她请。

"请张达？"路曼曼大惊小怪，"夏林果，你请张达，都不请丁文涛吗？"

路曼曼的生日会请了丁文涛，但是，夏林果觉得丁文涛一点都不好玩。

"你觉得张达好玩吗？他连话都讲不清楚，只会吃蛋糕。"

"我就是请张达去吃蛋糕的。"夏林果说，"生日蛋糕那么大，我吃了会发胖，你也吃不了那么多，只有请张达来帮忙啰……"

路曼曼觉得夏林果说得有道理，就去帮她请张达。夏林果还特别叮嘱路曼曼，不要让别人知道她的生日会只请了张达一个男生。路曼曼请夏林果放心，她的生日会也只请了丁文涛一个男生，所以她不会让别人知道的。

下课的时候，路曼曼找到张达，他正和马小跳、唐飞和毛超在一起。

"张达，你过来！"

跟他们还有一段距离，路曼曼不过去，大声地命令张达。

"什么……什么事？"

"我有话跟你说。"

"你说……说吧！"

"这话不能让他们听见！"

路曼曼说的"他们"，指的是马小跳、唐飞和毛超，立即引起众怒。

"张达，不过去，看她能把你怎么样！"

张达犹豫不决：是过去，还是不过去呢？

路曼曼下了最后通牒："张达，你再不过来，你会后悔的。"

张达怕后悔，如离弦的箭一般，射到路曼曼的面前。

"张达，夏林果请你去参加她的生日会，她只请了你一个男生，不许你跟他们几个说。"

路曼曼说的"他们"，仍然是指马小跳、唐飞和毛超。

张达回到他们几个中间，几乎是异口同声，他们都问路曼曼跟他说什么了。

张达不吭声。

"到底说什么啦？"马小跳最急，"你说呀！"

张达还是不吭声。在他们几个中，毛超最有心机，他会拐弯抹角："张达，你只告诉我们，路曼曼跟你说的，是好事还是坏事？"

张达老老实实地回答："是好事。"

唐飞生气了："是好事，为什么不告诉我们？"

马小跳比唐飞更生气："你跟路曼曼是好朋友，还是跟我们是好朋友？"

"当然跟我们是好朋友。"每当这种时候，毛超就会跳出来当和事老，"路曼曼是女生，不可以跟她做好朋友的，是不是，张达？"

张达招了，他怕他们说他是路曼曼的好朋友，不是他们的好朋友。

"路曼曼说，夏林果请……请我去参……参加她的生日会……"

"夏林果只请你一个人？"

张达老老实实地点头。

反应最强烈的是唐飞："会不会搞错？夏林果最应该请的人是我呀！我是她的同桌。"

毛超提醒他："现在不是。"

"现在不是原来是。"

毛超也觉得这里面有问题。班上的好多同学的生日会都会请他，因为他的废话多、笑话多，有他参加的生日会总是热热闹闹。冷冷清清的生日会有什么意思呢？

马小跳这时候只恨路曼曼，他和路曼曼是同桌冤家，也许人家夏林果是请了他的，就是她路曼曼在作怪。

他们各自怀着自己的想法，分别去找夏林果。

唐飞气急败坏，他是最先找夏林果的。

"夏林果……"

唐飞刚叫了声夏林果，眼睛眨巴眨巴，眼圈就红了。

夏林果不知道发生了什么事："唐飞，你哭了？"

唐飞真的哭了。他从小就爱哭，一哭起来眼泪就像断了线的珠子往下落，别人还以为他有什么伤心欲绝的事。

"你的生日会，为什么不请我？呜呜呜……"

夏林果被唐飞的满面泪水吓住了，赶紧说："唐飞，你别哭，我请你，我一定请你！"

唐飞有这种本事：说哭就哭，眼泪哗哗流；说不哭，眼珠子像可以吸水一样，把眼泪收回去。

唐飞欢天喜地地去找毛超："夏林果请我了！"

毛超坐不住了，也去找夏林果。

"夏林果，你知不知道，不请我的生日会会是什么样子？"

夏林果问："什么样子？"

"冷冷清清。"毛超骇人听闻，"冷冷清清的生日会根本就不叫生日会。总之，没有我，你那个生日会就不叫生日会。"

毛超真会缠人，他可以一直缠着夏林果说生日会。夏林果被他缠烦了，只好同意请他参加生日会。

毛超欢天喜地地去找马小跳："夏林果请我了。"

马小跳不去找夏林果，却去找路曼曼："是不是你在搞破坏？"

路曼曼每天都要和马小跳吵几场，已经吵烦了，所以不理他。

"你说，为什么夏林果请了张达、唐飞和毛超去参加她的生日会，偏偏不请我？"

"又不是我开生日会，你问我干什么？"

"我就问你！我偏问你！"

"马小跳，你别闹了！"夏林果快哭了，"我请你！我请你……呜呜……"

夏林果哭了，马小跳欢天喜地地跑了，跑去告诉张达、唐飞和毛超："夏林果请我了！"

导　读

·耐人寻味的男女生心思

在"淘气包马小跳系列"中，杨红樱不回避描写男女生之间的友谊和好感。这篇故事中，夏林果对于张达的好感，还有张达等四个调皮蛋对于夏林果的好感，也都一目了然。本来嘛，原本再正常不过的事情，何必遮遮掩掩不敢正视呢？明明很单纯美好的男女生友情，干吗要先入为主地把它想得复杂暧昧呢！

夏林果要请张达，自己不好意思说，让好朋友路曼曼代为转达；在回答路曼曼的质疑时，又以是请张达来帮助吃蛋糕自圆其说，还特别叮嘱不要让外人知道。小女孩曲里拐弯、细腻微妙的心思实在耐人寻味。要命的是，马小跳等三个男生知道后，都自我感觉良好，都觉得自己最有资本也最有理由"当选"，所以，不可能是一窝蜂去起哄，而是传接力棒似的都为着挤进"生日会"而各显神通了。

这时，故事结构、表达上出现了"相间反复"手法的运用：爱掉眼泪的唐飞用眼泪"吓住"了夏林果；擅说废话的毛超"缠烦"了夏林果；能找麻烦的马小跳急哭了夏林果；接下来便都是他们"欢天喜地"地去通报自己的好朋友"夏林果请我了"。这种有意味的"重章叠唱"不仅使作品富有自然韵律和节奏，增加了特殊的艺术魅力，还不断强化着"夏林果请我（一个）了"的信号刺激，而且推动着情节发展，让我们看到，夏林果末了请的男生远不止最初所想的"只请一个"，以及获准"入场"的男生们因为能得到漂亮女生的"垂青"而炫耀得意的情景。小说的幽默色彩益发浓厚了。

再看看夏林果，原本只想请张达一个男生，可是到后来，唐飞、毛超和马小跳都纷纷上榜，这实在是非她所愿，从被"吓住"过渡到被"缠烦"乃至于"呜呜"哭泣，她心情的转换实在是顺理成章的事情。所以，到后来，说话文绉绉也酸溜溜的丁文涛来讨生日会"入场券"时，这个不爱发脾气的已经受够委屈的女生能不跟丁文涛急嘛！

《丁克舅舅》

在咖啡馆里办公

不仅是马小跳迷上了他的丁克舅舅，就连他的好朋友张达、唐飞和毛超，也迷上了那个像谜一样的丁克舅舅。

丁克舅舅每天不上班，还挣那么多钱，他到底在干什么？

快放寒假了，那天期末考试，考完了还不到十点半钟。

这么早回去干什么？

毛超说："马小跳，丁克舅舅不是每天快到中午才出来吗？我们现在就去跟踪他，他走到哪儿，我们就跟到哪儿。"

马小跳的丁克舅舅，现在成了他们大家的丁克舅舅，叫来叫去，都分不清是谁的丁克舅舅了。

毛超经常出一些馊主意，但今天这个绝对是好主意！

不用马小跳带路——因为他们都去过一次了——七弯八拐，一跳狂奔，他们来到那座高级公寓楼的楼下，正好十一点，快到中午的时候。

张达最擅长寻找有利地形。正对着那座楼的地方，有一家书店，他们可以一边装作买书的样子，一边侦察楼上的动静。

他们冲进那家书店，把书店老板吓了一跳。那是一个很斯文的老头儿，脸白得像一张白纸。

"出去！出去！"书店老板像赶一群小鸡似的把他们往外赶，"这里没有中文书，只有英文书。"

"奇怪了，你卖书给中国人，还是英国人？"

毛超又找到打口水仗的机会了。

"小孩子别在这里胡闹！"书店老板训斥道，"我这里的书，是卖给懂英文的中国人的，你们懂英文吗？"

"你怎么知道我们不懂英文？"

几个人都各挑了一本英文书，装模作样地在那里看起来。

"你们……哎哟……"

书店老板一生气，牙就会痛。他捂着像白纸一样白的腮帮子，说不出话来。

马小跳叫了一声："出来了！"

他们合上英文书，都看那个从自动玻璃门里出来的人。只见他穿一身黑，宽大的裤子，宽大的棉袄，有许多金属的拉链和扣子，在冬日的阳光下闪着亮光。

"马小跳，你说丁克舅舅的头发像彩虹一样，是五颜六色的，怎么……"

马小跳一看丁克舅舅的头发，已经变成黑的了，只是在前额还搭着几缕卷曲的、银白色的头发。

"马小跳，他是不是丁克舅舅？"

"我还会认错吗？"马小跳带头冲了出去，"快，跟上！"

"可是，他……他的头发……"

张达的脑筋不会急转弯，毛超的脑筋可以急转弯。

"头发是染的。今天可以染成这样，明天可以染成那样。"

丁克舅舅的两条腿很长，他们要一路小跑才跟得上他。本来，他们很想学学电影、电视里那些盯梢的人，一会儿侧身藏在树后，一会儿站在商店的橱窗前，用眼角的余光盯着被跟踪的人……

丁克舅舅压根儿就没想到会有人盯梢，而且他走得太快，如果他们真要作秀的话，浪费表情是小事，把丁克舅舅跟丢了才是得不偿失。

丁克舅舅进了一家咖啡馆，在临窗的一张桌子旁坐下来。一缕温暖的阳光正照射在他的身上，他脱掉黑色的棉袄，露出里面一件宽大的白毛衣，肩上和胳膊肘上都打着灰色的真皮大补丁。

"你们猜一猜，丁克舅舅喝完咖啡，会去干什么？"

谁都猜不出来。他们准备等丁克舅舅喝完咖啡，再跟紧他，看他到底要干什么。

咖啡端来了，丁克舅舅只喝了一口，就从一个包里取出一台手提电脑，放在那张铺着小方格桌布的桌子上，然后又取出一沓资料，铺在桌上。

"丁克舅舅在干什么？"

"好像是在办公。"

"为什么要在咖啡馆里办公？"

他们决定去问问丁克舅舅：为什么要在咖啡馆里办公？

马小跳带头，进了咖啡馆，径直来到丁克舅舅那张桌前。

"丁克舅舅！"

丁克舅舅抬起头来，看看马小跳，又看看唐飞、张达和毛超，好像早就认识他们一样，十分随意地指指椅子："坐吧！"

丁克舅舅很忙的样子，
眼睛一会儿盯着资料，
一会儿盯着电脑，
就像他们几个根本不存在。

坐下来后，他们最想知道的是丁克舅舅是不是在这里办公。

"是。"

丁克舅舅的话少得不愿意多说一个字。

"你为什么要在这里办公？"

"舒服。"

他们不再说话，想感受感受这里是不是舒服。这里很安静，光线很柔和，有抒情的英文歌曲，桌子上都铺着上了浆的桌布，桌上摆放着盛开的鲜花，空气中暗香流动……

舒服，真的很舒服！

丁克舅舅很忙的样子，眼睛一会儿盯着资料，一会儿盯着电脑，就像他们几个根本不存在。

已经中午了，马小跳的肚子饿了，估计唐飞、张达和毛超的肚子也饿了。

马小跳问："丁克舅舅，中午吃什么？"

"一块三明治。"

唐飞提醒道："丁克舅舅，已经中午了。"

丁克舅舅举起手指一钩，打黑领结的侍者已来到他身边："三明治，五份。"

五份三明治很快端上来。唐飞他们以为三明治是点心，不是午饭。可丁克舅舅吃完三明治，又开始办公了，就像他们这几个人不存在一样。

唐飞又提醒道："丁克舅舅，你还没吃午饭呢！"

丁克舅舅头都不抬："三明治就是我的午饭。"

听这语气，丁克舅舅是不会请他们吃午饭了，他们也不能老坐在这里影响丁克舅舅办公。

几个人从咖啡馆里出来，都说知道什么是新新人类了。前些日子，他们几个老听马小跳说丁克舅舅是新新人类，问他什么是新新人类，他也说不清楚。

毛超说："新新人类，就是在咖啡馆里办公。"

唐飞说："新新人类的午饭，是一块三明治。"

张达说："新新人类穿的毛衣，要打上几块大补丁。"

马小跳说："新新人类的头发，今天是这种颜色，明天不知道会变成哪种颜色。"

　　"我说'菜鸟'本来是新手的意思，可他们教训我不能骂人；我说'我晕'，他们就会摸我的头，以为我发烧了；我说爸爸真'大虾'，是夸他厉害，可他会赶紧把腰板挺直起来，以为我是在批评他驼背……"一个小学生在抱怨父母听不懂他讲的新新人类的话语时如是说。

　　孩子们对一切新鲜的人、事都充满好奇心，而且接受得比成人都快。在外公外婆远不能理解丁克舅舅的怪异行为时，马小跳却已经对丁克舅舅产生了浓厚的兴味，成为一个追"新"族了。

　　丁克舅舅是对孩子们充满了诱惑力的谜一样的"新"人，所以孩子们会像"星探"似的，想尽一切办法跟踪追随丁克舅舅，试图揭开谜底，甚至也想感受一番新新人类的惬意生活。

　　当丁克舅舅说在咖啡馆里办公舒服时，他们会停止唧唧喳喳的询问，认真地实地感受那种"舒服"，并且在周围寻找一切能佐证"舒服"的例子。结果呢，他们的感受是"舒服，真的很舒服"。真是这样吗？四个调皮蛋真实却又有些肤浅的"粉丝"心理被作者杨红樱捕捉得多么精到！

小说结尾，四个孩子口口声声都知道什么是新新人类了。可是不消说，他们对于丁克舅舅基于不同角度的认知，都是片面的，像盲人摸象一样，都只抓住了新新人类的一个特征，很感性，很直观；但是这四个各说各话的特征拼凑在一起，丁克舅舅的"相貌"也就八九不离十了。

而且，你看唐飞，特别关注吃，在与丁克舅舅打交道的过程中也三句话不离"本行"，时刻忘不了提醒他"已经中午了"、"你还没吃午饭呢"，末了对新新人类的总结也还是与吃有关："新新人类的午饭，是一块三明治。"

《丁克舅舅》让我们看到了一个生活在孩子周围的与众不同的新新人类丁克舅舅：他既有自己的生活习惯和生活理念，使用新新语言，爱看卡通书、动画片，穿着空调裤，喜欢扮酷，不苟言笑，老大不小了还不肯结婚；也有社会责任感和道德底线，勇于承担。

丁克舅舅是一个健康向上、时髦前卫的另类人物，不光孩子们会喜欢，我们又有什么理由拒绝他呢？他的存在，恰好说明了我们今天多元社会的无限包容性。

英雄救美

　　红房子后面的草坪上，T型台已经搭好了。斗牛狗拉登和法国鬈毛狗雪儿的婚礼，还有"狗装秀"，定在这个周六的下午举行。

　　星期五的下午，那是一个阳光灿烂的下午。麦冬娜姐姐让拉登穿上她设计的狗服装，一遍一遍地走台。她又让雪儿披上新做好的婚纱，和拉登一起练习交换脚环。

　　脚环是麦冬娜姐姐专为它们俩设计的。她把拉登的照片和雪儿的照片粘上不干胶，在拉登的脚环上贴上拉登的照片，在雪儿的脚环上贴上雪儿的照片。在婚礼上一交换，拉登的脚上，便戴上了贴有雪儿照片的脚环；雪儿的脚上，也戴上了贴有拉登照片的脚环。

　　狗是聪明的动物。麦冬娜姐姐教了几遍，拉登和雪儿便学会了交换脚环，麦冬娜姐姐还给它们拍了交换脚环的照片。

　　"好啦，你们去玩吧！"

　　麦冬娜姐姐心满意足，她高兴地拍拍拉登的屁股，又拍拍雪儿的屁股。

拉登带着雪儿围着红房子跑了两圈，然后跑到铁栅门那里。

拉登会开铁栅门。它把铁栅门打开，带着雪儿跑出去了。

还没到放学、下班的时间，小巷里很安静。雪儿跟在拉登的后面撒着欢儿。

一辆白色的帕萨特开进了小巷。

雪儿突然停下脚步，看着那辆车，两眼闪闪发光。

——它以为它的主人来接它来啦。它主人的车，跟这辆车一模一样。

白色的帕萨特已经离雪儿很近了。

雪儿撒腿向车跑去。

"噢——"

拉登大叫一声，追了上去。

眼看着那车就要撞上雪儿了。拉登追上雪儿，把雪儿往旁边一撞。雪儿被拉登撞到一边去了，它自己却被车轮拦腰碾过。

嘎吱一声，车刹住了，从车上下来的并不是雪儿的主人。

拉登躺在地上，鲜红的血从它嘴角边流出来。它的一条后腿在抽搐着，两只眼睛瞪得好大。

雪儿嘴里发出呜呜的声音，它不停地舔着拉登的脸，还用嘴衔住拉登的一条前腿，使劲地拉，它想让拉登站起来。

拉登站不起来了。

就在这时候，马小跳、唐飞、张达和毛超来了，他们放学路过这里，正要到麦冬娜姐姐家去。

"看，这不是拉登吗?"

"拉登，你怎么啦?"

他们跪在地上，团团围住拉登。

拉登的腿不再抽搐，两只睁得大大的眼睛慢慢地闭上了。

马小跳哇的一声哭了起来:"拉登，你千万不要死啊!"

唐飞去摸拉登的脖子，脉搏已经不跳了。

"它已经死了。"

"拉登! 拉登!"

四个人一路哭哭啼啼，把拉登抬回麦冬娜姐姐家。

麦冬娜姐姐无论如何不能相信眼前这个事实: 拉登死了。

"不——"麦冬娜姐姐拼命地摇头，摇得披头散发，"拉登没有死，它刚才还在走台，还跟雪儿交换了脚环，它不会死，它是睡着了……"

麦冬娜姐姐把拉登抱到沙发上，把那件准备在明天的婚礼上给它穿的黑色燕尾服，轻轻地盖在它的身上。

拉登真的像睡着一样。它嘴角边的鲜血，刚才已经被雪儿舔得干干净净。

拉登瞪着两只大眼睛时，那样子看起来非常凶。但它睡觉的时候，两只大眼睛闭上了，那样子却非常和善。

平时，拉登喜欢在有太阳的下午，躺在草地上睡觉。马小跳他们最爱看它睡觉的样子:"你们看，拉登是不是在笑?"

"狗怎么会笑?"

"狗一定做梦了。"

"狗怎么会做梦?"

"人会做梦，狗就会做梦。"

"拉登会做一个什么样的梦?"

四个男孩子，给拉登编了四个梦。他们相信：狗是会做梦的，而且，做的都是好梦，所以它睡着的样子像在笑。

突然，他们听到一阵疯狂的狗叫声，是西施狗丑八怪。

丑八怪冲进来，对所有的人又叫又咬的，把他们都赶出了客厅。

"疯啦？丑八怪疯了吗？"

"你们忘啦？"毛超提醒他们，"丑八怪爱拉登。"

唐飞说："可拉登爱的是雪儿呀！"

"所以丑八怪是单相思。"

毛超什么都懂，连"单相思"他都懂。

"单相思很可怕的！"

"为什么？"

毛超是这样解释的：单相思，就是爱起来不要命。

看看丑八怪的表现，还真的有点像毛超说的那样。

大家趴在窗台上，看见丑八怪和雪儿在厮打，它们都想把对方赶出客厅，都想独占拉登。

张达为两只狗着急："死……死都死……死了，还争什么？"

"爱情是自私的。"

毛超又来这么一句。他这都是从肥皂剧里学来的台词，他妈妈每天都看肥皂剧。

丑八怪和雪儿互不相让，打不出胜负。自从雪儿瘦身后，它就跟丑八怪势均力敌了，再加上拉登活着时，有拉登护着，丑八怪也不敢像雪儿刚来时那样欺负它了。

两只互相视为情敌的狗妹妹打累了，又争着去舔拉登的脸。它们一边舔，一边流泪。

"嘿！嘿！"唐飞叫道，"你们还真流泪呢！"

"少见多怪！"毛超自以为见多识广，"流泪才是真伤心，不流泪是假伤心。"

死去的拉登，静静地躺在沙发上。它的身边，一边是它喜欢的狗妹妹雪儿，一边是喜欢它的狗妹妹丑八怪，它们都在为它伤心地流泪。

导 读

狗的爱情也美丽

屠格涅夫在《麻雀》中说过："爱,比死和死的恐惧更强大。只有依靠它,依靠这种爱,生命才能维持下去,发展下去。"《英雄救美》就是一个感人肺腑的充盈着爱的故事。在自己的"未婚妻"雪儿即将被车撞上时,斗牛狗拉登拼死营救,自己却被车轮拦腰碾过;其后,雪儿、丑八怪两只狗妹妹争相去舔拉登的脸,为拉登之死流下真心的眼泪,甚至在后来要以身殉葬⋯⋯

这个凄美的宠物故事,不仅仅印证着狗是有情有义的动物,也最形象地诠释了爱情:爱情不只是卿卿我我、两情相悦,它更是一种责任、一种付出;爱情是无私的,是伟大的,在关键时候,它甚至需要用生命来验证、来维护。同时,就像毛超鹦鹉学舌说的那样,"爱情是自私的",爱情具有排他性,不容许第三者的出现,雪儿、丑八怪两只互相视为情敌的狗妹妹为了争夺拉登而发生的厮打,就说明了这一切。在这里,作者杨红樱很巧妙地对小读者进行了一次很成功的也很严肃的爱情教育。

在《宠物集中营》中，杨红樱也未回避对麦冬娜姐姐与裴帆哥哥的爱情描写，但并没有写他们的"花前月下"，而是以很自然的笔调让小读者看到他们的爱情是建立在共同的爱好和追求基础之上的，并且是蜻蜓点水的一笔带过。杨红樱真正感兴味的、真正浓墨重彩书写的，还是动物间的恋情。

杨红樱在她的作品中让小读者屡次见证了动物的恋情：《暑假奇遇》中大黑猫对大白猫的恋情，《笑猫日记》中笑猫对于虎皮猫、麻花儿鸭对于黑鸭子的恋情等等。这当然是因为，对于人的爱情描写，会因为文学的类型、阅读者的接受特点而有着很大的局限性，而描写动物的恋情，因为有欣赏的距离，会更方便作者"托物言志"，也更利于小读者的接受；原因还在于，写童话出身的杨红樱一直擅长和喜欢"感时花溅泪，恨别鸟惊心"的艺术表达方式，所以以极其细腻感人的笔触刻写了狗的爱情，进而向小读者肯定和允诺了伟大爱情的存在。

顺带一提的是，麦冬娜姐姐是一个发展中的人物。她曾经因为缺少亲情陪伴而有着铁石心肠；但在马小跳们纯真心灵的濡染下，在人和动物真情故事的感化下，她那颗冰冷的心融化了，由最初嫌恶、抛弃小狗，而渐渐变得富有爱心，还成为一个出色的狗服装设计师，积极参与创建狗血库、收养流浪狗的公益事业中。这就是有着无穷伟力的爱对人的塑造。

品藏版

《小大人丁文涛》

穿裙子的小男人

马小跳从医院割完包皮，回到家里就叫痛。

"老爸，怎么这样痛啊？"

"你把裤子脱掉了，穿上你妈妈的裙子，会好一点。"

"我是男人，男人不可以穿裙子！"

"又没人看你。"

马小跳指着马天笑先生："你不是人吗？"

"我马上就要出去办点事儿。"

马天笑先生真的开门出去了。

马小跳叉开腿像螃蟹那样走路，还是痛得厉害，都是裤子害的。反正现在又没人看他，马小跳脱掉裤子，去找了一条他妈妈的裙子穿上。

马小跳站在穿衣镜前，镜子里的马小跳像个小怪物。穿裙子的样子是很可笑，但真的不那么痛了。

马小跳马上想到了丁文涛，他刚才也去医院割了包皮，一定也很痛，让他也穿裙子。

马小跳给丁文涛家打电话，是他爸爸接的。

"喂，我找丁文涛。"

"丁文涛有点不舒服。"

"我知道，他刚在医院割了包皮。"

丁爸爸的脸都白了："你，你是谁呀？"

"我是马小跳，我也刚割了包皮。你忘了，丁叔叔？刚才我们还见过呢！"

"我记得。"丁爸爸几乎在求马小跳，"我说马小跳，你不要再把'割包皮割包皮'挂在嘴上，好不好？"

"为什么？"

"这又不是什么光彩的事情，人家会笑话的。马小跳同学，你找我们丁文涛有什么事儿？"

"我想问问他，割了包皮痛不痛？"

丁爸爸皱皱眉头："马小跳同学，你又说'割包皮'！"

"本来就割了包皮嘛。"

马小跳终于明白了，为什么跟丁文涛说话费劲，原来跟他爸爸说话，也这么费劲。

"丁叔叔，你让丁文涛脱掉裤子穿裙子，走路就不会那么痛了。"

这个孩子真麻烦！

"爸爸，谁来的电话？"

丁文涛叉开两腿，也像螃蟹一样走路，从他的房间里走出来。

"那个马小跳打来的。他问你痛不痛，还说穿裙子会好一点。"

"讨厌死了！"丁文涛用手捂着脸，"马小跳一定会到处讲，

我还怎么去上学呀！哎哟——"

"是不是很痛呀？要不要穿裙子？"

丁文涛刚换上他妈妈的裙子，电话铃又响了。这次是丁文涛接的。一听是马小跳的声音，他差一点没昏过去。

"丁文涛，你穿上裙子没有？"

丁文涛明明穿着一条大花长裙子，他却对马小跳说："没有，我是男的，又不是女的，为什么要穿裙子？"

"你不是割了包皮吗？"

真是哪壶不开提哪壶。现在，丁文涛最怕听见的，就是"割包皮"三个字。

"马小跳，我俩订个君子协议好不好？"

"什么叫君子协议？"

"就是两个君子订的合同。"

"我又不跟你做生意，订什么合同？"

马小跳以为，只有做生意才订合同。

"我不把你'那个'的事告诉任何人，你也不许把我'那个'的事告诉任何人。"

马小跳一时不明白"那个"是什么事情。

"就是今天在医院的'那个'。"

哦，马小跳明白了："那个"就是"割包皮"。

"马小跳，这种事情，更不能跟女生说。"

"我知道。"穿着裙子的马小跳说，"这是我们男人的事情，不能跟女生说，也不能跟秦老师说，因为秦老师也是女的。"

丁文涛还是不放心，他不太相信马小跳。

"马小跳，我们干脆订个书面合同，好不好？"

"好！"马小跳同意，"但是，我当甲方，你当乙方。"

甲方排在乙方的前面，所以马小跳要当甲方。

"马小跳，我就让你当甲方，你说，如果甲方或者乙方，违反协议，怎么罚？"

马小跳还不太明白："什么协议？"

"就是不能把我们'那个'的事说出去。如果说出去了，怎么罚？"

马小跳说："谁说出去，谁是小狗。"

"不行！"丁文涛说，"现在小狗是宠物，我还愿意当小狗呢！这根本就不叫惩罚。"

丁文涛坚信自己能管住嘴巴，马小跳管不住嘴巴，就想把协议上的惩罚订得重重的。

"马小跳，违反交通规则都罚款，我们也罚款，好不好？"

马小跳问罚多少。

丁文涛反问道："你有多少？"

马小跳的压岁钱已经用得差不多了，现在只剩下二百七十元。

"二百七十元。"

"那就罚二百七十元。"

丁文涛一定要罚得马小跳一穷二白，这样才能让他管住自己的嘴巴。

丁文涛心中狂喜，他怕马小跳翻悔，又给马小跳打了一个电话过去："马小跳，君子一言，驷马难追，一言九鼎，一锤定音……"

丁文涛的老毛病又犯了，说起成语来就没完没了。

马小跳大喝一声："丁文涛，不许你说成语！"

丁文涛这才收住口:"马小跳,我马上起草一份文件,明天带到学校,你签你的名字。"

马小跳又不明白了:"什么文件?"

"就是不说'那个'的协议。"

马小跳同意明天在书面协议上签字。

丁文涛刚放下电话,电话铃又响了。

又是马小跳。

"丁文涛,你现在还痛不痛?"

"痛又怎么样? 不痛又怎么样?"

马小跳说:"如果痛呢,你就去穿裙子。告诉你吧,我都不痛了。"

"哈哈,马小跳,你穿裙子了?"

马小跳不知该说什么好。

丁文涛穿的裙子,腰太大了。他把裙子往上提提:"马小跳,我告诉你吧,我就是痛死,也不会穿裙子。"

马小跳放下电话,就脱下裙子:男子汉大丈夫,怎么可以因为一点点痛,就去穿裙子?

马小跳又穿上裤子,刚走一步,哎哟——

两种性格的碰撞 ■

品藏版

对于男孩子来说，割包皮是健康成长过程中的一个小手术，是再平常不过的事情。童心未泯、内心干净的马天笑先生对此毫不避讳，大大咧咧的，马小跳自然也秉承着这样的风格，直来直去，不会绕弯弯。可是到了会鱼吐泡泡似的背成语的丁文涛那里，不光是他，还有他的在单位里当大官的爸爸，却都紧张兮兮，讳莫如深，说起此事来也吞吞吐吐的。

偏巧在丁氏父子面前，马小跳是哪壶不开提哪壶，张口来闭口去都是"割包皮"，"逼迫"得丁氏父子躲躲藏藏、咬牙切齿、欲说还"羞"。于是，两种截然不同的性格、处事风格在割包皮这一话题上的碰撞，就造成了本篇故事令人捧腹的效果。

马小跳是很感性的孩子，他富有同情心，能由自己的"痛"想到与自己有同"病"的丁文涛，并接二连三地打电话慰问丁文涛、关照丁文涛穿裙子以消除疼痛。比较起来，丁文涛就太成人化了。明明穿着裙子，却矢口否认，信誓旦旦地表示"我就是痛死，也不会穿裙子"。

马小跳却是表里如一，没有那么多的弯弯绕，很容易就掉进了丁文涛为他设计的"陷阱"中——与丁文涛订合同；很男子气地脱下裙子。所以，"穿裙子的小男人"也许在这里指的仅仅是丁文涛，他在还应该是一个男孩的时候，却成为了男人——一个"小"男人，这"小"不仅仅是个子、年岁的"小"，更是心胸不够宽广的"小"。

小大人丁文涛是一个很耐人寻味的孩子。这样一个成人眼中的好孩子，在为人处世上处处表现出与他的年龄很不相称的理性色彩来。诸如要比马小跳们缺乏同情心，工于心计，有经济头脑，会向同学提供作业抄写并以此收取"版权费"，还懂得"防患于未然"，免掉了这件事情对自己可能的不利影响。

在本篇故事中，丁文涛会想到和马小跳订立书面合同，以罚款作为制裁手段以保证"丑事"不为外人知道。这是一个过早受世俗浸染而失去了童心的孩子。出现这样一个表面学习成绩辉煌但缺失了童年快乐和自由的"问题"孩子，该是多么令人揪心的事情啊。

做好事太难

"不能算分!"

"为什么不能算分!"丁文涛总是有很多的理由,"一个人做点好事并不难,难的是天天做好事。"

马小跳站起来说:"你是班上的数学课代表,每天收数学作业,是你应该做的事情,不能算做好事。"

"什么叫应该做的?"丁文涛说,"我又没有挣大家一分钱。"

丁文涛这么一说,好像也有点道理。丁文涛又给自己往"积善银行"存进了好几分。

看丁文涛已经在"积善银行"存进了那么多分了,马小跳还一分都没存进去,他急了。

"丁文涛,该我存了!"

"马小跳,你现在要叫我丁行长。"丁文涛还真把自己当成了丁行长,"你说吧,看能不能存进去。"

"我……"马小跳挠着脑袋瓜,"我忘了。"

"做过的好事怎么可能忘呢?"丁文涛很惊讶,"说明你根本就没做过好事。"

"我做过的。"

安琪儿说她能证明马小跳做过好事的。

"有一天，我忘记带家里的钥匙了，马小跳就让我到他家去做作业，还请我吃水晶果冻。"

安琪儿是跟马小跳住在一层楼上的邻居，马小跳宁愿没有做过好事，也不愿意安琪儿把这些事情说出来。果然，已经有同学在小声地笑马小跳了，丁文涛也在笑。

"同学们，这算马小跳做的好事吗？"

"不算。"唐飞说，"那是马小跳喜欢安琪儿。"

哈哈哈！

教室里笑翻了天。

马小跳就坐在唐飞的前面，他转过身来就给了唐飞一拳。马小跳最讨厌别人说他喜欢安琪儿。

眼看着马小跳和唐飞就要打起来，丁文涛为了控制好局面，赶紧叫唐飞说他做的好事。

其实，唐飞跟马小跳一样，现在要他说他做过的好事，一件都想不起来。

"我说！我说！"毛超等不及了，"昨天，哦，不对，是前天，我在路上看见有一张十元的钞票，我没有捡。"

丁文涛问："谁能证明你没有捡呢？"

"没人证明。"毛超说，"当时周围没有人。"

"没人证明，怎么行呢？"丁文涛说，"我还可以说，我在路上看见一张一百元的大钞，我没有捡。毛超，你当时为什么不把那十元钱捡起来，交到学校里来呢？"

毛超说："那又不是我的钱，我为什么要捡？"

丁文涛马上作了一个规定：凡是在路上见到钱，都要捡起来交公，才能算是做了一件好事。

反正那一天，丁文涛给自己往"积善银行"里存进了许多分。马小跳、唐飞和毛超却一分都没有存进去。

马小跳他们心里着急，恨不得一天做一百件好事，往"积善银行"里存进一百分，一天就能做尖端客户。

放学路上，马小跳他们看到一个老奶奶，提着满满一篮鸡蛋，马小跳他们就像猎人见到猎物一样，扑了上去。

"你……你们，干什么？"

提鸡蛋的老奶奶大惊失色。

"老奶奶，我们帮你提鸡蛋。"

几个人都争着去抢老奶奶手中的篮子，结果盛鸡蛋的篮子摔在地上，一篮子鸡蛋竟摔碎了一半。

老奶奶坐在地上哭起来："你们这群小强盗，你们到底要干什么？"

马小跳他们几个也没想到会这样，他们都太想做好事了。

倒霉的事情还在后头呢！

就在把老奶奶的鸡蛋打碎的第二天，马小跳上卫生间，看见洗手池的水龙头没关。如果在平时，马小跳肯定会随手把水关掉。可这样，没有人看见，怎么能证明他马小跳做了好事呢？

马小跳要去把丁文涛找来，让他亲眼看见是他马小跳把卫生间的水龙头关掉的。

"丁文涛！丁文涛！"

马小跳把丁文涛往卫生间里拽。

丁文涛拼命地挣扎："你要干什么？我不去！"

"你必须去!"

马小跳正跟丁文涛扭作一团的时候,校长突然出现在他们面前。

"马小跳!"

因为调皮捣蛋,马小跳也算得上是学校的名人,所以校长认识他。

一看校长的样子很严肃,马小跳眨巴眨巴眼睛:他觉得他没犯什么事儿呀!

"校长,我没有……"

"马小跳,你刚才在卫生间,为什么不关水龙头就走了?"

啊,原来刚才的事情,被校长看见了。

"校长,我本来是要关的,但我必须找到一个证人,证明是我关的。"

校长不知道马小跳乱七八糟地说些什么,反正他更加生气。

"我们天天都在讲,要节约每一滴水,可是,你看见水在哗哗地白流,却视而不见……"校长在教育马小跳的时候,丁文涛就在一旁偷偷地笑。其实,他心里也承认:马小跳挺冤的。

等校长一走,丁文涛就拿马小跳开心:"你真是弄巧成拙、掩耳盗铃、画蛇添足、拔苗助长、聪明反被聪明误……"

"丁文涛,不许你说成语!"马小跳愤怒地大叫一声,"都是你把我害的!"

如果不是丁文涛开创什么"积善银行",如果不是马小跳太想当"积善银行"的尖端客户,马小跳昨天就不会打碎老奶奶的鸡蛋,今天也不会被校长教训了。

唉,马小跳想要做好事,怎么就这么难呢?

慧眼难找

前两年在全国各地从小学到大学、由学校到社区鳞次栉比开办的"道德银行"，很是红火了一阵。始终关注孩子健康成长的杨红樱，对于这一发生在身边的关乎教育的新鲜事情同样很关注，注入了很认真的思考，并且很及时地用文学手法加以表达，含蓄地表明了自己的看法。于是我们就看到了小大人丁文涛在大人撺掇下而在班级开办的"积善银行"，看到了在"积善银行"利益驱动下孩子们浮躁而功利的心了。

道德是来自良心和良知的一种自律，是通过风俗和惯例形成的对人行为的一种限制和规范，它是最朴素和最含蓄的。做好事本来是道德的升华，是自然而然的事情。可是当人们要把"积善"（"道德"）和"银行"两个毫不搭界的范畴硬性结合在一起，想通过外在的量化形式和外在的奖励方式来刺激人心做好事，并且需要有无处不在的见证者和记录者及时出现以将积善行为存入"银行"时，就恰恰背叛了"积善"("道德")的本质。

　　本来，马小跳、唐飞们心地很善良，做好事是发自内心的，做过以后也从来都不记得。但是在"积善银行"运行之后，为了做所谓的"尖端客户"，他们着了魔似的到处找好事做，可谓无所不用其极。结果怎么样？他们做好事心切，打碎了老奶奶的鸡蛋；甚至于为了找一个积善的见证者而任由自来水哗哗白流。还有呢，到后来，毛超把自己的十元钱变成捡来的钱而且前后分十次交了"公"，马小跳和张达强行背一个脚伤已好的小男孩上学……这不都是弄巧成拙吗？这些已经存进银行的"钱"不都是制造出来的道德"伪钞"吗？可是，到哪里找一个鉴定积善钞票真伪的仪器啊！

　　没想着做好事的时候，好事似乎处处有；当刻意去找好事做时，好事偏又找不到。"事与愿违"，这是杨红樱幽默作品中常见的情境。《做好事太难》似乎是再度书写"踏破铁鞋无觅处"一类的黑色幽默，但杨红樱用意并不仅在于此。她是要用形象的故事告诉我们：做好事之所以太难，只是因为孩子们必须要在善行之外让自己的善行能时时被一双全知全能的"慧眼"有效地发现。这才是一件比做好事还难的事啊！

疯丫头来了

　　一遇到马天笑先生对马小跳笑得不是那么自然，还带着讨好的意思，而马小跳的宝贝儿妈妈又做出格外温柔的样子，不停地问他吃不吃这样，吃不吃那样，马小跳就知道，他们肯定有不好讲的话要对他讲，而这些话，马小跳听了可能会跳起来。

　　"马小跳，有一件事情……唉，还是宝贝儿妈妈讲吧！"

　　马天笑先生一直叫马小跳的妈妈"宝贝儿"，所以马小跳也一直叫妈妈为"宝贝儿妈妈"。

　　"是这样的，马小跳。"宝贝儿妈妈挨着马小跳坐下来，手就在他的脊背上摸来摸去，像对付不好对付的猫一样，希望这样能把马小跳安抚下来，"你姨妈要去美国住半年，杜真子要来我们家住半年。"

　　"我坚决不同意！"

　　马小跳果然跳了起来。

　　杜真子是马小跳姨妈的女儿，是他的表妹，比他小三个月。杜真子的爸爸在美国做访问学者，开始说访问一年，到现在已经访问了三年，还不回来，说要把一个尖端课题研究完了再回来。结果，姨妈隔三差五地往美国跑，把杜真子一会儿寄放在她奶奶家，一会儿寄放在她外婆家。她的外婆，也是马小跳的外婆。

"她为什么不去她奶奶家，不去外婆家？"

宝贝儿妈妈说："她奶奶、外婆都管不了她。"

"马小跳，你是杜真子的表哥，也许你能管住她。"

马天笑先生的这句话，马小跳爱听，但是他确实不喜欢杜真子。

在这个世界上，马小跳最讨厌两个女孩子：一个是他的同桌路曼曼；一个就是他的表妹杜真子。如果杜真子是夏林果那种类型的女孩子，别说在他家住半年，就是住一年、三年、八年，就是一辈子住在他家，马小跳也热烈欢迎。

杜真子有一样东西，可以动摇马小跳那颗坚定的心。杜真子有一只心爱的猫，这猫很怪，它会笑。她走到哪儿，就把猫带到哪儿。她的奶奶、外婆都不喜欢这只猫，说它是猫精、猫怪。马小跳却对这只猫特别感兴趣，他怎么也想不通：这只猫为什么会笑？

"杜真子会带那只猫来吗？"

"猫？"马天笑先生也知道那只猫，"那只会笑的猫？"

马小跳松口了："如果杜真子把那只猫带来，我还可以考虑考虑。"

"她肯定会带来的。"宝贝儿妈妈说，"杜真子跟猫，比跟她妈妈还亲。"

第二天，杜真子就来了，风风火火地来了。她一手抱着那

第二天，
杜真子就来了，
风风火火地来了。
她一手抱着那只会笑的猫，
一手拖着一个大轮箱，
一进门便大呼小叫。

只会笑的猫，一手拖着一个大轮箱，一进门便大呼小叫。

"最最亲爱的姨妈！最最亲爱的姨父！"

可一看见马小跳，她眼睛一闭，嘴巴一撇："讨厌！"

马小跳有一些时候没见到杜真子了，今天一见她，突然发现，杜真子原来一张圆圆的脸，现在怎么变成了一张短短的猫脸？还有，她原来的眼睛也没有现在这么大呀，还闪着绿光。

"杜真子，你越长越像猫了！"

杜真子一点都不生马小跳的气，她说爱跟谁在一起，就会跟谁长得一样。她爱跟猫在一起，自然会越长越像猫。

"你会不会像猫那样长出一条尾巴来？"

"马小跳，你想气死我吗？"

杜真子尖叫着朝马小跳扑去，马小跳躲闪开，杜真子一头栽在沙发上。

如果是别的女孩，早就哭鼻子了，或者去向大人告状了。杜真子可不，她像什么事都没发生一样，一本正经地问马小跳："我住哪儿？"

马小跳说："沙发。"

杜真子可不买马小跳的账，她拖起轮箱就往马小跳的房间里走。

"干什么？干什么？"马小跳追了过去，"那是我们男生的房间，女生不能进去！"

"从今天起，本小姐住这个房间了。"杜真子把她的轮箱横在门口，"女生房间，男生免进！"

砰的一声，杜真子关上了房门。

"宝贝儿妈妈，杜真子把我的房间占了！"

"马小跳，你是男孩子，杜真子是女孩子，要有点绅士风度嘛！"马天笑先生拍拍马小跳的肩膀，"你做表哥的，就把房间让给表妹住吧！"

如果不把房间让给杜真子，就没有绅士风度。马小跳怕落个"没有绅士风度"的恶名，只好把房间让给杜真子住。

"我睡哪儿呢？"

"沙发。"

马小跳顿时觉得他在这个家里的地位，一落千丈。

宝贝儿妈妈赶紧说："如果你不愿睡沙发，睡在书房里也行。"

马天笑先生却说："如果你在灯光的照射下也睡得着的话，你就在书房里睡吧！"

马天笑先生白天在玩具厂当厂长，晚上在书房里搞设计，经常搞到半夜。书房里亮着灯，怎么睡得着？

马小跳说："我还是睡客厅的沙发吧！"

嘭！嘭！嘭！

有三大包东西从马小跳的房间里被扔出来，一包是马小跳的衣服，一包是马小跳的书，一包是马小跳的玩具。

"杜真子，你把门打开！"

马小跳使劲地拍着门。拍不开，又推。

门一下子开了，马小跳扑进房间里。

"出去！"

"这是我的房间！"

"现在是我的！"

啪的一声，杜真子把一张写着大字的纸，贴在了门上：

女生寝室

男生免进

有这样的表妹，马小跳只好自认倒霉。他安慰自己"好男不与女斗"，从他的房间里退了出来。

导 读

杜真子的"疯"

写杜真子时，作者杨红樱全力渲染她"疯"的特点。故事开篇，马小跳爸爸妈妈说到杜真子时的难以启齿、吞吞吐吐，就做好了一定的铺垫，已经暗示出杜真子会是一个难缠的"主"，善者不来嘛。接下来，杨红樱从语言和动作描写两方面入手，抓住了杜真子"疯"的特点大做文章。这个不善的来者"一进门便大呼小叫"，一句修饰性的"最最亲爱的"，足以让姨妈姨父心生温暖；而看见马小跳时神情的变换"眼睛一闭，嘴巴一撇"，外加一句简洁的"讨厌"，让人看到杜真子的"爱憎分明"。

论起来，杜真子和路曼曼都是马小跳讨厌的对象，因为她们都挺霸道。可同是霸道，杜真子和路曼曼还大有不同呢。后者有章法可循，只动口不动手，使用语言暴力，向老师打小报告，借"师"发威；杜真子则是双管齐下，动口又动手，自己解决问题，不借助第三方力量。因为马小跳"要气死"自己，遂尖叫着扑去，一旦扑空而吃亏了，还挺"识闹"，不愠不恼，没事人似的继续与"对手"商量自己的住处；一旦不称自己的心，不必下情上达，更无须商量，便强行入住马小跳的房间。

她言语中"本小姐"长啊短的，透着傲慢与不逊；把马小跳的东西"嘭嘭嘭"都扫地出门，大大方方、泼泼辣辣，巾帼不让须眉。"砰"、"嘭"、"啪"几个模仿关门、扔东西、贴告示的拟声词的使用，把杜真子做事麻利、动作迅猛、风风火火的劲头全恰如其分地表现出来了。这样一个疯劲十足的动感女孩能不让人把她牢牢记住？

这场两个人的战争本来就够幽默了，杨红樱一定还嫌味道不够，又撒了点"味精"：天真妈妈对于马小跳落脚地方的评价还有那么点人情味儿——"如果你不愿睡沙发，睡在书房里也行"；可贪玩老爸一句"如果你在灯光的照射下也睡得着的话，你就在书房里睡吧"，就只能使马小跳老老实实在沙发上安营扎寨了。

马小跳的无奈和落寞不正好衬托出杜真子的嚣张和得意了吗？所以，"疯丫头来了"，对马小跳来说，无异于"狼来了"。看来，杨红樱对标题也是很讲求艺术的，标题看着简单，却是一语双关。

《疯丫头杜真子》

白雪公主和四个小矮人

　　杜真子本来就高，穿上宝贝儿妈妈的高跟鞋后，就比马小跳、唐飞和毛超高出一头来，他们成了名副其实的小矮人。张达的个子本来很高，但他知道自己演的是小矮人，必须弓着背，弯着腰。

　　"你们等着，我去换白雪公主的衣服。"

　　马小跳纳闷：杜真子怎么会有白雪公主的衣服？

　　杜真子跑进宝贝儿妈妈的房间。不一会儿，她穿着一身雪白的婚纱出来了。

　　马小跳又叫起来："那是我宝贝儿妈妈结婚穿的衣服，你快脱下来。"

　　杜真子根本不理马小跳，她问那几个小男生："你们说，我像不像白雪公主？"

　　唐飞的眼睛都直了："像，太像了！"

　　毛超更是夸大其词："杜真子，你比白雪公主还像白雪公主。"

　　杜真子双手提着裙裾，旋转到张达的身边，逼着他问："张达，你说像不像？"

张达怕那只会笑的猫，不敢说不像。

杜真子双手提着裙裾，又旋转到马小跳的身边，还没问马小跳，马小跳就先说了："不像不像。你穿的是婚纱，你又没有结婚。"

杜真子说："小矮人找到白雪公主，王子就会来和白雪公主结婚。"

"可惜这里没有王子。"

唐飞和毛超异口同声："我来演王子！"

唐飞和毛超争起来，都说自己像王子，还相互进行人身攻击。

"有你这么胖的王子吗？"

"有你这么瘦的王子吗？"

"你们不要争了！"杜真子站在唐飞和毛超的中间，"你们都不像王子，张达最像王子。"唐飞和毛超马上结成统一战线，联合攻击张达。

"他话都说不清楚，哪里像王子？"

"说话不清楚不要紧，只要个子高就像王子。"

唐飞、毛超和和马小跳都想不通：张达的魅力究竟在哪里？为什么漂亮女孩都喜欢他？比如夏林果，比如杜真子。

其实，张达一点都不想当王子。

"你们谁想……想当王子，谁当。反正，我……我不当。"

"我也不当。"马小跳一本正经地说，"我爸爸说，近亲不能结婚。"

"马小跳！"

　　杜真子尖叫一声，那只会笑的猫纵身一跳，跳到电视机上。它弓起背，眼睛一眯一眯，闪着一道一道的绿光。猫的嘴巴一歪一歪，耳朵一动一动。一看它这样子，四个男生安静下来了，特别是马小跳，变得格外老实。

　　还是猫的威力大，把四个不安分的家伙都镇住了。

　　杜真子说："你们都演小矮人，谁的小矮人演得好，我就让谁当王子。"

　　有当王子的希望了，唐飞和毛超摩拳擦掌。

　　马小跳心想：反正我不当王子，可以乱演。

　　张达心想：千万别演好了，我可不想当王子。

　　杜真子说演小矮人，要蹲着走路，她叫他们蹲在门边，准备出场。她自己从冰箱里拿出一个又大又红的苹果，大口大口地啃起来。

　　唐飞从地上站起来："我也要吃苹果！"

　　"这是演戏的道具！"杜真子说，"我在吃道具。"

　　毛超拉拉唐飞："这个苹果有毒。"

　　唐飞说："没有毒！我看见她从冰箱里拿出来的。"

　　"唐飞！"杜真子的猫眼睛瞪得圆圆的，"你再乱说话，我就不许你演了。"

　　唐飞赶紧蹲下身子，不再说话。

　　杜真子吃掉半个苹果，身子一歪，晕倒在沙发上。

　　四个小矮人出场了。他们蹲在地上走路，围着客厅转呀转呀，一边转一边听毛超喋喋不休地讲着废话。

　　四个小矮人似乎把白雪公主忘了。

　　等他们转到沙发边，杜真子踢了一脚，正踢在马小跳的屁股上。

"我的屁股!"马小跳叫起来,"这里怎么躺着一个人?"

唐飞:"啊,是个漂亮的公主!"

毛超:"她穿着这么白的衣服,像白雪一样纯洁、美丽,我们就叫她白雪公主吧!"

张达:"这个……名字真好……好听!"

唐飞:"她怎么会倒在荒地里呢?"

马小跳:"是沙发上。"

唐飞踢了马小跳一脚:"这不是演戏吗?"

毛超:"狠心的王后,就是白雪公主的后妈,派恶巫婆拿一个有毒的苹果给白雪公主吃,现在她中毒了,快拿药来!"

马小跳去拿药。他记得他感冒时吃过的藿香正气水,要多难吃有多难吃。对,就拿这个给杜真子吃。

马小跳一脸坏笑,把一瓶藿香正气水全灌进杜真子的嘴里。

"噗——"

杜真子把藿香正气水全喷在了马小跳的脸上。马小跳正要发作,毛超却要把戏接着往下演:"啊,白雪公主醒啦!"

杜真子坐了起来:"啊,我要喝可乐!马矮人,快去给我拿!"

马矮人就是马小跳。因为是在演戏,马小跳只好给杜真子拿来一听罐装的可口可乐。

杜真子咕咚咕咚喝完一听可乐,伸了一个懒腰:"我好了。你们去劳动吧,我给你们做饭。"

张达:"你要我们干……干什么?"

杜真子:"擦地板。把每个房间的地板都擦一遍。擦不干净

的，不准吃饭。"

四个小矮人，每个人拿一块抹布，跪在地上，擦起地板来。

杜真子真的进厨房，给四个小矮人做起饭来。

毛超："白雪公主，我们要擦到什么时候，才可以吃饭？"

杜真子："当太阳落山的时候，当鸟儿回树林的时候，你们就可以收工了。"

真真假假过家家

　　杨红樱的作品不但"好玩"，她也"好"在作品中表现孩子们各种各样的"玩"，诸如脑筋急转弯、成语接龙、变魔术、过家家等等游戏，甚至杜真子那真刀真功夫的烹调也可算作一种别致的"玩"。游戏是孩子的天性，是快乐孩子生活中必不可少的重要内容，就连马天笑、唐明这些家长们还对"斗鸡"、滚铁环、打玻璃弹珠这些童年游戏津津乐道，并在时机"成熟"时抛开堂堂大设计师、董事长的身份不顾而身体力行着；那么，在孩子们的"玩"上面花费些笔墨，实在是题中应有之意了。

　　杜真子与四个调皮蛋的"演出"，属于现学现卖、即兴发挥，甚至原作也遭到了"篡改"——小矮人都可以升格为王子，但是他们的童真和鲜活的性格令这出游戏横生了许多妙趣。尤其是杜真子，她以宝贝儿妈妈的高跟鞋和婚纱来装扮自己，自以为是地做着公主梦，憧憬着童话中的白马王子；出演起角色来也半真半假：吃苹果、喝可乐，

似乎是"剧情"所需，但也是她吃喝的正当借口；对几个男孩子颐指气使，稍有不满，就踢一脚或者将药水喷口而出，与她的"疯"劲儿正般配。

马小跳呢，因为反感杜真子而"假戏真做"地屡屡蓄意破坏，却总是事与愿违，还不得不对杜真子俯首帖耳奉上可乐。张达笨嘴拙舌，说话尽可能言简意赅；唐飞贪吃本色不变，看到杜真子吃苹果，一再"溢"出了角色——"我也要吃苹果"、"没有毒！我看见她从冰箱里拿出来的"，完全忘"我"了。毛超为了争当王子，对唐飞人身攻击之后，演戏颇为卖力。他们的身份在游戏（幻想）和现实中来回穿梭。

四个"小矮人"在玩中还得实实在在地擦地板，杜真子在玩中要真真实实地一展厨艺，说的台词却充满抒情色彩——"当太阳落山的时候，当鸟儿飞回树林的时候，你们就可以收工了"。不消说，这场游戏距离正版的"白雪公主"还差了好多，但孩子们的性情与梦想都在这真真假假里逐一浮现，孩子的创造力和想象力就在玩中勃发。

有教育专家指出，教育的核心不是传授知识，而是培养健康人格。一个人格健康的孩子也应该在智商、情商和玩商三方面都具备相应的能力。在对孩子玩的生活的展示中，杨红樱真心欣赏着孩子的这种天性和能力并认真呵护着。该玩的时候尽兴地玩，爽爽快快地过一把孩子瘾，这该是杨红樱对健康、快乐的孩子抱持的期许。

《寻找大熊猫》

蓝眼睛温迪

才放暑假不过三天，唐飞就给马小跳打电话来了。

"马小跳，我上次跟你说的那个美国人，他真的来啦！"

马小跳刚睡了午觉，头脑还有些不清醒："哪个美国人？"

"就是那个想拍熊猫照片的美国人……美国国家地理杂志的摄影师……"

马小跳模模糊糊地记得：唐飞有个什么舅舅在藏龙山熊猫自然保护区研究熊猫，他还有个三叔在美国研究环境学，这个三叔要介绍一个热爱野生动物的美国摄影师到中国来拍熊猫。

现在这个美国人已经来了，要去找唐飞的舅舅。唐飞家的叔叔舅舅一大堆，遍布地球每个角落，世界各国人民在他家常来常往，马小跳他们已习以为常。所以，唐飞今天打这个电话来，一点都没引起马小跳格外的重视。

电话那头，唐飞还在没完没了地说。他平时懒洋洋的，恨不得三句话并成一句话说，可一打电话，他就有些婆婆妈妈了。

"马小跳，那个美国人还带了个女的来。"

"是不是他的老婆？"

"不是他老婆，才十一岁，是他女儿。唉，为什么他不带一个儿子来？所以马小跳，我迫不得已，只好让你跟我一起去。"

去藏龙山看大熊猫？马小跳欣喜若狂，他才不在乎唐飞的"迫不得已"，他压根儿就没听出这意思来。

唐飞还在电话那头喋喋不休："我本来想让张达去，可张达这人话太少，叫人闷得慌；又想让毛超去，可毛超这人话又太多，叫人想安静一会儿都不能，最后才想到你……"

马小跳赶紧说："我，我的话不多不少——刚好。"

唐飞说："不是这个原因。"

"那是什么原因？"

"不是因为你，是因为杜真子。"唐飞在电话那头咯咯地笑起来，"张达和毛超又没有表妹。"

杜真子是马小跳的表妹，唐飞对她很有好感。唐飞的如意算盘是让杜真子去跟那个金发碧眼、纠缠不休的温迪纠缠，她有无穷多的问题，问得唐飞见她就躲。

原来马小跳是沾了他表妹杜真子的光。

"杜真子会讲美国话吗？"

马小跳知道，美国话就是英语。杜真子还真会几句简单的英语，但马小跳却告诉唐飞：杜真子只会讲中国话，不会讲美国话。

"那怎么办？温迪她爸爸，就是那个摄影师说了，我们当中，一定要有一个懂英语的人。"

马小跳马上想到了 Miss 张。

"Miss 张是英语老师，她说起英语来，比英国人说得还好。"

这事唐飞也做不了主，他叫马小跳带Miss张过来，直接见那个摄影师。

Miss 张目前是马小跳的丁克舅舅的女朋友，马小跳找她太容易了。现在，她也放假了，听马小跳这么一说，她还真跟着马小跳来到了唐飞的家。

Miss 张一见那个美国摄影师和他女儿温迪，就跟他们叽里呱啦说起来，好像她和他们已经认识了好久好久。

他们在说什么，马小跳和唐飞一句都听不懂。

唐飞看着 Miss 张，看着看着便笑起来："马小跳，Miss张的嘴巴怎么那么大呀？"

马小跳第一次见 Miss 张的时候，也有这样的感觉，日子长了，已经习惯了她那与众不同的嘴巴。

"唐飞，这你就不懂了。"马小跳一本正经地说，"嘴巴大，说英语时发音才准。"

"OK！"

"OK！"

那边，摄影师和他女儿对 Miss 张非常满意，不停地"OK"、"OK"。看来，Miss 张是非去不可了。

唐飞急了："那，那杜真子呢？"

"杜真子？"摄影师摊开双手，耸着肩膀问 Miss 张，"杜真子是什么？"

他以为"杜真子"是一样什么东西。

Miss张当然知道"杜真子"不是东西。

"杜真子是一个跟温迪一般大的小姑娘。"

摄影师还是不明白，这个叫杜真子的小姑娘跟他们这次"熊猫故乡之行"有什么关系。

唐飞心里的小算盘，马小跳一清二楚。唐飞一门心思地想让杜真子去。马小跳怕杜真子去了，他就去不了。

果然，唐飞跟他挑明了："马小跳，其实我们只需要两个人：一个翻译；一个既可以陪着我玩、又可以给温迪解答各种问题的人。"

马小跳说："这个人除了我，还是我。"

"马小跳，你怎么那么自信啊？"唐飞终于把他想说的话说出来了，"我怎么觉得杜真子是最合适的人选呢？"

马小跳急了："那你叫我来干什么？"

眼看着马小跳就要和唐飞打起来，Miss 张赶紧插在两个人的中间。

"唐飞，你还是不是我的好朋友？"马小跳告诉 Miss 张，"他想让杜真子去，不让我去！"

马小跳曾经跟Miss张和丁克舅舅出去旅行过，Miss 张觉得马小跳是个令人愉快的小旅伴，再说，她和丁克舅舅还是马小跳促成的，所以她希望这次能跟他们同行的不是杜真子，而是马小跳。Miss 张要在暗中帮马小跳一把。

"你俩不用打，我们让温迪来决定吧！"

Miss 张把马小跳推到温迪的面前，用英语说道："这个男孩子非常幽默，如果他能够跟我们一起到熊猫的故乡去，我相信我们一路上将会非常有趣。温迪，你希望这个男孩子跟我们一起去吗？"

美国女孩绝对喜欢幽默的男孩子。听Miss张说马小跳非常幽默，温迪立刻对马小跳产生好感，热情洋溢地对马小跳说了一大堆话，可惜马小跳一句也没听懂。

唐飞问Miss张："她说的什么意思?"

Miss张拣主要的翻译成汉语："温迪的态度十分坚决，她一定要请马小跳跟我们一块儿去。"

"可他是男的，你不希望有一个女孩子陪着你吗?"

Miss张把唐飞的话翻译给温迪听，温迪直摇头。

唐飞没辙了，恶狠狠地对马小跳说了句："算你走运!"

马小跳这才好好地看了一眼温迪。从进门起，他就没把这个黄毛丫头放在眼里，全部心思都在唐飞身上。最后还是人家这个黄毛丫头一锤定音，才让他马小跳去的。

马小跳看温迪的时候，温迪也正在看他，马小跳的目光马上闪开了。但他记住了她的眼睛，像他曾经在一部魔幻电影里看见过的蓝色水晶球，又像在阳光下波光荡漾的海洋，还像……现在在马小跳的脑海里，凡是蓝色的、闪亮的东西，都可以用来比喻温迪的眼睛。

导 读

有特点的外貌描写

基于对孩子阅读心理的了解，杨红樱在写作中一直比较注重叙述的节奏。我们不难发现，她作品中的静态描写比较少，更多的是通过有力度、视觉性强的语言、动作来表现人物。

本篇故事中，唐飞变得像毛超一样喋喋不休，是因为他一门心思想让他喜欢的杜真子去藏龙山，而有可能被"挤"掉的马小跳则要力争"胜出"。所以，到底谁最终能拿到去藏龙山的"车票"，这不仅是唐飞、马小跳所关心的，也是小读者急于知道的。

由此，杨红樱着眼于这场"纠纷"的谁胜谁负，叙述节奏一直比较快；当尘埃落定，读者都松了一口气时，她才放慢了节奏，让我们注意起温迪这个已经在前面出场却很容易就被忽视了的女孩。读者自然会像马小跳一样，开始注意到这个对马小跳"进山"握有决定权的美国女孩到底是怎样一方"神圣"。

注意到没？在对温迪的外貌描写上，杨红樱只突出了她的一个特征，那就是她的眼睛、她眼睛的蓝色。杨红樱用了一系列生动贴切、很容易让人产生联想、唤起人想象的比喻，说她的眼睛像蓝色水晶球，像波光荡漾的海洋。这里没有艰涩的词语，也没有让人摸不着头脑的喻体，"凡是蓝色的、闪亮的东西，都可以用来比喻温迪的眼睛"。这充分考虑到了小读者的接受心理和阅读兴趣。而小读者也很容易就像马小跳那样牢牢"记住了她的眼睛"，还有从她眼睛——这扇心灵窗户反射出来的人性的善良。

杨红樱为人画像时的一个显著特点，就是抓住每个人物的一个突出特征，稍事渲染，就足够了，笔墨绝不粘连。这篇故事中的Miss张，最大特点就是有一张与众不同的大嘴巴;《宠物集中营》里那个漂亮的麦冬娜姐姐也只是"穿着很短很短的裙子、很长很长的靴子"。比较起来，那种大段大段的从头到脚、从长相到穿着的外貌描写反倒会显得机械、呆板，最终还很难给人留下什么印象，小读者看了，不急死，也得"跳"过去。

《巨人的城堡》

值得炫耀的秘密

　　几个男孩子心里揣着一个秘密，兴奋得好几天都睡不着觉。他们自认为把这个秘密藏得很好，滴水不漏，殊不知在言谈举止上，他们的态度已发生了一些变化，一副不屑与人一般见识的样子，别人讲什么都引不起他们的兴趣。他们会在心里说：我知道有一个巨人，他的名字叫阿空，他住在一座像城堡一样的房子里，开着一辆像集装箱一样的房车，你知道吗？

　　这是一个值得炫耀的秘密。向谁炫耀呢？除了唐飞，他们都同时想到了一个人——他们班上长得最漂亮的女生夏林果。

　　自从放暑假后，他们就没有见过她。有时候真想给她打个电话，可是在电话里跟她说什么呢？夏林果骄傲得像个公主，她是不喜欢听废话的。如果把这个秘密告诉她，她肯定会……

　　当然，他们曾经对巨人阿空发过誓，他们相互之间也发过誓，不把这个秘密说出去，但他们自己给自己发誓，却是这样的：我只告诉夏林果一个人，除了夏林果，我谁也不告诉。

　　第一个给夏林果打电话的人，居然是张达。

　　"夏……林果，本来……我不会……给你打电……但是有一个秘……秘密，你千万……不……要跟别……人说。"

张达本来就结巴，给夏林果打电话，他更结巴。

"什么秘密？"夏林果懒洋洋的，"你说吧，我不跟别人说。"

"我们发……发现……一个巨……巨人……"

"巨人？"夏林果不相信，她只知道童话里有巨人，"张达，你在做梦吧？"

张达迷迷糊糊，常常处于半睡半醒的状态，夏林果以为他在说梦话，便把电话挂了。

第二个给夏林果打电话的人是毛超。

"夏林果，我本来不想给你打电话，但是，如果我有一个秘密，一定要有一个人与我分享的话，那么这个人，我想来想去，除了你，还是你。"

毛超是废话大王，他说十句话，有九句都是废话。

"毛超，别跟我弯弯绕，有话就说。"

毛超继续说："在我说之前，你得先发誓。"

夏林果说："我都不知道你要说什么，我凭什么发誓？"

"你不发誓，我就不说。"

"不说就不说。"

夏林果啪地把电话挂了。漂亮女孩就是有脾气。

过了一会儿，电话铃又响了，还是毛超打来的。

"夏林果，既然我决定了要把这个秘密告诉你，我就一定要告诉你。"

夏林果沉默着。

毛超怕夏林果挂电话，不敢再绕："你知道吗，在我们这个城市里，有一个巨人……"

怎么又是巨人？夏林果不动声色，继续沉默。

"他起码有两米五，比那个篮球明星姚明还高呢。他住在……"

毛超把他知道的，全部告诉了夏林果。

夏林果有点相信了。她知道毛超会编，但编不了这么圆。只是那只来路不明的瘫痪狗，那些来路不明的乌龟，让她觉得不可思议，让她半信半疑。

这太离奇了！

毛超第三次打电话来，他一再声明，这个秘密他只告诉了她，要她一定不能再告诉第二个人，特别不能告诉马小跳、唐飞和张达。

夏林果向他保证，绝不告诉马小跳、唐飞和张达。

毛超还是不放心："你会不会因为张达是个四肢发达、头脑简单的人，你就告诉他？"

谁都知道，在他们四个男生中，夏林果对张达最好。

夏林果再一次保证，她不会。

马小跳是在思想斗争了许久后，才给夏林果打电话的。他知道他是发过誓的，他知道他这样做不对，出尔反尔，没有诚信，但是，只要夏林果不告诉别人，还是算守住秘密的。一想到他和夏林果共同拥有一个秘密，马小跳就有一种幸福的感觉。

从放暑假的第一天起，马小跳就想给夏林果打电话，天天都想打，但又不知该说些什么，这下有说的了。

"夏林果，我本来不想给你打电话……"

又是这样的话开头。张达、毛超都说了同样的话，怎么一给她打电话，都没了创意？

夏林果要逗逗马小跳："不想打就不打呗，又没有人拿着枪顶在你的背上,非打不可。"

马小跳急了:"但是,我有一个秘密,必须要告诉你。"

夏林果已经知道他的秘密是什么了,所以并不急于知道。

"马小跳,什么叫'秘密'呀?"夏林果要逗逗马小跳,"秘密就是一个人或者很少人知道的事情,你到处跟人讲,还叫秘密吗?"

马小跳更急了:"我没有到处跟人讲,我只跟你一个人讲。"

"你为什么要跟我讲?"

"因为……因为……"

马小跳也不知道他为什么要告诉夏林果,但就是想告诉她。

马小跳不管三七二十一,上气不接下气地把那个秘密对夏林果讲了。跟张达、毛超讲的差不多,夏林果相信,马小跳讲的是真的。

跟张达和毛超一样,马小跳也没忘了叮嘱夏林果:"我只告诉了你一个人,你千万别再告诉别人,特别是唐飞、毛超,还有张达。"

夏林果大笑:怎么这几个人开头结尾的话都一样?

马小跳不知道夏林果在笑什么,他心虚了。

"夏林果,我知道你喜欢张达,我知道你会告诉张达的。"

"马小跳!你再胡说,我一辈子不理你。"

马小跳就怕夏林果一辈子不理他,赶紧闭嘴。

夏林果就等唐飞的电话了。唐飞也是知道这个秘密的,她十分自信,唐飞一定会给她打电话的,而且,开头结尾说的话,也跟他们几个一样。

唐飞的电话,一等不来,二等不来,夏林果奇怪了——这唐飞怎么啦?

导 读

·破解童心的秘密

　　杨红樱的作品能受到孩子们的欢迎，很大程度上得益于她对童心的成功破解。这篇故事中，男孩子知晓巨人阿空的秘密后，言谈举止中表现出不屑与人一般见识的样子来；本来已经彼此郑重其事地发过誓要保守这个秘密，但又禁不住炫耀心理的"作祟"，又先后要与心目中的"偶像"女孩夏林果共同分享这个秘密。杨红樱就像钻进了铁扇公主肚子中的孙猴子一样，几个孩子微妙的心思变化难逃她的"火眼金睛"。

　　同是向同一个女孩诉说同一个秘密，开头结尾的话大同小异，但是三个男孩的诉说顺序前后有别：张达四肢发达、头脑简单，第一个非他莫属；毛超爱说爱道，自然接踵而来；马小跳呢，有道德感，懂得诚信，所以"是在思想斗争了许久后"打来电话的。而三个男孩的性格特征和心理世界又同时体现在迥然有别的诉说方式上。

　　张达本来说话就结结巴巴，诉说秘密时又吞吞吐吐上气不接下气，能不让人以为他是在说梦话，就怪了。毛超呢，果真不愧对"废话大王"的称号，为了诉说这个秘密，前后打了三次电话：第一次没来由地先绕来绕去让人家发誓，结果是有脾气的漂亮女孩把电话挂了；第二次打电话来不再饶舌和盘托出；第三次电话则是一再要求夏林果保证不告诉别人。够贫嘴的了吧？再看马小跳，明知不守秘密不道德，但还是禁不住内心的驱使讲述一切，夏林果偏慢悠悠猫捉耗子似的欲擒故纵，马小跳能不"急"和"心虚"吗？

　　三个男孩不同的诉说在夏林果那里出现了截然不同的"反馈"：从不把张达所说当成一回事时的"懒洋洋"，到对毛超的"秘密"半信半疑时的"不动声色"，再到洞若观火时的"逗"弄马小跳，一切都是那么自然。而接下来，漂亮女孩的虚荣心也抬头了，她满心以为唐飞也会像另外三个男孩子一样讲述这个秘密来讨她的好，而十分自信地等待唐飞的电话，结果呢，"一等不来，二等不来"，都让她"奇怪"了。夏林果的心理变化够耐人寻味的吧？

　　就像旋转心理魔方似的，四个孩子心理的方方面面都被杨红樱明察秋毫地掌控住并全面呈现出来了，小读者当然会感觉作者与自己心有灵犀。

《超级市长》

如野马般的想象力

马小跳的爸爸马天笑先生特别贪玩，他就是读一份报纸，也能从中读出好玩的事情来。

"哈，我们这座城市越来越好玩了。"

马小跳正在写作文，半个多小时过去了，一个字都没憋出来。马天笑先生的话，刚好把马小跳从憋闷中解放出来。

"是不是要建迪士尼乐园?"

"马小跳，为什么我一说好玩，你马上就会想到迪士尼乐园?"

"香港刚刚建了一座迪士尼乐园，唐飞都去过了。"

"这是一种玩法。但是，肯定还有更高级的玩法。"马天笑先生从很多张报纸中抽出一张花花绿绿的报纸来，上面画着很有宫崎骏风格的城市，"如果咱们来玩一个模拟城市的游戏……"

"老爸!"马小跳打断马天笑先生的话，"什么叫模拟城市?"

"模拟城市完全是你想象中的城市。你可以去竞选这个城市的市长或者部长，你的那几个好朋友，像唐飞、张达，还有毛超，都可以去竞选嘛。"马天笑先生把报纸放在马小跳的面前，

"想去就赶快哦，已经开始报名了。"

马小跳没有看报纸，他已沉浸在一座想象的城市中，而他马小跳，就是这座城市的市长……

今天，秦老师布置的作文题是半命题作文《我第一次……》，本来应该在作文课上完成的，马小跳一个字都没写出来。秦老师问他为什么写不出来，他说他的"第一次"太多了，不知道应该写哪一个"第一次"。现在，马小跳终于找到了一个"第一次"，他在作文本上写下《我第一次当市长》。

马小跳心潮澎湃，文思汹涌，他的想象乘上飞翔的翅膀，飞得很高，飞得很远；又像一匹野马，一路狂奔。然而，他手上的笔，完全驾驭不了这匹想象的野马。作文写出来了，洋洋洒洒写了三页半，马小跳从来没有写过这么长的作文，从头到尾读了一遍，有些词不达意，有些颠三倒四。总之，马小跳不太满意，他觉得写的不如他想的好。

第二天到学校，秦老师堵在教室门口，等着收马小跳的作文本。

上午第一节课是语文课。语文课不教课文，秦老师又在说昨天作文课上的作文题——《我第一次……》。

"路曼曼，你来说，你昨天写的作文是什么?"

路曼曼是班上的中队长，是秦老师最喜欢的学生。路曼曼回答说，她昨天写的是《我第一次包饺子》。秦老师表扬说，路曼曼把第一次包饺子的过程写得又具体又生动，还突出了第一次的感受。

"现在，我来念丁文涛写的作文，他写的题目是《我第一次乘飞机》。"

丁文涛是班上的学习委员，是老师们公认的成绩最好的学生，他还是个成语大王。就他这一篇作文，起码用了上百个成语，完全就是用成语串起来的一篇文章，课堂上一片啧啧声，那是同学们望尘莫及的感叹声。

念完丁文涛的作文，秦老师总的评语是：路曼曼和丁文涛的作文，他们有一个共同的优点，都是写自己亲身经历的事情。秦老师话锋一转，说到了马小跳的作文。

"马小跳，你来说说，你的作文写的是什么？"

马小跳没有听见。刚才，秦老师点评路曼曼的作文，念丁文涛的作文，他都没听见，他还沉浸在一座想象的城市之中。

马小跳的同桌路曼曼用手肘撞一下马小跳："秦老师叫你说……"

"说什么？"

马小跳两眼迷茫，望着秦老师。

秦老师手里拿着马小跳的作文本："说说昨天的作文，你写的是什么？"

马小跳说："我第一次当市长。"

全班笑得人仰马翻。

"马小跳没睡醒，在做白日梦。"

"他连小组长都没当过，还想当市长。"

马小跳奋起反驳："我怎么没当过小组长？我当过野炊组小组长。"

路曼曼马上揭穿他："你只不过当了一天。"

马小跳说："我还当过纪律委员。"

路曼曼又揭穿他："你只不过当了七天……不，除掉两天周末，才当了五天。"

马小跳没话可说，气得喘粗气。

秦老师走到马小跳的课桌前："马小跳，你当过市长吗？"

马小跳摇摇头，但又说："我想……"

秦老师不让马小跳往下说："你想归想，但是你到底没有当过，所以你这篇作文怎么写得出真情实感？完全是一派胡言。如果是考试，你这篇作文肯定不能及格。"

秦老师拿马小跳的作文说了一节课，念一段，评一段，同学们笑一段。马小跳的脸上却毫无表情，仿佛这篇作文与他完全不相干，他依然沉浸在他想象的城市里。

下课了，马小跳木木地坐在他的座位上，没有像往日那样，一听到下课铃声，就像冲锋陷阵的战士，拼命地往教室外面冲。

马小跳的三个铁杆哥们儿，都围在马小跳的身边。毛超做出巴结的样子："马小跳，刚才全班的人都在笑你，只有我没有笑。"

"笑了又怎样？马小跳的作文，那是相当的怪头怪脑，想让我不笑都不行。"

唐飞刚才笑了，所以他这么说。

"无情无义。"

唐飞像一只胖企鹅，向长得像猿猴的毛超扑过去："你说谁无情无义？"

毛超被唐飞压在身底下，但他还是不屈服："如果你还是马小跳的好朋友，你就不应该笑。你说是不是，张达？"

张达刚才也笑了，所以他不说"是"，也不说"不是"。他只是伸出手，把唐飞从毛超的身上拉起来。

夏林果人长得漂亮，心眼儿也好，是极有同情心的女生。她问马小跳怎么了，毛超悄悄地说："受刺激了。"

"马小跳今天不正常，相当的不正常。他又不是第一次被秦老师刺激。"

最近一段时间，唐飞不知吃错了什么药，几乎每句话都要加一个修饰语"相当的"。

"马小跳的作文虽然写得有点乱，但想象很丰富，我不觉得有那么可笑。"

夏林果一半是安慰马小跳，一半是她的真心话。刚才，秦老师在念马小跳的作文时，尽管是念一段批一段，但她还是为马小跳的想象力感到惊讶，她甚至觉得全班人的想象力加起来，也抵不过马小跳一个人的想象力。

一直没有说话的马小跳，终于说话了："你们去不去报名？"

"报什么名？"

"竞选市长。"

大家都不明白马小跳在说什么。

毛超说："马小跳，你真的受刺激了？"

"不正常，"唐飞说，"相当的不正常。"

需要保护的想象力

老师问："雪化了变成什么？"一个孩子的回答是"变成了春天"。这个答案因为不靠"雪化了变成水"这个标准答案的"谱"，而被判为错。可是，我们仔细想一想，"变成春天"是多么的富有创意和想象力啊！

同样的，马小跳原本在写《我第一次……》这个半命题作文时，吭哧了半天连一个字都没有写出来，可是在任想象的野马狂奔后，洋洋洒洒地写出了平生第一篇长作文《我第一次当市长》。这是多么值得肯定的事情！可秦老师视之为"完全是一派胡言"，由此拿马小跳的作文说了一节课，"念一段，评一段，同学们笑一段"。

1972年，联合国教科文组织国际教育发展委员会提出的《学会生存》报告中有这样一段对人的创造能力的精彩阐述：它"是一种最容易受到文化影响的能力，是最能发展并超越人类自身成就的能力，也是最容易受到压抑和挫伤的能力"，"教育有着开发创造精神和窒息创造精神这样双重的力量。"负着开发孩子创造精神责任的秦老师，在这节作文课上着着实实充当了一回窒息创造精神的"杀手"。不过，令人欣慰的是，马小跳的心理耐受力相当的强，他没有理会别人的嘲讽，也并没有停留在想象的原地踏步，却是付诸实施，开始了自己的"征程"，在友情的扶持下一步步登上了超级市长的宝座。

秦老师为什么会变成"杀手"？她说的没错，"如果是考试，你这篇作文肯定不能及格"。按照应试教育这根指挥棒的要求，马小跳的作文当然是胡言乱语；但是在"胡言乱语"中，我们却看到了马小跳可贵的想象力，看到他无拘无束的快乐和气象万千的生命气息。从素质培养的角度来看，马小跳的想象力是令人称美的。所以，归根结底，马小跳的想象力被老师无情地封杀，就在于我们的教育评价机制、教育体制出现了问题。

《超级市长》是有生活原型的。一个有着许多令人叫绝的施政计划的男孩，由于没有出色的才艺表现，在超级市长初赛时被淘汰了。由此杨红樱认真地想到这样一个问题："面对格式化的孩子和个性化的孩子，我们怎么去评判谁更优秀？"

在此，杨红樱借着"作文事件"告诫人们：教育者面对孩子，应该有一颗博大宽容的心，学会采取多元的、欣赏的评价方式对待孩子的言行，我们要注意保护孩子的想象力，这也是在捍卫孩子的人格尊严。

为什么同一个黑板上的粉笔圆点，大学生们会嗤之以鼻、不屑一顾，仅仅看到这是一个"点"，而天真烂漫的孩子们却能对这一"点"产生多姿多彩的想象？孩子的想象力是需要鼓励、理解和保护的。当千万个马小跳的想象力真正得到了重视和呵护时，我们民族神奇、瑰丽的创造力之门也就能由此得以开启。

《超级市长》

八十份民意调查

离初赛还有三天的时间。

丁文涛已经把他的施政纲领背得滚瓜烂熟了。这个施政纲领是他爸爸写的，像毛超从他姑父那里拿来的施政纲领一样，很正规，也很全面。虽然里面好多东西，比如"财政预算"、"市政建设"、"外资引进"等等一系列，丁文涛也不懂，但他还是照着他爸爸写的施政纲领，一字不漏地背下来了。

下课了，丁文涛也不去玩，他把施政纲领放在课桌下面，还在那里背。

路曼曼来到他的身边："丁文涛，你准备得怎么样了？"

"万事俱备，只欠东风。"丁文涛踌躇满志，"我已经把施政纲领背得滚瓜烂熟，熟能生巧，巧夺天工……"

一不小心，丁文涛又开始了成语接龙。他赶紧向路曼曼打探马小跳的消息："马小跳怎么样？"

"他能怎么样？"路曼曼翻翻白眼撇撇嘴，"初赛就会被刷下来。"

夏林果在一旁听不下去了："路曼曼，你也太小看人家马小跳了。"

"我怎么小看他了？"路曼曼句句是理，"就他那木瓜脑袋，能把施政纲领背下来吗？还有才艺展示，你说他有什么才艺？"

夏林果也说不出马小跳有什么才艺，但她还是觉得，路曼曼在丁文涛面前那么轻视马小跳，太过分。

"马小跳敢去报名，说明他还是很勇敢的。"

"对，马小跳是很勇敢，但如果勇敢得没有自知之明，这勇敢就是缺点了。"

路曼曼幼儿园就当班长，上了小学又当中队长，能言善辩。夏林果虽然是大队委，但她从五岁起就开始跳芭蕾舞，她站在台上，几乎都是用舞蹈在表达，所以她的口头表达能力跟路曼曼相比，简直就不是一个级别的。

夏林果也是个高傲的漂亮女孩，她是不肯轻易服输的："反正我相信马小跳还是有实力的。"

"那好吧，我们来打赌。"

夏林果问路曼曼："赌什么？"

"赌第一场初赛，马小跳就会被刷下来。"

夏林果骑虎难下，和路曼曼击了掌。

"你们还是不要赌吧！"

有路曼曼这么铁杆的支持者，丁文涛应该感激才是。可是，丁文涛却很生路曼曼的气，他在乎的是夏林果，并不是路曼曼。本来，他完全可以争取到夏林果的支持，就是因为路曼曼要和夏林果打赌，把夏林果完全推到马小跳那边去了。

既然击了掌，这个输赢，路曼曼和夏林果是一定要赌下去的。

全班同学，包括老师，都以为路曼曼和夏林果是一对好朋友，其实只有她俩自己心里明白，她们不是知心朋友。两个人爱在一起，是因为两人都是心高气傲的女孩，都是老师眼中的佼佼者，都觉得只有对方才配做自己的朋友。

现在为马小跳打赌，中队长路曼曼和大队委夏林果，开始了暗中较量。而这一切，马小跳一点都不知道。

这几天，马小跳和他那三个铁杆哥们儿，紧锣密鼓，已经开始了民意调查。马小跳准备了厚厚一沓扑克牌大小的白纸，给唐飞、毛超和张达，每人分了二十张，叫他们去分头调查。

"这事做起来相当的简单。"马小跳对他们说，"你们就问：想过什么样的幸福生活？然后把他们的回答写在这个纸片上，就可以了。"

"找什……么人调查……"

毛超抢在马小跳之前回答张达："男人、女人、老人、小人，只要是人，都可以是调查对象，是不是，马小跳？"

马小跳拍拍毛超的肩膀，他现在的一举一动，都是市长的派头。

放学走出校门，见校门口围着许多接孩子的家长，正好进行民意调查，四个人分头行动。

马小跳盯住了一个高大男人，他正伸长脖子向学校里张望。

"叔叔您好！请问：你想过什么样的幸福生活？"

高大男人看都不看马小跳一眼："走开，别烦我！"

"哼！"马小跳走开了，"等我当了市长，你会为你今天这句话后悔的。"

马小跳在人群中挑选，他要选一个面目和善的人，这样的人不会拒绝他。

马小跳挑了一个穿大花衣服、眉毛弯弯、眼睛弯弯、嘴巴弯弯的女人。

"阿姨您好！我想知道，你想过什么样的幸福生活？"

这个阿姨果然没有拒绝马小跳，而且还十分认真地对待马小跳的问题。

"我想过的幸福生活呀——"阿姨偏着头想了一会儿，"哎呀，几句话根本说不完，起码要说三天三夜。"

马小跳拿出笔和纸准备记录："说最想的就可以了。"

"最想……最想我的女儿上学、放学能自己回家，不用我天天来学校接送。"

马小跳把阿姨的话记下来了。

那边，唐飞见一个跟他爸爸差不多胖的男人正从一辆轿车里钻出来，好像是他爸爸生意上的朋友，唐飞便大模大样地朝人家走去。

那个胖男人好像也认出了唐飞："你是唐总的公子吧？"

"你的记忆力相当的好。"唐飞直奔主题，"你最想过的幸福生活是什么？"

胖男人一头雾水，但看唐飞拿着笔，拿着纸，不像捣蛋的样子，想起刚才开车的辛苦，才两条街就开了一个多小时，便说："我最想过的幸福生活是开车不堵车。"

唐飞认真地把胖男人的话记录下来。

毛超最擅长死缠烂打。现在他缠住了一位老奶奶，老奶奶是来接她读一年级的小孙子的。毛超问了她好多遍，她都懒得回答。后来被毛超缠得想赶紧把他打发走，就说她想天天吃没

有洒过农药的蔬菜。

　　毛超搞不懂了："为什么天天吃没有洒过农药的蔬菜，就算是过最幸福的生活？"

　　"我想活到一百岁。"老奶奶说，"吃洒过农药的蔬菜，会缩短寿命。"

　　这个问题很重要，毛超记在了纸片上。

　　张达拦住一个低年级的小男生。因为张达是学校里的体育明星，这个小男生十分崇拜他，尽管听了几遍，才听张达结结巴巴地把问题讲明白，他还是直接在那张扑克牌大小的纸上，一笔一画地写下他最想过的幸福生活："老师不要布置家庭作业！"

眼观六路，耳听八方·

能把小说写得有滋有味、疏密有致，杨红樱靠的是"眼观六路，耳听八方"的本领，她能把方方面面各色人等的反应井然有序地照顾到，再有声有色地现于笔端。

这篇故事的前一篇结尾交代得很清楚：是马天笑先生让马小跳懂得了市长的施政纲领就是让市民过想要过的幸福生活。而在本篇开始，杨红樱采取"花开两朵，各表一枝"的方式，先"表"马小跳的竞争对手丁文涛阵营的动向。丁文涛把施政纲领"一字不漏地背下来了"，可谓胸有成竹，但也恰好与马小跳形成了鲜明对比：一个是靠爸爸，空对空，不知纲领所云为何而死记硬背；一个是靠自己，实打实，有的放矢地步入社会调查民意。

两个心高气傲的女孩对马小跳的态度也不同：同桌冤家是鄙夷不屑，漂亮女孩是钦佩有加，她们针尖对麦芒的谈话充满"火药味"，也构成了本篇故事的戏剧性冲突。最终路曼曼"把夏林果完全推到马小跳那边去了"，这在

《超级市长》一书中可是个重要环节，马小跳能在日后一步步地登上超级市长的宝座，相当大的动力来自于夏林果的支持。

在描写马小跳的竞选班子调查民意时，杨红樱充分注意到了写法的变化万端，所以这一段描写情趣迭生。调查者一面，既有马小跳那种"见风使舵"的，也有唐飞那种"大模大样"的；既有毛超那种"死缠烂打"的，也有张达那种"结结巴巴"的。被调查者一面，男女老幼都有，构成了有代表性的群体；而且被调查者不光是性别有交错、年龄有差异，就是态度也各有不同：高大男人是"看都不看"，"眉毛弯弯、眼睛弯弯、嘴巴弯弯"的阿姨是"十分认真"，胖男人是"一头雾水"，老奶奶是"懒得回答"，小男生是"十分崇拜"。

在写到调查者记录民意的地方，杨红樱在表述上也注意方式多样而避免了单调呆板：马小跳是一般的"记下来"；在唐飞那里，态度有不同了，是"认真地把胖男人的话记录下来"；写到毛超时，陈述的句式发生了变化，毛超的态度也隐含于其中——"这个问题很重要，毛超记在了纸片上"；至于张达，他只消做"壁上观"即可，崇拜他的小男生"反客为主"，"直接在那张扑克牌大小的纸上，一笔一画地写下他最想过的幸福生活"。

能把一次在很多人看起来索然无味的"调查"，写得花团锦簇、绚烂多姿、疏密有致，这得归功于杨红樱那支变化无常的妙笔和对生活细致入微的观察与体悟。

如果不出意外

　　尽管马小跳和唐飞也都说得上是见多识广，但是，他们拍的DV要在电视上播放（不是学校的闭路电视，是家家户户都能看见的卫星电视），对他俩来说，还是一件大事情。

　　唐飞天天给电视台那位把长头发扎起来的导演打电话："我们送去的DV作品什么时候播呀？"

　　那天在唐飞家里，经导演一点拨，唐飞和马小跳明白了：他们在野生动物园拍了那么多，都是素材，有很多素材是不能用的。那些有用的素材还要经过编辑，才能成为作品。所以，唐飞郑重其事地称他们送到电视台的是作品。

　　导演心里装的事情太多，哪里记得住哪个作品在哪天播？这种事情，对唐飞和马小跳来说，是天大的事情，对电视台的导演来说，根本就不算事情。

　　"如果不出意外，就在这周吧！"

　　于是，毛超把这消息在班上广为传播："特大喜讯！特大喜讯！如果不出意外，这一周每晚六点半，电视上要播我们'跳跳电视台'拍的DV作品。"

很多同学都还不知道，就在自己班上，还有一个"跳跳电视台"。

他们都问："'跳跳电视台'在哪儿？"

"远在天边，近在眼前。"

同学们都不把毛超说的话当真，谁叫他是"废话大王"呢？

"我说的是真的。"毛超赌咒发誓，"马小跳是台长，所以叫'跳跳电视台'。我、唐飞、张达都是副台长。"

"马小跳都能当台长，你们几个都能当副台长，不难想象，不出所料，意料之中，可想而知，这是一个什么破电视台！"

"丁文涛，我要告你诽谤！"

"你去告呀！"丁文涛根本不怕告，"你往哪儿告？"

"我告诉秦老师！"

不等毛超去告诉秦老师，路曼曼已先去告诉秦老师了："马小跳他们私自成立了一个电视台，马小跳自任台长，所以叫'跳跳电视台'。唐飞、张达、毛超都是副台长。"

办公室里的老师都笑了，只有秦老师没有笑，她已经习惯了马小跳层出不穷的花招。

秦老师不动声色，问路曼曼："还有呢？"

"毛超到处宣扬，说在这一周，电视上要播他们的DV作品。"

秦老师终于笑了。她压根儿就不相信有这种事情。她笑马小跳他们几个真是异想天开。

"你去把马小跳给我叫来。"

两分钟之后，马小跳已经十分诚恳地站在秦老师的跟前了。

"马小跳，听说你成立了个'跳跳电视台'，参加的人全部都是台长？"

"还有两个不是。"马小跳老老实实地说，"夏林果和安琪儿不是。"

"嗬，夏林果也是你旗下的？"数学老师端着茶杯，来到马小跳的身边，"她可是大队委，你们四个都能当台长，人家夏林果为什么不能当？"

马小跳说："我本来让她当副台长的，她不当，她只当主持人。"

办公室里的老师又笑。

秦老师只当马小跳在玩过家家。她十分严肃地告诫马小跳："国家的电视台，是十分正规的机构，要经过十分严格的审查，节目才能在电视上播。我知道你用唐飞的摄像机拍的一段录像，在我们学校的闭路电视上放过，但那毕竟不是正规的电视台。千万不能再胡说了，听见没有？"

马小跳说："唐飞问过电视台的导演，导演说，如果不出意外，这一周就要播。"

"播什么呀？"

"播我们拍的。"

"你们拍的什么呀？"

"就是……你看了就知道了。"

"拍的什么都说不出来，还播呢！"

马小跳沉默了，他听出秦老师话中的意思。

这一周都快过完了，电视台确实天天都在展播DV作品，但就是没有看见"跳跳电视台"送上去的。

唐飞又打电话去问那个把长头发扎起来的导演："这一周都快过完了，怎么还没播？"

"我的话你没完全明白。"导演说，"如果不出意外，肯定是

会播的。那么现在没有播，就是出意外了。"

唐飞还想知道出了什么意外，人家导演根本就不想说，他只是说电视台每天都有太多太多的意外。

当"跳跳电视台"的所有成员知道这个不幸的消息时，都有一种想哭又哭不出来的感觉。

对这样的挫折，马小跳他们几个是有心理承受能力的，但对凡事都风调雨顺的夏林果来说，她觉得这件事情让她很没面子。

"都怪毛超，是毛超把消息散布出去的。"

果然，丁文涛来找毛超了："这一周都快过完了，你们拍的DV怎么还没播呀？"

"我的话你没完全听明白。"毛超原封不动地套用导演的话来应对，"如果不出意外，肯定是要播的。既然现在没有播，那就是出意外了。"

"对我来说，一点儿都不意外。"丁文涛才不吃毛超那一套，"从头到尾，都是弥天大谎，以讹传讹，巧立名目，弄虚作假……"

当然，秦老师也不会放过马小跳。

"马小跳，我早就告诉过你：国家的电视台，是十分正规的机构，不是学校的闭路电视，你们拍的那些东西，怎么可能拿到正规的电视台去播呢？"

　　"如果不出意外……"这明显是导演对小孩子的敷衍之语。而毛超一帮孩子在班上的广而告之，就不仅仅是单纯的重复了，更多的还是表现出来宣扬和矜夸的姿态。这也难怪，成立了自己的电视台，在大人指点下制作出了自己的作品，并且有可能在正规的电视台播出，这对孩子们来说，当然是额手称庆的事情。

　　可是秦老师就不这样看，包括路曼曼、丁文涛这样的学习优等生，也认为这些调皮蛋不可能做出什么"惊天动地"的大事情。所以，马小跳的"意外"和秦老师的"意中"之间构成的矛盾形成了这个故事的主干。当马小跳们为"不出意外"而企望和为"出意外"而失望、情绪大起大落时，秦老师却安之若素，认为事事全在自己意料之中。

　　在秦老师的"意中"，马小跳是没有"意外"的，他所做的、所说的一切都是儿戏。小说中对早就料定马小跳们不会出什么"意外"的秦老师的描写，都是关乎其语言、神情的，既简洁又传神，把一个自以为是的偏心老师的形象活灵活现地勾勒出来。你看，在办公室里初听路曼曼有关跳跳电视台的汇报，别的老师都笑了时，她"没有笑"，多么老成！这是她见怪不怪的表现。到听说电视上要播马小跳的DV作品的消息时，"终于笑了"，这可是她"看破"马小跳"把戏"时成竹在胸的写照！赶紧把马小跳找来，是为着"十分严肃地告诫"他"千万不能再胡说了"。

不必讳言，秦老师是给了马小跳申说的权利的，但并不是为着平等对话、了解事实真相，而是在循循善诱地"引蛇出洞"，以戳破马小跳的"弥天大谎"。"不出意外"之前，轻口薄舌的一句"拍的什么都说不出来，还播呢"，对于马小跳的创造力和自尊心该有多大的杀伤力啊！"出意外"之后，再找马小跳谈话，不是为着安慰他，而是要证明自己的料事如神，苦口婆心的一番"我早就告诉过你"，轻而易举地抹杀了马小跳的"工作"。

教育孩子的前提是了解孩子、尊重孩子，可作为教育者的秦老师偏偏不去认真了解马小跳，更谈不上尊重马小跳的人格尊严了。好在马小跳是"曾经沧海难为水"，永远能以快乐弥合自己受伤的心。

"人人都说小孩小，谁知人小心不小；你若小看小孩子，便比小孩还要小。"陶行知这首《小孩不小歌》太值得教育者牢记了。

《开甲壳虫车的女校长》

戴珍珠项链的女人

这一天，是这个暑假最后一个返校日。

昨天晚上，马小跳很早就上床了，但翻来覆去睡不着。这个暑假太长了，他开始怀念在学校的日子——每天和唐飞、张达、毛超在一起，每天能见到夏林果，每天和路曼曼吵来吵去，甚至那个不喜欢他的秦老师和他不喜欢的丁文涛，也成了他怀念的人。

睡不着觉的马小跳跳下床来打电话。

他打通了毛超家的电话，是毛超的妈妈接的。

"是马小跳吧？我一听就知道你是马小跳。这么晚了你还打电话？明天要返校你知道吗？你作业做完没有？毛超这会儿还在赶呢！我现在去叫他。但是，你们通话不能超过一分钟。"

现在，马小跳终于明白，毛超的废话那么多，真的不怪他，要怪就怪遗传吧。

"马小跳，原来你有一道数学题要请教我？这么简单的题你都不会做？我经常对你讲，上课要专心听讲，你不听。妈，你听见没有，马小跳的作业也没做完，所以，这不是我一人的错。

马小跳，你有什么问题，快点问！"

毛超叽里呱啦说了这么多，把马小跳的脑袋都说晕了。他并没有什么问题要问毛超，是毛超用他来开脱自己。毛超那装腔作势的语气，是在暗示马小跳他妈就在他身边，马小跳只好长话短说："明天早上八点老地方见，不见不散。"

马小跳说的老地方，就是那一片把一座豪华厕所包围起来的小树林，那是他们去学校的必经之地，他们四个经常在那里会合。

接着，马小跳又打通了张达家的电话。

"返校时间……是九点，你……为什么……要……八点？"

马小跳也不知道为什么要八点，刚才就那么随便一说。

"反正我已经通知毛超八点了。"

"好……吧，八点就……八点……"

毛超和张达都稀里糊涂地答应明早八点在老地方集合，唐飞可不稀里糊涂，他一定要问出个为什么来。

"马小跳，返校时间是九点钟，八点钟我还没起床呢！"

"唐飞，你长那么胖，就是因为睡得太多。"

"从小树林到学校要不了十分钟，八点五十分集合也不迟呀！"

马小跳没辙了，只好硬着头皮说："我有重要的事情要宣布。"

"你现在宣布不行吗？"

"现在就宣布，我怕你睡不着。"

马小跳啪的一声，把电话挂了。

马小跳回到床上，更睡不着了，他得杜撰一件"重要的事情"明早去宣布。

"重要的事情"最终没有杜撰出来。这天早晨不到八点，马小跳还是硬着头皮去了小树林，"车到山前必有路"，马小跳一向对自己有信心。马小跳来到小树林的时候，张达和毛超已经在那里了。

"马……小跳，我早饭都没……没吃……"

马小跳奇怪地问张达："你为什么不吃早饭？"

"我怕……迟到……"

"迟到怕什么，又不是赶飞机。"

"马小跳，昨晚我妈在旁边，我没问你，你这么早把我们叫到这里，到底有什么事？"

马小跳不理毛超，踮起脚，伸长脖子，一副翘首盼望的样子："唐飞怎么还不来？"

"我明白了！"毛超似乎看透了马小跳，"你什么事都没有，你就是心急。"

"我心急？"马小跳莫名其妙，"我急什么？"

"你急着见夏林果。上一次的返校日，你不是没见着她吗？"

上一次的返校日，夏林果没有来。马小跳去问路曼曼，路曼曼朝他翻白眼，说你是人家夏林果的什么人哪，管那么多！马小跳还是不放心，鼓足了勇气去问秦老师，秦老师盯着马小跳的脸足足看了有三分钟，对马小跳来说，这三分钟长得好像有三年。马小跳被秦老师看得脸红筋胀，可秦老师还是没告诉马小跳，夏林果为什么没有来，只说夏林果请了假。马小跳还想问夏林果是不是生病了，可一看秦老师那沉下来的脸和垮下来的嘴角，吓得马小跳把想问的话又咽了回去。

其实马小跳从昨天就开始担心，担心今天返校又见不着夏林果，他是被毛超说中了，所以他有些恼羞成怒。

"毛超，你……"

马小跳朝毛超扑去，张达插身在他俩中间，然后把他俩分开。在四个人当中，一般都是马小跳、毛超、唐飞三个人之间打来打去，他们从来不和张达打，因为他们有自知之明，知道自己不是张达的对手。而张达也决不和他们打，他是练跆拳道的，他怕他一出手就要打死人。所以，他成了他们三人当中专门劝架的，只要他们一打，张达就会把他们拉开。所以，只要张达在，他们都要做出生猛的样子、拼命的样子，因为他们知道张达一定会把他们拉开。

这时候，唐飞满头大汗地跑来了："马小跳，有什么重要的事情，你快点宣布！"

毛超扑过来搂住马小跳："马小跳，原来你有重要的事情要宣布，你怎么不早说？"

自从马小跳发现了巨人的城堡，自从马小跳参加了"超级市长"的选拔，自从马小跳当了"跳跳电视台"的台长，如果马小跳要说"重要的事情"，那么这个事情一定是重要的，不容忽视的。

三个人都盯着马小跳，等着他宣布"重要的事情"。马小跳眨巴着眼睛，他多么希望这时候有一些惊天动地的事情发生，比如外星人从天而降，比如恐龙复活，从地铁出口里跑出来，比如这座城市眨眼间成了海底世界，马路上的汽车都变成了鱼……

马小跳眨巴的眼睛不眨了，他看见一辆红色的甲壳虫车缓缓地驶过来，停在路边。这种甲壳虫车十分少见，在来来往往的汽车中显得格外扎眼。马小跳想，这辆甲壳虫车一定能抢去

所以，只要张达在，
他们都要做出生猛的样子、拼命的样子，
因为他们知道张达一定会把他们拉开。

唐飞他们在他身上的注意力。

"唐飞，你看那是什么车？"

唐飞是个车迷，几乎没有他不知道的车型，所以，他最喜欢别人向他请教有关车的问题。

唐飞拿腔拿调的："你们看这车像什么，它就是什么车。"

马小跳说："像甲壳虫。"

"相当的正确，这种车就叫甲壳虫车。"唐飞滔滔不绝，"甲壳虫车是德国大众的第一款车型，是汽车发展史上最最成功的车型，是经典和流行的象征……"

唐飞一边说，一边向那辆红色的甲壳虫车走去，马小跳、毛超和张达紧跟在后。

甲壳虫车在颤抖，唐飞凑近车窗看了一眼，回头对马小跳他们说："这车开不走了！"

果然，颤抖的甲壳虫车安静下来。左边的车门开了，从里面走出一个穿一身白衣裙、戴一串珍珠项链的女人，看不出她的年龄，说她二十几岁、三十几岁甚至四十岁都可以。

几乎就在马小跳看见这个女人的第一眼，便对她产生了好感。人是分类型的，这女人跟他的宝贝儿妈妈是一个类型，都披一头像海藻一样弯曲的长发，都穿飘逸的连衣裙，都戴珍珠项链。马小跳还注意到，她脖子上的珍珠项链，跟宝贝儿妈妈的珍珠项链一模一样，每一粒都如樱桃般大小，每一粒都闪耀着洁白的光芒。

导 读

别致的开场

　　相信"马小跳"的小书迷们大都希望马小跳能继续一如既往地"出事"，由此可以随同马小跳一同展开精彩冒险。这是因为小孩子大都有些唯恐天下不乱的心理。

　　具体到这篇作品中，在经历了一个漫长暑假的沉寂后，马小跳又开始"蠢蠢欲动"了。明天就要返校，就能够见到日思夜想的同学了，甚至那些他不喜欢的和不喜欢他的人都成为他的怀念对象，而潜意识中更可能是因为担心见不到夏林果而难以入眠。由于这种说不清道不明的焦渴心理，他要求好朋友们提前一个小时就到老地方会合。毛超、张达稀里糊涂地答应了，精明的唐飞却不依不饶，马小跳就不得不信口开河他有一件"重要的事情"宣布。杨红樱花费了大量笔墨来准确细致地拿捏孩子们的这一渴盼"出事"、无事生非的心理。

　　但如果认为这篇故事仅仅是要透析孩子没事找事的心理的话，就不免低估了杨红樱谋篇布局的能力。杨红樱是要以此为契机，把它作为一件"重要的事情"不可缺少的引子。最终没能杜撰出"重要的事情"而硬着头皮按时赴约的马小跳，为转移同伴的注意力，让唐飞们关注一辆很别致的甲壳虫车。而此时，"重要的事情"出其不意地发生了：欧阳雪这个开着甲壳虫车的女校长走进了孩子们的视线。接下来乐于助人的孩子们帮助了正陷入困境的女校长，为此迟到挨训被秦老师误解，孩子们也为此念念不忘这位戴珍珠项链的女人能为他们洗雪"冤屈"。但直到小说进行了三分之一的篇幅，马小跳他们才终于有机会把新校长与他们最早见到并施加帮助的对象"对号入座"。

所以说，作为《开甲壳虫车的女校长》一书中的女主角，欧阳雪尽管一开始就已经亮相了，但她的正式出场却是"千呼万唤始出来"的。这个戴珍珠项链的女人在较长的篇幅里，都在孩子心中葆有着神秘的色彩；而即将到任的女校长究竟何许人也，也一直吊足了孩子们的胃口。欧阳雪"吞吞吐吐"的出场方式令故事充满了"变数"，也是能吸引读者往下阅读的动力。

杨红樱设计了一个很别致的、颇具匠心的开场，以云山雾罩的方式让这位要认真捍卫孩子童年、积极践行着科学而前卫的教育理念的新校长逐渐露出峥嵘来。她是一个与马小跳喜爱的林老师、《漂亮老师和坏小子》中的米兰老师一样富于神采和魅力、敢于打破陈规的新型教育者，她是寄寓着杨红樱教育理想的人物。

爱上语文课

走进教室里来的是欧阳校长。

"同学们好!"

欧阳校长一说话,脸上就有笑容。这笑容如灿烂的阳光,照亮了教室。

欧阳校长没有给大家上新课。她说,教与学有个相互适应的过程,所以,她选了一篇大家既熟悉又喜欢的课文《白雪公主》来上。

"今天,我们就来说说这个故事的两个主要人物。"

欧阳校长在黑板的一端贴上写着"白雪公主"的词条,在黑板的另一端贴上写着"王后"的词条。

"王后和白雪公主是什么关系呢?"

有同学答:"是母女关系。"

"不对不对!"马小跳把手举得高高的,等不及欧阳校长请他,便急着说了,"白雪公主不是这个王后亲生的。"

欧阳校长问马小跳:"你能准确地说出这种关系吗?"

马小跳摇摇头,怏怏地坐下了。

丁文涛站起来回答："她们是继母和继女的关系。"

欧阳校长表扬丁文涛的回答非常准确。

丁文涛沾沾自喜，轻蔑地看了马小跳一眼。

"得什么意？"马小跳心里不服，"谁不知道继母就是后妈。"

欧阳校长："虽然白雪公主不是王后亲生的，但她们有一个相似之处——"

有同学回答："她们都长得很漂亮。"

"还有还有！"马小跳又按捺不住了，"她们都是女的。"

"哈哈——"同学们都笑起来。如果是秦老师，她一定会批评马小跳在课堂上故意捣蛋，但是，欧阳校长不仅没有批评马小跳，还接着马小跳的话往下说："同样都是女性，同样都长得很漂亮，她们的性格却有天壤之别……"

欧阳校长在黑板上贴满了各种各样的词条："美丽"、"恶毒"、"可怜"、"阴险"、"妒忌"、"可爱"、"仇恨"、"单纯"、"聪慧"、"善良"、"虚伪"、"勤劳"、"友好"、"狡猾"、"丑陋"、"真善美"、"假恶丑"。

欧阳校长："黑板上的这些形容词，哪些可以形容白雪公主，哪些可以形容王后？"

欧阳校长请安琪儿上讲台，在黑板上贴词条。从一年级到现在，秦老师很少给安琪儿这样的机会，所以安琪儿一脸憋得难受的表情——熟悉她的同学都知道，那是高兴、激动的表情，可是欧阳校长不知道，她以为安琪儿紧张。

"别紧张！"欧阳校长轻轻拍拍安琪儿的肩膀，"把每一个词都看清楚了，想明白了再贴。"

安琪儿在黑板上是这样贴的：

白雪公主

美丽　单纯　可爱　可怜　善良

勤劳　友好　聪慧　真善美

王后

仇恨　狡猾　虚伪　假恶丑

美丽　阴险　恶毒　妒忌　聪慧

安琪儿刚走下讲台，就有很多同学举起手来要发言。

有同学说："'美丽'是个褒义词，不能用在阴险恶毒的王后身上。"

"女人是因为可爱而美丽。王后可爱吗？"

当得到全班同学异口同声"不可爱"的回答时，欧阳校长问道："我们在用一个词的时候，一定要注意这个词的感情色彩。那么，可以换一个什么词来形容王后的长相呢？"

唐飞："可以用'漂亮'这个词。"

欧阳校长："能说说你的理由吗？"

唐飞："王后虽然很坏，但是人家长得还是很可以，'漂亮'是一个中性词，好人可以说漂亮，坏人也可以说漂亮。"

欧阳校长赞许地点点头，用"漂亮"的词条换下"美丽"的词条。她见马小跳把手举得很高，又请马小跳说。

"我觉得'聪慧'这个词也不能用在王后的身上。"马小跳还说出了他的理由，"'聪慧'的意思是聪明智慧，王后满脑子都是害白雪公主的阴谋，只能用'阴险'、'狡猾'来形容她。"

见马小跳和唐飞都受到了欧阳校长的表扬，丁文涛坐不住了，他不等欧阳校长请他，便站起来说："我觉得'聪慧'这个词也不能用来形容白雪公主。"

欧阳校长："为什么？"

丁文涛："因为白雪公主老是上当受骗。第一次，王后扮作卖丝带的老太婆，白雪公主让她把丝带系在自己的脖子上，差一点被勒死；第二次，王后又扮作卖梳子的老太婆，白雪公主让她把有毒的梳子插在自己的头上，差一点被毒死；第三次，王后又扮作一个卖苹果的农妇，把一个有毒的苹果给白雪公主吃，白雪公主居然吃了，又差一点被毒死。事实说明，白雪公主一而再、再而三地上当受骗，不仅不能说她聪慧，反而，我还怀疑她的智商是不是有问题。"

丁文涛是"语不惊人死不休"，他的话音刚落，很多女生都把手举起来，她们都是反对他的。

女生甲："白雪公主是因为自己太天真、太善良，所以她很容易相信人。"

女生乙："白雪公主还是一个孩子，她哪里知道，美丽也会招来杀身之祸。等她长大以后，她就不会再上当受骗了。所以，不能说白雪公主的智商低。"

丁文涛："我也是孩子，可我知道人世间人心险恶，我绝不会轻易相信别人的话。所以，我也绝不会犯白雪公主那样的低级错误。"

丁文涛的话引来一片嘘声，还有女生不满地向他翻白眼。

夏林果上课很少举手，现在她把手举得高高的。

夏林果："也许白雪公主没有小聪明，但是她有生活的大智

慧。她待人真诚善良，所以在危急关头，她总能得到别人的帮助，转危为安，最后过上幸福的生活。而王后呢？尽管她诡计多端，但因为她有害人之心，所以善有善报，恶有恶报，最后落得一个悲惨的下场。"

"说得好！"

马小跳带头鼓起掌来，别人都是鼓几下便停下来了，马小跳不停地鼓，最后，只剩下他一个人的掌声。除了夏林果，全班同学都在看他，马小跳这才意识到他必须转移大家的注意力，于是，他又把手举起来。

欧阳校长笑眯眯地请他说。

马小跳指着黑板："我发现有个词'丑陋'，安琪儿还没有贴。"

欧阳校长让马小跳上去贴。马小跳把"丑陋"这个词贴在王后那边。

欧阳校长指着"漂亮"的词条问马小跳："漂亮和丑陋是一对反义词，你认为能把这两个词放在一起形容王后吗？"

马小跳说："王后的样子是漂亮的，灵魂却是丑陋的。"

这一次，是欧阳校长带头为马小跳鼓掌。

下课铃响了，马小跳第一次觉得上语文课时间过得这么快，平时上语文课，他总是嫌时间过得太慢。马小跳还惊喜地发现，原来语文课还可以这样上。如果天天都这样上，他一定会爱上语文课。

别开生面的课堂 ■

一提到语文课，很多孩子都会头疼，因为它似乎总是与划分段落、归纳段意和中心思想这样干枯、抽象、教条的讲述联系在一起。这篇故事尽管是对一次语文课的"实录"，却并不让我们觉得枯燥，原因有二。

其一，这节课的讲授方式和内容新颖。这是一个注重启发、平等对话的课堂，每一个孩子的积极性都被调动起来，孩子们可以就对文章的理解而畅所欲言，思维活跃的马小跳不会再被视作"故意捣蛋"；一直很少被秦老师给予机会的安琪儿终于能一显身手。

在这样的课堂上，欧阳雪没有把鲜活形象的文章肢解撕裂变成程式化的贴标签，而是更注重学生对课文的感性认识，由此学生学习的热情被激发起来，理解、分析能力反倒无形地得到了提升。那句精当的概括——"王后的样子是漂亮的，灵魂却是丑陋的"，不仅让人感觉到马小跳语文能力的升华、人文教育的贯穿其中，也让人看到汉语言自身散发的诱人魅力。这样的语文课不仅马小跳爱上了，大人也饶有兴味。

其二，在"实录"这节课时，杨红樱细致地描述了成语大王、淘气包、笨女孩等各色学生在课堂上的不同表现和明里暗里的"较量"。同样回答问题，马小跳抢出风头"急着说"，说不清楚，则"快快地坐下"；丁文涛胜出了，就很"轻蔑"败北的马小跳，马小跳呢，却在心里跟丁文涛较劲；一旦马小跳受到表扬，丁文涛就"坐不住了"，不请自答，且"语不惊人死不休"，招致嘘声一片；夏林果对丁文涛的惊人之语回应得好，马小跳则带头鼓掌喝彩，以致自己成了众人的焦点……两个"阵营"在课堂上的"较量"与交锋，在让我们领略到这个别开生面的课堂上活跃气氛的同时，也让我们见识到其中的"刀光剑影"，最终窥探到孩子们各异的性格、风采。

由这节语文课的描写，我们也看到了杨红樱——一个曾经的语文教师、一个持续的教育关注者，对于现代语文教育很严肃很认真的思考。她用生花妙笔为我们描述了未来语文课应该有的美好前景。语文课是可以这样上的！

取一个中国名字叫"牛皮"

本说中国话像唱歌，将每个字音都弯来拐去，汉字的四声，从他嘴里出来全变了调。但是，本的听力却没有问题，他不仅能听懂每一句中国话，连"本"和"笨"这两个字声调的差别，他也能听出来。

唐飞是故意的，每次叫"本"，他都故意降成第四声"笨"。

"笨，我跟你说……"

本反应极快："我不笨。"

"难道你不叫'笨'吗?"

"我不叫'本'，我叫'笨'。"

本想说他不叫"笨"，他叫"本"，可这两个字音从他嘴里弯出来，刚好说反，唐飞又笑得打嗝。

马小跳对唐飞极其不满："唐飞，本都是我们的好朋友了，你还老把'本'叫成'笨'，真没劲!"

毛超息事宁人："我们干脆给本取一个中国名字。"

"好得很!"本拍着毛超的肩膀，"你是我肚子里的蛔虫。"

这一声"好得很"，说明本也很愿意有一个中国名字，这让马小跳他们兴奋不已。在他们的想象中，只有大人才能给小孩子取名字，也就是说，要等他们以后做了爸爸，才有权力给自己的儿子或者女儿取名字，没想到现在，他们还是小孩子的时候，就可以给别人取名字了。

毛超问本："我们中国有百家姓，你想要一个什么姓？"

本眨巴着他的绿眼睛："什么叫百家姓？我不懂。"

"这样跟你说吧，比如我马小跳，姓马，名小跳。"

"我明白了。"本点着头，"我想姓马。"

"姓马有什么意思呢？你还是随我姓唐吧。"

本问唐飞："为什么要姓唐？我不懂。"

"'唐'是中国最牛的姓。"

"'最牛'是什么东西？我弄不懂。"

"中国的唐朝是历史上最强大的朝代，在你们美国，中国人常去的那条街叫'唐人街'，你说姓唐是不是最牛的？"

本说："我姓'最牛'好不好？"

"'最牛'不是姓。"毛超问马小跳，"不知道百家姓中，有没有姓牛的？"

马小跳想当然地说："有马，就应该有牛。"

"有姓牛的……"张达很肯定地，"有一个说相声的……叫牛群……"

"既然百家姓中有'牛'，就让他姓牛吧。"马小跳替本做主姓了牛，但名字还没有，"牛什么呢？"

毛超想把他的姓作为本的名字："牛毛。"

"叫牛毛还不如叫牛皮。"唐飞又嘎嘎地笑起来，"牛皮还可以吹一吹。"

本不一定明白"吹牛皮"是什么意思，在他的想象中，"吹牛皮"一定非常好玩，所以他一拍手："我喜欢'牛皮'这个名字！从今天起，不，从现在起，你们只能叫我的中国名字，我叫牛皮。"

第二天在学校，本——不，现在只能叫他牛皮——不管见到班上的男生还是女生，他都会说："我有一个中国名字，请你以后叫我牛皮。"

同学们都觉得好笑，只有路曼曼觉得生气："本，你为什么要取这么奇怪的名字？"

牛皮郑重地说："我喜欢牛皮这个名字。"

路曼曼十分霸道地说："我不许你叫牛皮！"

牛皮笑嘻嘻地、慢条斯理地说："有没有人不许你叫路曼曼？"

马小跳和唐飞都在暗中握牛皮的手，为他助威。

路曼曼有所警觉，她突然问牛皮："你告诉我，谁给你取的这个名字？"

"这……"

牛皮瞪着绿眼睛，在寻找毛超。毛超不知从什么地方冒出来："牛皮想说的是，谁取的这个名字并不重要，重要的是他喜欢这个名字，他只要这个名字。"

"好得很！"牛皮跟毛超来了一个紧紧的拥抱，"你是我肚子里的蛔虫。"

"你不说，我也知道是谁给你取的这个怪名字。"

路曼曼怀疑，乱给本取名字的人，不是马小跳就是唐飞，她要把这个情况报告给秦老师。

不一会儿，马小跳和唐飞便毕恭毕敬地站在了秦老师的面前。

秦老师那像探照灯一样的目光，在马小跳和唐飞的脸上轮流地扫了几个来回后，问道："牛皮这个名字是谁取的?"

唐飞说："我本来想给他取一个具有中国特色的名字，比如黄河，比如长江，他都不要。"

马小跳说："我本来想给他取一个威武的名字，比如金刚，比如泰山，他也不要。"

"我在问你们是谁取的牛皮这个名字? 你们考虑过国际影响没有?"秦老师不想跟他们两个绕下去，直截了当地说，"你们不说，我也知道就是你们两个取的。这种奇奇怪怪的名字，也只有你们两个才想得出来。"

"不只是我和马小跳两个，还有一个——"唐飞把毛超供出来了，"毛超先取的是'牛毛'，我说'牛毛'不如'牛皮'，没想到本一下子就铁了心，非要用'牛皮'做他的中国名字不可。秦老师，真的不怪我……"

秦老师怕再跟他们说下去自己的血压又要升高了。

"你们去把本叫来，我另给他取一个名字。"

马小跳和唐飞把牛皮带到秦老师的跟前。秦老师对牛皮的态度不像对马小跳和唐飞那样严厉，毕竟人家是国际小友人，而秦老师是相当注意国际影响的。

"本，听说你现在有了一个中国名字?"

"秦老师，请您以后叫我牛皮。"

"你知道'牛皮'是什么意思吗?"

"不用知道。我喜欢牛皮这个名字。"

秦老师耐着性子:"我们中国人的名字都是有意义的。所以,我要重新给你取一个有意义的名字。"

"谢谢秦老师!不用麻烦了!"牛皮很有礼貌,但也很固执,"我只要牛皮这个名字。"

经验丰富的秦老师,面对这个太有主见的美国男孩,一筹莫展,竟按中国老师的惯性思维,搬出他的父母来。

"如果你爸爸妈妈不喜欢牛皮这个名字,你会考虑重新取一个中国名字吗?"

牛皮轻描淡写地说:"他们尊重我,也会尊重我的喜欢。"

秦老师无话可说了。人家外国孩子就这么自我,人家的父母就那么民主。他喜欢叫牛皮,就随他吧。

导 读

牛皮的"牛"

　　在对人物性格进行展示时，杨红樱喜欢抓住人物的某一个突出特性着力渲染，由此给读者留下很深的印象。诸如唐飞的贪吃、毛超的废话连篇、张达的笨嘴拙舌、丁文涛的鱼吐泡泡似的说成语等等。《名叫牛皮的插班生》中出场的重要角色——美国小男孩牛皮，同样有一个突出的性格特征，那就是一个"牛"字。

　　本篇故事是围绕着牛皮起中国名字这件事来做文章的，牛皮不折不扣的"牛"脾气已经初现端倪了——后来还有更令人叫绝的表现呢。尽管唐飞是开玩笑地提出了"牛皮"的命名，牛皮却当真喜欢、欣然接受；尽管同学们都觉得这个名字可笑，牛皮却一本正经、有板有眼地要求同学接受它；尽管霸道的路曼曼不许他叫这个名字，牛皮却反唇相讥，绝不放弃自己的"喜欢"；尽管秦老师以师道尊严，搬出传统习俗乃至家长权威来要求牛皮改名换姓，牛皮仍然固执己见、本"姓"难移。我的名字我做主，够有个性的吧？

牛皮的"牛"性格是在中西两种教育观念"碰撞"中展现出来的，小说的喜剧效果也源于此。

但杨红樱的用意并不仅止于提供一些笑料。牛皮的出现，不仅仅是故事发展的需要，让"固若金汤"的四个调皮蛋联盟与一个性情相投的美国男孩再来一次中西合璧的组合以进行"升级换代"的淘气秀；她更有意把有着美国教育背景的牛皮作为一面镜子，从中照见我们教育当中的某种缺陷："人家外国孩子就这么自我，人家的父母就那么民主"，尊重孩子，尊重孩子的"喜欢"。

反观中国家庭，有着多强烈的反差！家长总是处处插手干预孩子的一切，就像安妈妈监视安琪儿那样，孩子始终被束缚着，完全失去了自己自由的空间。这不是太值得玩味了吗？

《名叫牛皮的插班生》

丁文涛的如意算盘

丁文涛在寻求一切机会接近牛皮，这是他爸爸布置给他的任务。他爸爸告诉他，学外语最需要的是语言环境，而丁文涛学了几年英语，老是派不上用场，没有一个令人满意的飞跃，就是因为没有一个人完全用英语和他对话。

"你要千方百计地接近他，跟他做好朋友，上课下课都跟他在一起，只用英语和他对话。这等于一分钱不花，就给自己请了一个陪练英语的外教。你知道现在外教的市场价吗？一小时三百元呢！"

丁爸爸两只眼睛在闪闪发光，丁文涛的两只眼睛也在闪闪发光，他在做心算：如果他每天和牛皮说一个小时的英语，就等于他每天赚了三百元；说两个小时，就等于他每天赚了六百元；说三个小时，就等于他每天赚了九百元……

可是，丁文涛的眼睛很快又暗淡下来："一到下课或放学的时候，牛皮就跟马小跳他们几个在一起，我根本接近不了他。"

丁爸爸一挥手："你要像攻克一座堡垒一样，将他拿下！"

"可是，马小跳他们几个老是在他的身边……"

"你要想办法吸引他，把他从马小跳他们身边吸引到你身边来。"

丁文涛能吸引牛皮的唯一优势，就是他能够用英语直接与牛皮对话。所以，尽管牛皮跟马小跳他们形影不离，但他们听不懂丁文涛和牛皮在说什么，这时候的语言，就会像一堵墙，将说英语的人和听不懂英语的人完全分开。

丁文涛的心里打着这样的如意算盘，瞅准一个牛皮上卫生间的机会，死死地缠住了牛皮。他用英语跟牛皮说了半天，牛皮瞪着一双小小的绿眼睛看着他，不回答他一句话。

丁文涛第一次对自己不自信：难道我说的英语有那么糟糕吗？人家美国人都听不懂？

丁文涛只好改用中文问牛皮："我说的英语你听不懂？"

"原来你会说中国话。"牛皮反问丁文涛，"你为什么不说中国话？"

"因为你是外国人，我才对你说你们国家的语言。"

"不用客气！"牛皮拍拍丁文涛的肩膀，"我在中国，只说中国话。所以，请你以后不要跟我讲英语。"

够精的！丁文涛在心里说，我倒成了他的外教陪练。

丁文涛还是不甘心，想继续说服牛皮："英语是全世界的通用语言，你不用学中国话。"

"你好老土！你还不知道，现在全世界的人都在学中文！"牛皮惊愕不已：这个班上成绩最优秀的学生，怎么如此孤陋寡闻？

"为什么要学中文？"

牛皮用他"不是太好的中国话"告诉丁文涛，因为中国已

经成为世界上最令人向往的国家、最有活力的国家，很多人都想到中国来工作，因为不懂中文，所以没来成。牛皮的意思是他必须学好中文，以后才能来中国工作。

丁文涛还真不知道这股世界潮流。他只知道中国人都在拼命地学外语，想到国外去，不知道外国人却在拼命地学中文，想到中国来。

丁文涛回到家，沮丧地告诉他爸爸，他没能"把牛皮拿下"。

"他真的一句英语也不跟你讲？"

"爸，牛皮的想法跟我们一样。"丁文涛说，"他一心想学好中文，当然不肯跟我讲英语。"

丁爸爸问牛皮的中文水平如何，丁文涛说听力还可以，说得不怎么样。

"那就好！"丁爸爸又想出一招来，"你们可以交换嘛，你跟他说一个小时中文，他跟你说一个小时的英文。"

第二天，丁文涛直接找牛皮说了交换条件。

"为什么？为什么要交换？"牛皮觉得丁文涛这位同学跟马小跳他们几个太不一样了，实在令人费解，"我有这么多中国同学，我跟他们说中国话，不用交换的。"

"你应该学会选择。"

这话也令人费解，牛皮眨巴着绿眼睛。

"中国人说中国话，也有说得好说得坏之分。"

"我知道。"牛皮同意丁文涛的说法，"我觉得张达的中国话说得最好。"

牛皮最喜欢跟张达说中国话，张达说得慢，他也说得慢，他俩之间交流的节奏是最合拍的、最畅通无阻的，所以他认为张达的中国话是说得最好的。

丁文涛告诉牛皮，张达的中国话说得最不好，因为他是结巴。

"结巴是什么？我不懂。"

"结巴就是舌头有毛病。"丁文涛吓唬牛皮，"你再跟张达在一起说中国话，你也会成结巴的。"

牛皮伸出他的舌头让丁文涛看："你看看，我的舌头一点毛病都没有。"

鬼精鬼精的丁文涛，他猜不透牛皮是真傻，还是比他更精，无论如何不进他的套。最后，还是丁爸爸亲自去找了秦老师。秦老师非常赞同这种英文中文共同提高的双赢思路，她一口应承下来，说她负责找牛皮谈。

"牛皮，你的中文水平进步很快啊！你想不想进步得再快一点呢？"

牛皮使劲地点头："想得很！"

"那就好！"秦老师胸有成竹，"我准备派我们班上中文水平最高的一个同学来帮助你。"

"好得很！"牛皮问，"这个同学是不是张达？"

"你说谁？"秦老师以为自己的耳朵出了问题，"你再说一遍，慢慢说。"

当秦老师明明白白听清楚从牛皮嘴里说出的是张达时，她差点没晕过去。这个国际影响可太大了！一个话都说不利索的结巴，牛皮却认为他说中国话说得最好，真不知道这位国际小友人的脑瓜里是怎么想的。

"牛皮，秦老师可以负责任地告诉你，张达的中文水平是最不好的，不是他不努力，而是他先天条件不好。所以我建议你，要尽量少和张达在一起，我怕你说话也跟着他结巴。"

"张达是我的朋友，我不会抛弃他！"牛皮坚决地摇头，"我也不怕结巴。"

这国际小友人的牛脾气又上来了。秦老师撇开张达，直奔主题说丁文涛。她说丁文涛才是班上中文水平最高的同学，他还是个成语大王。

"丁文涛一口气能说出好多好多的成语，而且，他的英语水平也是班上最高的，我想派他来帮助你。"

"好得很！但是——"牛皮把"是"字的尾音拖得老长，"我有一个条件，就是丁文涛只能和我说中国话，不能和我说英语。"

可想而知，丁文涛是不会接受牛皮这个条件的。用丁爸爸的话来说：这种只赔不赚的事，咱们不做。

鬼精鬼精的丁文涛削尖脑袋寻求一切机会要"把牛皮拿下",实现自己的免费外教梦,可他使尽浑身解数,牛气冲天的牛皮都能从容不迫地做到水来土掩、兵来将挡。在这两个人的三次交锋中,杨红樱注意不时变换写法,让每一次交锋的内容、方式、招数都各有不同。第一次是丁文涛"死死地缠住了牛皮",游说对方只和自己说英语;第二次是直奔主题谈判交换条件,还连唬带吓。可牛皮不为所动,不是把丁文涛变成了自己的外教陪练,就是"装疯卖傻"不进丁文涛的圈套。在无计可施的情况下,丁文涛搬来了"救兵"秦老师,在这次侧面交锋中,看起来至少应该是个平局了,可牛皮尾音拖得老长的"但是——"还是让丁文涛悻悻然地败下场来。

正是在两个人的较量中,我们再度领教了牛皮的牛脾气。丁文涛的如意算盘、秦老师的师道尊严,都没能降服他,够绝的吧?他"独具慧眼"地认为张达的中国话说得最好，坚决谢绝秦老师"要尽量少和张达在一起"的好意劝说，因为"张达是我的朋友，我不会抛弃他"，"我也不怕结巴"，完全是我行我素的架势，够倔的吧？

故事主角自然是丁文涛，可如影随形的丁爸爸更值得玩味。毕竟拨弄丁文涛的如意算盘的人是丁爸爸啊。从在幕后运筹帷幄，到老帅出马去找秦老师寻求"双赢"，丁爸爸处处显示出他超凡的经济头脑，他自始至终都从商业原则出发来促成这桩"做好朋友"的买卖：起始，两只眼睛"闪闪发光"，"一挥手"地对儿子发号施令"要千方百计地接近他"，"要像攻克一座堡垒一样，将他拿下"，目的是要"一分钱不花，就给自己请了一个陪练英语的外教"；当此招不行，再出新招，让儿子与牛皮等价"交换"；到末了否决牛皮只说中国话不说英语的条件，也还是用经济眼光来衡量这一切——"这种只赔不赚的事，咱们不做"。连友谊都充满了算计和铜臭味，这样的"友谊"谁能接受？

很显然，在这里，杨红樱精妙细微地透析了当下一些机关算尽太聪明的家长在家庭教育上的市侩哲学，对他们的"势利眼"温婉地批评了一回。"眨巴着绿眼睛"的国际小友人也许还会费解，但我们却不难理解，"两只眼睛也在闪闪发光"的丁文涛为什么会跟马小跳他们几个不一样——有其父必有其子嘛。

我是班长

　　小非洲虽然是个山里的孩子，但他生性活泼开朗，爱说爱笑，这些日子，每天都有采访，他在镜头面前，从来没有紧张过。但是现在，他有点紧张，因为夏林果离他这么近，他从来没见过长得这么好看的女生，他眼睛不看夏林果，只看马小跳。

　　夏林果不愧是有经验的主持人，她一说话就让小非洲进入到最佳的自然状态。

　　夏林果："虽然我今天是第一次见到你，但我早就听马小跳说起过你，他总叫你小非洲……"

　　小非洲："哦，我们村子里的人都叫我小非洲。"

　　夏林果："能给我们讲讲，他们为什么都叫你小非洲吗？"

　　"因为我的皮肤特别特别黑，牙齿又特别特别白，嘴唇特别特别厚，村子里的人都说我长得像非洲黑人，所以都叫我小非洲。"小非洲话题一转，转到马小跳身上，"我也不叫他马小跳，我叫他跳跳娃。其实，跳跳娃该叫我幺叔。"

　　"不会吧？"牛皮搞不懂了，"你比马小跳还小，你应该叫他一声哥。"

小非洲："我们那里幺房出老辈，我叫马天宝，他爸爸叫马天笑，都是天字辈的，我叫他爸爸哥，所以马小跳该叫我叔。"

唐飞他们几个最想知道马小跳叫过小非洲幺叔没有。小非洲说没有。这让唐飞他们几个非常失望，如果能亲耳听见马小跳叫小非洲一声幺叔，那肯定很好玩。

小非洲："虽然我是跳跳娃的幺叔，但我最崇拜的人还是跳跳娃……"

"你怎么能崇拜马小跳呢？"毛超忍不住打断小非洲，"你是小英雄，马小跳应该崇拜你。"

小非洲："那时候，如果跳跳娃也在我们教室里，他也会像我那么做的。还有你们，都会像我那么做，都可以当小英雄的。"

小非洲突然不说话了。

马小跳："小非洲，你怎么啦？"

小非洲小声地说："我们班一共有三十一人，活下来的只有十人，老师也……"

马小跳："这活下来的十个同学中，就有两个是小非洲救出来的。"

小非洲："是郑老师救了他们。地震的时候，郑老师正在给我们上语文课，她离教室的门最近，完全可以在房子倒塌下来之前跑出去的，可是她用手撑着教室已经变形的门框，让我们先跑。我刚跑出去，房子轰的一声就倒了，郑老师和我们班的二十三个同学都还在里面。"

夏林果："你觉得害怕吗？"

小非洲："那种时候，已经不知道害怕，就想冲进去把老师和同学都救出来。我冲进去找到了郑老师，有几块预制板压在她的身上，她一手抱着牛壮壮，一手抱着田小燕。郑老师还活着。我去拉她，她对我说：'快救田小燕！'我把田小燕从她身下拉出来，背着她跑了出来，把她交给正在那里指挥的校长。然后，我又跑了进去，我还是想把郑老师救出来。可是，郑老师一定要我先救牛壮壮。我又从郑老师身下把牛壮壮拉出来，背着他跑了出来。我再一次冲进去的时候，房子又摇晃起来，我刚跑到郑老师的身边，又有一块预制板掉下来，砸在我的身上，我就什么都不知道了。"

牛皮："后来呢？"

"我醒过来的时候已经在医院里了，头上的皮被掀掉一大块，一只手也没有了，我都没有哭。可是，他们告诉我郑老师和班上二十一个同学都……我就哭了，一直哭，哭累了睡一会儿，睡觉时也在哭……"

唐飞："你都从教室里跑出来了，又跑进去两次，你是怎么想的？"

小非洲："什么都没想，我是班长！"

毛超："我们来想象一下，如果你不再跑进去，或者你跑进去一次，不再跑进去第二次，那么，你头上的皮也不会失去一大块，你的手也不会……"

"哪能这么想象？"小非洲打断毛超的话，"我是班长，我必须这么做！"

牛皮："给我们讲讲，你是怎么当班长的？"

"我也当不好！"小非洲嘿嘿一笑，"有一次，有几个男同学拿毛毛虫来吓班上的女同学，我就去管他们，他们不听，我就

和他们打起来，他们三个人打我一个人……"

牛皮："哇，一个人对付三个人，你太酷了！你打赢了吗？"

夏林果却为小非洲担心："他们打疼你没有？"

小非洲："没有，他们也不会真打我。"

班长怎么能跟同学打架？路曼曼觉得小非洲班长当得太不靠谱，她必须把"打架"这个话题转移开："马天宝同学，当了小英雄，你今后有什么打算吗？"

路曼曼一开口，小非洲就觉得这个女生说话的语气跟其他人都不一样，他们都跟着马小跳叫他小非洲，而她却称呼他马天宝同学。毛超忙给他介绍路曼曼："她是我们班的中队长，也就是班长，级别跟你一样。"

小非洲："哦，你问我今后有什么打算啊？我要做的事情太多了：先养好伤，多吃饭，让头上那块掉了头皮的地方快点长出头发来。"

牛皮："啊？多吃饭头发就能长出来吗？"

小非洲："那当然！你看那些荒地，只要有水、有肥料，就能长出草来。我现在没有右手了，必须练习用左手写字，左手吃饭；我最大的愿望还是想上学，可是，我们的学校不在了……"

马小跳："你可以上我们的学校！"

夏林果："你还可以到我们班上来！"

"OK！"络腮胡子眉开眼笑，向几个孩子竖起了大拇指，"非常棒！"

络腮胡子想要的就是这样的效果，让这几个孩子来陪衬小英雄身上的孩子气，他不仅勇敢，还很可爱，这样的小英雄不仅仅令人敬佩，还惹人怜爱。

　　络腮胡子带着他的摄制组，满意地离开了病房。护士长说小天宝该休息了，言外之意是在给马小跳他们下逐客令。

　　"护士阿姨，求求您让他们再陪我一会儿吧！"

　　"好吧！"护士长对小非洲说，"就十分钟。"

　　只有十分钟的时间，可马小跳有好多问题要问小非洲。

　　"小非洲，你知道我爷爷奶奶在哪儿吗？"

　　"不知道。"小非洲说，"我的爸爸妈妈到现在还没找到呢。"

　　马小跳又问："我奶奶家的房子还在吗？"

　　"不在了。"小非洲说，"村子里所有的房子都不在了。"

　　"我奶奶家的猪、狗、猫，还有鹩哥，它们呢？"

　　"它们都跑到山上去了。"

　　马小跳问小非洲："你怎么知道的？"

　　"猜的呗。"小非洲说，"你想想，猪、狗、猫都有四条腿，比人还多两条腿呢，当然比人跑得快；鹩哥有翅膀，它们一定还活着。"

　　十分钟很快就到了，马小跳他们必须要走了，他们都舍不得小非洲，眼里都含着泪。倒是小非洲笑眯眯地："你们可以天天来看我嘛。说不定哪天我把伤养好了，就到你们班上去，跟你们做同学！"

导 读

英雄原是普通人

即使马小跳做过那么多的"大事"：当上超级市长，操办跳跳电视台，做过小侦探，抓过小偷，帮过被拐的女孩……他也还是会有这样那样的缺点：不尊重安琪儿，好表现，既有虚荣心，也有嫉妒心，等等。毕竟他是一个普普通通的孩子。杨红樱自始至终都注意到了这个"度"，所以并没有把他写得高大完美。

同样的，在描写有着救人壮举的小英雄小非洲时，杨红樱也是始终把他当成普通孩子来写的，正是他身上散发出的浓浓人情味、郁郁孩子气，让我们感受到小非洲的有血有肉、真实可信。普通人与英雄其实只有一步之遥，或者说英雄原本就是普通人，只是在关键时刻能挺身而出，迸发出人性和道德的光辉而显出了他们的与众不同。小非洲不是说过嘛："那时候，如果跳跳娃也在我们教室里，他也会像我那么做的。还有你们，都会像我那么做，都可以当小英雄的。"所以，"我是班长，我必须这么做"不是什么豪言壮语，也不是身份的炫耀，而是小非洲责任感的显示。而"责任感"、"有担当"是杨红樱一直强调的人的最重要的品质。

和马小跳一样，小非洲也是一个有情有义的孩子：他没有为自己救出两个同学而居功自傲，倒是会为自己辈分比马小跳大而在同龄伙伴面前显着得意；他没有为自己失去一只手、头皮被掀掉一大块而独自伤悲，倒是为老师和同学的不幸遇难而连连落泪。杨红樱注意到从公、私两方面来展现小非洲身上十足的孩子气，不论是在媒体采访的公众场合里，还是在与伙伴交心的私下相处中，小非洲都表里如一，处处现出他的"真"来。

在摄像机镜头前，小非洲也会自曝其短——当班长"气场"不足的时候，也会和被管理的同学发生肢体冲突；对未来的打算也实实在在——多吃饭、练习用左手做事、想上学。而且不为自己的残疾而悲戚，言辞中对未来充满着美好的想象："你看那些荒地，只要有水、有肥料，就能长出草来。"看到没？对于班长和同学打架这件事情，几个孩子的关注点各异：看重个性、注重魅力的美国孩子牛皮是崇敬："你太酷了！"温情善良的漂亮女孩夏林果是担心："他们打疼你没有？"说话、想法上带着点官员腔的小大人路曼曼则转移话题，避免不良影响。当事人小非洲在回首往事时是释放善意："他们也不会真打我。"

在私下十分钟的攀谈中，小非洲进一步显现出他作为孩子的幽默感和想象力来。小非洲对马小跳奶奶家的猪呀

狗呀猫呀命运的合理猜想让人感觉出他的俏皮和机智来："你想想，猪、狗、猫都有四条腿，比人还多两条腿呢，当然比人跑得快；鹩哥有翅膀，它们一定还活着。"从"笑眯眯"的小非洲身上，我们不难体会到灾区儿童开朗乐观、自信坚强的精神面貌。真的就像杨红樱在这本小说中着重表达的那样："灾难可以摧毁人的身体，不可摧毁的是人的梦想！"

有一个叫老杜的人

走着走着，毛超做出很诡异的样子，让他们把耳朵伸过来："有一个人十分可疑，他一直跟着我们。"

马小跳蹲下来，假装系鞋带："是那个穿 T 恤的吗？"

唐飞假装挠后脑勺，把头偏过去："是那个秃顶吗？"

张达假装东西掉了，回头去找："是那个……啤酒肚吗……"

黄菊掏出身上的小镜子，从小镜子里找到那个人："是那个红鼻头吗？"

就是这个人，他可能也意识到他跟踪的人已发现他，假装东张西望，仿佛在寻找什么。

马小跳他们突然来了一个大转身："什么人？"

那人一怔，随即露出笑脸。他不笑时，脸上一条皱纹都没有，是一张婴儿脸；笑的时候，满脸的皱纹像盛开的菊花瓣。

"误会！误会！"那人很有交际能力，一副"自来熟"的样子，"我跟你们一样，也是想帮助这个小姑娘的热心人。"

马小跳纠正道："我们跟你不一样，我们是她的同学。"

"一样，我们的心一样，目的也一样。"那人不把自己当外人，"从现在起，你们干什么，我就干什么。"

"不行！"马小跳对这个陌生人还存有戒心，"我们是一个侦探小组，我是组长。"

唐飞再一次提醒马小跳："临时的。"

"我听你的！你就是临时小组长，我也听你的指挥，绝对听你的！"

一个大男人，愿意绝对地听一个小孩子的指挥，这让马小跳动了恻隐之心。他马上松口道："你先回避一下，我们商量商量。"

那人知趣地退到一边。

"他到底什么动机呀？"唐飞见多识广，他看那人也不像一个没事干的闲人，"不好好干自己的事业，跟我们瞎闹什么呀？"

在张达眼里，人只分两种：好人和坏人。

"……我看他……不像坏人……"

唐飞说："也不像个好人。"

"人多力量大嘛。我看他是个很有办法的人，说不定对我们有用。"

马小跳完全同意毛超的说法，这人已经给他留下一点好感，再说这么大的一个人，居然愿意听从他的指挥，这让他很有成就感。

侦探小组的四个成员，除了唐飞的态度不明朗外，马小跳、张达和毛超都同意那人加入他们的侦探小组。

马小跳向那人招招手："我正式通知你，你被批准加入我们的侦探小组了。"

"我很荣幸！"那人的态度十分谦卑，"你们就叫我老杜吧！"

按理说，老杜这样的年纪，马小跳他们应该尊称他一声叔叔，但目前他们跟他都在一个侦探小组里，算同事关系，老杜就老杜吧。他们一起向紫荆苑的大门走去。

紫荆苑的大门是仿照罗马的凯旋门修的，门气派，守门的保安也挺神气，大檐帽，挺括的制服上扛着两个肩章，把肩膀衬托得宽宽的。见马小跳他们走来，保安伸出戴着雪白手套的手，不让他们进去。他的旁边立着一个告示牌："私人住宅，非请免进"。

"我们不进去。"唐飞眼睛也不看保安，大模大样地说，"就找你调查调查。"

唐飞这目中无人的派头，还真把保安给镇住了，他问唐飞："什么事？"

"就是那天晚上 11 点左右……"

"哪天晚上？"

"17 号晚上。"毛超对唐飞很不满，"侦探工作，注意严谨，一定要严谨。"

"我严谨，我来问。"马小跳问道，"17 号晚上 11 点左右，有没有车从这里边开出去？"

"有啊！"保安说，"每晚都有车开进来，也有车开出去。"

"我希望你回答问题严谨一点。"马小跳做出严谨的样子，"我问的是 17 号晚上，下着毛毛雨，从里面开出来的车，没问从外面开进去的车。"

"下毛毛雨的晚上，我有印象……"保安欲言又止，"你们是干什么的？我为什么要接受你们的调查？"

唐飞把黄菊推到保安面前："她爸爸是这附近工地的农民工，

被从这儿开出去的车给撞了，现在还躺在床上呢！"

"你们怎么就断定是从这里面开出去的车撞了人呢？"

"我们已经找到了目击者，她亲眼看见那撞人的车是从紫荆苑开出去的，因为距离太远，没看清楚是什么车，只看见那车灯雪亮……"

"说到车灯，我有印象。"保安回忆道，"那晚，我11点刚接班，就有一辆车摇摇晃晃冲出来，那远光灯射得我眼睛都睁不开。"

老杜比谁都急："你看清楚了是什么车？"

"是宝马。"

"车牌号呢？"

"车速很快，只记得最后一个数字好像是8。"

"既然车速很快，你怎么看得清楚呢？"老杜比谁都较真，"你能肯定车牌号的最后一个数字是8吗？"

保安说他敢肯定。

"那宝马车是几系的？什么车型的？"

唐飞的问话让老杜大吃一惊："你人不大，懂得还不少。"

"他是超级车迷。"毛超向老杜隆重推出唐飞，"全世界的名牌车，他都能倒背如流。不信，你随便考他。"

"毛超，现在正搞调查，你不要东拉西扯。"唐飞追问保安，"你还没回答我的问题呢！"

"还真没看清楚。"保安似乎很为难，"那颜色挺特别的，是那种不是黑，也不是白，也不是红……"

"什么都不是？不可能。"

"好像有点黄，黄得有点暗……"

"我知道了，是香槟色。那是宝马7系最新款740。"

保安问："什么是香槟色？"

"香槟酒见过吗？就是那颜色。"

保安点点头，又摇摇头，很茫然的样子。

"人家保安都不敢确定，我们可不能乱下定论。是不是，组长？"

唐飞纠正老杜道："临时组长。"

"老杜说得有道理。"马小跳问保安，"当时，还有谁看见这辆车了？"

保安说："还有一个跟我一块儿值班的保安，可他今天休息，明天上午在。"

"那我们明天再来。"

老杜问："明天还来呀？"

"老杜，你可能还不了解我们。我们做事情从不半途而废，不达目的，誓不罢休！"马小跳一本正经地说，"你如果有事，明天我们来，你可以不来。"

老杜赶紧说："不，我没事，我必须来。"

导 读

精彩的细节描写

　　杨红樱提到过古典名著《水浒传》写作上的一个特点："《水浒传》有一百零八将，会一个一个出来，而且每一个新人物出场，都会有非常精彩的铺垫和描写。"同样的，《侦探小组在行动》中重要人物老杜的出场，也是很精彩，耐人玩味的。

　　老杜的现身完全是落在孩子们的眼眸里的。爱饶舌、也爱咋咋呼呼的毛超是从老杜的行踪上觉出这个人的可疑的，所以毛超"做出很诡异的样子"，让伙伴们把耳朵伸过来。别的几个孩子为避免打草惊蛇，也都有着很个性的观察方式：马小跳是"蹲下来，假装系鞋带"；唐飞是"假装挠后脑勺，把头偏过去"；张达"假装东西掉了，回头去找"；黄菊是典型的女孩子，要比前面几个男孩的"装腔作势"更聪明委婉一些，她是"掏出身上的小镜子，从小镜子里找到那个人"。几个孩子是从不同敏感带和各异的角度出发对老杜产生了不同印象的，合拢在一起也就恰好形成了老杜的全像：穿T恤，秃顶，啤酒肚，红鼻头。小侦探们是以"假装"的方式来观察老杜的，老杜也以牙还牙来反侦察，"假装东张西望，仿佛在寻找什么"。两方面"假装"对"假装"，再加上马小跳他们的突然"大转身"和"什么人"的诘问，孩子们和老杜"过招"时暗斗明争剑拔弩张般的架势为小说增色不少。

借孩子们之势推出老杜的外貌，显然要比由杨红樱直接描绘出来更巧妙更生动，而让老杜的外貌"动"起来也更会给人留下深刻的印象："他不笑时，脸上一条皱纹都没有，是一张婴儿脸；笑的时候，满脸的皱纹像盛开的菊花瓣。"老杜表情的丰富性和独特性足以让人对他那张"变脸"过目不忘。在和孩子们的语言交锋中，老杜这么一个大男人不再躲躲闪闪，讨好的言语、谦卑的态度和知趣的行为中处处表现出对侦探小组领导的服帖和逢迎，极大地满足了小侦探们的虚荣心，让自命不凡的孩子们从最初的存有戒心到后来"动了恻隐之心"，老杜和孩子们刚开始的紧张关系全然化解，他被接纳为侦探小组的一员，也就顺理成章了。在接下来对保安的询问中，老杜"比谁都急"、"比谁都较真"、"大吃一惊"的诸般情态和显得思虑深熟沉稳的问话以及"我必须来"的表态，都述说着老杜不同寻常的来头和可能的隐情，同时杨红樱又以此为后面故事的发展蓄势铺垫。

杨红樱说过作文当中细节的重要性："细节就像一颗颗珠子，作文就是一颗颗珠子串起来的，好看、生动，能

吸引人往下读。所谓的生动形象都是细节描写，没有细节就干巴巴的。"这一篇中诸多生动的细节描写，就让我们对老杜这么一个"不像坏人"可"也不像个好人"的大人产生了浓厚的兴味，急巴巴地想知道不好好干自己的事业却跟孩子们"瞎闹"的老杜到底会在侦探小组中扮演怎样的角色。在整个"淘气包马小跳系列"中，诸多人物之所以能质感鲜活地出现在我们面前并被读者津津乐道念念不忘，依靠的也正是杨红樱出神入化的细节描写。

有华人的地方，就有马小跳

受访人：杨红樱
采访人：乔世华（辽宁师范大学文学院副教授、文学博士）
地　点：大连——北京

乔世华：马小跳已是家喻户晓的儿童形象，在中国的孩子们当中，更是被津津乐道的明星。对你来说，马小跳意味着什么？

杨红樱：马小跳一直是我想写的一个儿童形象，可以说，他是我的理想，我在他的身上，寄予了太多的东西：比如我的教育理想，家庭教育的和学校教育的；我对当今教育现状的思考；我对童年的理解，对孩子天性的理解；这里面还包括我做老师、做母亲的人生体验。我笔下的马小跳是一个真正的孩子，我想通过这个真正的孩子，呈现出一个完整的童心世界。

乔世华：马小跳有没有生活原型呢？还有，为什么会想到写这样一个淘气包呢？

杨红樱：马小跳是有原型的，但不是具体的哪一个，是我以前教的几个男学生。我虽然早就不教书了，但常常会想起我的学生，特别是那些调皮捣蛋甚至把我气哭过的"坏孩子"。他们该调皮的时候调皮了，爽爽快快地过了把孩子瘾。

　　作为童书作家，我一直想写一个真正的孩子，让小读者在他的身上找到成长的力量，书里主人公的烦恼就是他们的烦恼，他们能在我的书中找到自己的影子。在写马小跳时，我常常写得热泪盈眶，像马小跳这样有情有义的孩子真是太少了，在秦老师

236

病了的时候，无论如何想着去看她，而丁文涛、路曼曼就不曾想到过。

现在社会一般比较看重智商，培养了很多太聪明的孩子。相对智商，我更看重情商，马小跳和安琪儿都属于情商特别高的孩子。我是喜欢木讷一些的孩子，因为他们做事情很执著。我小时候就很木讷，安琪儿身上有我的影子，所不同的是我小时候比较漂亮。相比其他的同学，我显得有点笨，笨人比较认真，会一心一意地把手边的事情做好。直到今天，我也是这样。

乔世华：在"淘气包马小跳系列"的写作中，你一开始似乎有走超现实表达路线的倾向，如《贪玩老爸》中的《吹泡泡糖吹上了天花板》和《袁隆隆老师》中的《瞌睡虫在教室里飞》、《吹泡泡糖飞过了木马》等多篇。但从后来的写作路向来看，你最终还是选择了写实的路线。请问你是出于怎样的考虑做出了这种调整的？

杨红樱："淘气包马小跳"的前身是"顽皮巴浪"。1998年，我担任《小学生生活》的主编，上面登着我写的两篇连载，一篇是童话《仙女蜜儿》，另一篇是小说《顽皮巴浪》。《顽皮巴浪》的写作有很浓厚的童话色彩，是因为我写了十几年的童话，刚开始写小说，小说和童话的界限还不是分得很清，就会出现这种"超现实"表达的情形。

其实，小孩子对现实和幻想分得不是很清楚，他们常说读我的书有"飞"的感觉。有时我自己对现实和幻想也不是分得很清。

乔世华：你从2003年开始推出"淘气包马小跳系列"，到现在已经先后推出了20种之多，累计销量早已经超过了2000万册。在这20种书中，我们能很清晰地看到你写作的路径越来越宽，已经从单纯对孩子日常生活的表现，过渡到更有意义的话题，属于大手笔了。比如《寻找大熊猫》涉及到的是生态保护命题，《开甲壳虫车的女校长》中有对新颖前卫的教育理念的表达，《名叫牛皮的插班生》中通过牛皮的出场展示了中西两种教育观念的差异，贯穿《侦探小组在行动》始终的是现代公民教育，《小英雄和芭蕾公主》则直接取材 2008 年的汶川地震，关注灾后儿童心理干预问题。

杨红樱：在这 20 本书中，前 12 本是人物形象的铺垫，当这些人物形象都立起来后，当然会出现大手笔的。因为有了前面的人物铺垫，越到后来，越显得游刃有余，只要保持一点——"好看"，那么会有好多我要表达的东西都能纳入其中。在《巨人的城堡》中，其实就写到了后工业时代出现的问题是人的心理问题，而不是生理、生存问题。

我写东西，是要滋养孩子的心灵成长，要展现一个孩子完整的成长过程。凡是孩子成长中必须要接受的教育，我都要通过马小跳的童心世界来展示出来。很多成人包括未生育孩子的都市白领也都喜欢阅读马小跳，认为在里面看到了小孩完整的成长过程。我对于自己的要求是，如果有下一本的话，一定要比前一本写得好，绝不硬写，所以写作的时候我也常有如履薄冰的感觉。

乔世华：2008 年出版的《小英雄和芭蕾公主》的写作似乎又与前面几本不同，比较"实"一些，比如坐实了地震的时间，小非洲和芭蕾公主也都有生活原型。在那以后，你一直没有再出马小跳的"下一本"。而据我所知，很多孩子是仍然热切盼望着"下一本"的。能否说一下《小英雄和芭蕾公主》写作的相关情况？

杨红樱：在写了《侦探小组在行动》后，我就觉得孩子童年的方方面面我都已经写到了，我想要表达的东西都已经在其中了。当汶川地震之后，很多人问过我，是否会去写点什么东西，当时我曾明确表示不会。汶川有我的大量读者，那时我前前后后去灾区七八次，都是想着能为那里的孩子提供一点力所能及的帮助，所以也就根本没有积累什么素材。我去医院看望那些因为地震而截肢的孩子时，真为他们的命运和未来而揪心，可他们见到我却笑得一脸的灿烂，争相和我一起拍照。他们觉得那么多的老师、同学都死了，自己活下来就已经很幸运了，根本来不及难过。

当我回到成都，痛定思痛后，感到自己作为一个四川作家，这么大的一场发生在家乡的灾难，主观上我是回避不了的，这里有作家的社会担当问题。而且，大自然的这场灾难是当下孩子所处的特殊历史时期，不可能不进入到马小跳的生活当中。所以在2008年9、10月份的时候，我开始动笔写作了。俗话说，画鬼容易画狗难，这一本写得确实很难，写完后我曾推倒重写。应该说，这是"淘气包马小跳系列"的最后一本。

乔世华：从你过去的教学经历以及目前的文学创作来看，你是一直比较关注教育的。你作品中的一些人物是有你早年从教的影子的，如《漂亮老师和坏小子》中的米兰、"淘气包马小跳系列"中的林老师、欧阳雪等；你在马小跳的写作中一直对发生在教育界的一些新鲜事物表现出特别的关注，比如心情卡、道德银行、带轮子的书包等等。所以，你其实是在教育的圈子外继续着你早年的教育思考。你曾说过：生命的终极目标，应该是充分地享受自由和快乐。从这个角度来看，说到底，"淘气包马小跳系列"所传递出来的就是自由和快乐的精神，它承载着你的教育观、人生观和文学观。

杨红樱：我教书的时间不长，仅仅是把一个班从一年级教到六年级，然后离开学校去出版社做了童书编辑。在学校期间，我对教育的认识更多的是感性的。离开学校后，特别是做了母亲以后，我开始对教育有了更多的理性思考。比如，对秦老师这样的老师，我自始至终肯定她是一个好老师，但是她对学生造成了伤害，没有达到教育的目的，所以我对她是有着善意的讽刺的。

还有，我们应怎样评价马小跳这种个性化的快乐孩子和丁文涛这类标准格式化的孩子的优劣？尽管用公认的标准来衡量马小跳，他算不上是一个好学生。在《超级市长》中，老校长终于开始反思：在马小跳和丁文涛这两个孩子身上，究竟谁的综合素质更高。还有，在我看来，快乐是一种能力，教育的一项重要内容应该是培养孩子快乐的能力。所以，在这套书中，我的写作重点不是要塑造某一种形象，而是要表现马小跳的快乐。马小跳是一个具有快乐能力的孩子，他在生活际遇中遇到各种各样的问题，但都能保持健康的心态。其实人到了最后一刻，是要扪心自问"我一生是否快乐"的。真正有快乐童年的孩子会有非凡的想象力，将来才有可能做成大事。

乔世华：马小跳的快乐性格确实让人感觉很健康，一旦他遇到什么不开心的事情，往往自己能想方设法很好地调节心理。偏偏是传统意义上的好学生，容易出现心理问题：路曼曼因为没能当选大队委，就哭过好几回以致生病了；丁文涛呢，在超级市长竞选中败北，就萎靡不振；自拍的电视节目没上电视，马小跳们有心理承受能力，而夏林果却感觉很没面子。

还有，你在写到四个调皮蛋的理想的时候，他们的理想都很简单，或者当游乐园经理，或者当美食评委，或者当快递员；而丁文涛呢，是要做经济学家，在丁爸爸看来这才是出类拔萃的儿子。你以很委婉的笔调对于这种公认的标准进行了讽刺。

杨红樱：社会是由各种各样的职业的人构成的。中国的家长把职业分成了三六九等，总是希望孩子做这个"家"那个"家"，要他们从小立下各种雄心壮志，但很少考虑孩子是否快乐。国外家长一般希望孩子做快乐、幸福的人。其实，人首先是要做一个好公民，能自得其乐自食其力。我做老师时，是孩子们喜欢的好老师；做编辑时，在业内也有很好的口碑。那时，我是一个快乐而知足的人。现在成了所谓的名人，也并没有觉得就比过去好。要紧的是，人要永远保持一颗平常心。

乔世华： 说到"快乐"，让我想到了你作品中的幽默。可能人们一般会认为你是从2000年校园小说创作之后开始的幽默文学写作。但事实上，通读你的作品后，我感觉幽默是你骨子里的东西，从你写作之初就已经内蕴在写作中了。能否谈一下你对幽默的认识？

杨红樱： 幽默应该是含而不露的，不是人刻意追求就能得到的。有人说我的童话写作很优美很温暖，其实我的童话也是很有幽默感的，属于那种冷幽默。这可能和我居住的成都这座城市有关，成都人都不是追求"闹"的那种。如果你看过我们四川作家马识途的《夜谭十记》，就会体味到这种典型的冷幽默风格。小时候，我阅读亲戚家的藏书，其中有全套的川剧剧本，像《柜中缘》、《御河桥》什么的，那里的幽默就都是带出来的，属于藏而不露。

　　说到幽默，钱锺书的《围城》给我的影响也挺大的。我个人说话不幽默，但是处理人和事挺有幽默感的，也特别能理解别人讲话中的意味。我的童话《没有尾巴的狼》、《亲爱的笨笨猪》、《流浪狗和流浪猫》、《会走路的小房子》、《森林谜案》等就都是幽默感很强、很好读的作品。

乔世华： 看你的作品感觉还是有理想化色彩的。比如在《超级市长》中你让马小跳这样传统意义上的后进生登上超级市长的宝座；还有在《开甲壳虫车的女校长》中你塑造了欧阳雪校长这样一位坚持捍卫孩子童年的人物，也给人理想化的感觉。

杨红樱：欧阳雪是有生活原型的，是成都几个女校长的集合体，她们都很漂亮，有先进、甚至超前的教育理念，为捍卫孩子的童年，为给孩子们减负，她们做了许多大胆的尝试。

　　书中写到的欧阳校长上的那堂语文课，是我在台湾一个小学听的一堂课，那个女校长讲的就是《白雪公主》，学生坐在地板上听课，眼神里都透着兴奋，看起来很简单，却让孩子喜欢上了语文，教育目的达到了，所有情感因素也在其中。这是我很欣赏的一堂课。

乔世华：我曾问过一些"马小跳"的铁杆书迷，他们是否希望马小跳也和他们一样长大。他们的回答惊人的一致：不希望。因为长大了，就不可爱了。由此我也想到了你在"淘气包马小跳系列"的写作中是否考虑过这套书的目标读者？

杨红樱：小孩子一天一个样，五岁和四岁、六岁和五岁都不一样，小孩子的认知程度也就不一样。我们都知道一岁孩子吃的东西必须是糊糊，虽然有的东西有营养，但是他不能吃。一岁孩子跟两岁孩子吃的东西绝对不一样，两岁孩子跟三岁孩子吃的东西又不一样，这需要具备一定的儿童心理学和儿童教育学的专业素养，才能顾及不同年龄特征孩子的认知程度、接受程度。

　　童书写作其实是一件专业性很强的事情，它要求作家对不同年龄的儿童心理一定要把握得相当准确。童书比较发达的国家，在这个领域里年龄段划分地很细，比如日本，零岁、一岁、两岁，都有对应的不同读物。这是非常科学的。其实有一个简单的道理：医院为什么要专门设置儿科医生？因为儿童身体和成人身体不一样嘛。孩子在阅读时，几乎都会把自己放进一个角色中，好的儿童书就是要满足他们的想象力，满足他们的求知欲，满足他们心灵成长的需要。要让孩子爱上阅读，这是童书作家的责任。我写马小跳其实就是写给小学生看的。

乔世华：能否从写作技巧的角度来谈一下，你究竟施展了什么样的"魔力"，让孩子对你作品如此痴迷？

杨红樱：给孩子写东西，难度相当大，心里知道怎样的表达会更直接一些，但在给儿童写的东西里这么说就不行。它需要一些技巧的。比如我在写作中，就注意叙述节奏，静态描写要少。你可能会注意到，我在描写上不超过三个句子，否则孩子会感觉节奏慢。在外貌描写上，我主要突出人物的某一点，表现人物更多的是通过语言和动作。

　　"淘气包马小跳系列"中的废话大王毛超，我主要就是通过语言表现，十句话中有九句是废话。"河马"张达主要描写的是他的动作，他的语言是结巴的。唐飞就是贪吃，各种各样的吃。经过这么多年的语言锤炼，我基本上可以把语言用得干净、动感、富有节奏。

　　在《开甲壳虫车的女校长》开篇写到马小跳看到女校长时，就是用一个孩子的眼睛在打量她，因为他太小，对女人构不成整体的印象，所以我这时抓住跟天真妈妈很像的欧阳雪的珍珠项链，还有海藻一样弯曲的长发，从而让马小跳一下子对她产生了好感。儿童文学是浅语的艺术，但是要使用好浅语，确实很难。《超级市长》中马小跳和真正的市长在一起时，两人都在笑，其中有这样一句，"马小跳的嘴巴笑得有点歪"，这个"歪"字就给人很多想象空间。

乔世华：从"淘气包马小跳系列"的内容来看，你的游历对你的写作很有帮助，像《暑假奇遇》、《寻找大熊猫》、《名叫牛皮的插班生》等书中，写到孩子们去望龙山区、藏龙山、雪山等，很有真实感。即使在《宠物集中营》中，也因为你有过在宠物医院的

243

生活体验，而赋予了日常动物以丰富的情感乃至产生艺术美感。

杨红樱：这些书中写到的山，我都去过。我最大的爱好就是旅行，每一年都要去一些地方。马天笑先生的原型是我的父亲，他很会玩，也很会享受生活。小时候，父亲常常带着我们去乡间看荷花，去地里采摘成熟的瓜果，所以我从小就对大自然十分敏感。现在的孩子往往不知道感动，没有感觉，没有对生活、对自然感恩的心理。

有孩子来信说，我的书对他们作文能力提高特别有帮助，他们发现作文原来可以这样写，也觉得有东西可写了。只要生活中有感动的东西，就能写出好文章来。语言是为内容服务的。所以有的孩子很不解，为什么老师、家长不让他们看这样的书，因为成人觉得这对考试没有帮助。我也感到，我的作品，往往是孩子读懂了，大人却没读懂。

乔世华：你书中不回避孩子们对异性的纯洁而朦胧的好感，如马小跳、张达、丁文涛们对夏林果，唐飞对杜真子，安琪儿对马小跳、牛皮对安琪儿，也包括马小跳对漂亮的林老师等等。这其实是很符合小孩子也包括成年人心理特点的——"爱美之心，人皆有之"。但就像你小说中写到的那样，人们不愿意去承认这一切。还有，你是怎样看待这种小孩子间的对异性的好感的？恐怕很多家长都会像安琪儿妈妈那样担心这会导致孩子早恋之类的。

杨红樱：其实每个孩子在小的时候都会有他特别关注的异性，这是很自然的。我作品中写到这些，也是在进行情感教育。这是一种生命现象，植物有雌雄之分，只有在一起才能生长得更好。无论是在童年期还是在青春期，都会有某一类男生吸引某一类女生，或某一类女生吸引某一类男生，这是必然要发生的，我认为根本不需回避，只需告诉他们，这其实不是爱情，却是一生当中最没有功利、最干净的情感。

乔世华：你说的话提醒了我。我在上小学的女儿就经常做着公主
　　梦，在玩过家家的游戏中要找她心中的王子。所以就不难理解，
　　在诸多孩子家长闻"爱"色变的今天，你的作品中为什么不回避
　　写爱情了。以"淘气包马小跳系列"来说，主要表现在孩子们对
　　成人爱情的关注上。如在《丁克舅舅》中，写到马小跳对于丁克
　　舅舅和林老师、Miss 张牵线搭桥；《寻找大熊猫》中，唐飞和马
　　小跳关于 Miss 张的"归属"的争执等等，饶有趣味。

　　　　还有你写到的动物之间的爱情，如《暑假奇遇》中的大黑猫
　　与大白猫之间的爱情，《宠物集中营》中拉登与雪儿的爱情等，
　　也包括在"笑猫日记系列"中，笑猫与虎皮猫、麻花儿与黑鸭子的
　　爱情描写等等，都让人非常难忘。你是怎样看待你书中的爱情以及
　　爱情描写的？你觉得这对于今天的孩子来说具有什么样的意义？

杨红樱：童书的写作不仅仅是要给孩子提供阅读上的快感，更要
　　让孩子能从其中的描写找到安慰、梦想，得到有意义的东西。我
　　提倡正面的爱情教育、爱情憧憬。

　　　　国外家庭里，就比较注重表达夫妻情感，诸如夫妻之间说
　　"我爱你"、"你是我最心爱的宝贝"等等。在中国，没有爱情教
　　育，父母之间不表达，甚至经常吵来吵去，在孩子的眼睛里，他
　　们看到的婚姻就是这样子的。所以常有小孩子给我来信说，原本
　　感觉婚姻家庭、生小孩子这些事情没有意思，长大了不想结婚，
　　但是在看了我的小说后，开始向往这样的生活，女孩子想找一个
　　马天笑这样的有幽默感、有责任感的人做丈夫；男孩子想找宝贝
　　儿妈妈这样温柔优雅、又有独立人格的人做妻子。对爱情、婚姻
　　有了憧憬，这是一件好的事情。

乔世华：在"淘气包马小跳系列"中，除了马天笑等童心未泯的家

深度访谈

245

长们，你还比较喜欢哪一个人物呢？

杨红樱：我还是很喜欢丁克舅舅这样的人。过去，社会不允许多元化，人是单一的；现在社会有了包容性，人们可以有不同的生活方式，但是一定要有社会公德，要有做人最起码的道德底线。作为新新人类，丁克舅舅有自己的事业、生活理念和人生追求，同时也具备做人的道德品质，非常有社会责任感。

乔世华："淘气包马小跳系列"创造了中国原创童书的奇迹，从最初出版到现在已经是第九个年头，这么长时间的热读热销，已成了大家不得不说的"杨红樱现象"和"马小跳现象"。随之而来的是童书市场上出现的大量跟风之作，甚至还有大量印着你的名字的伪书。而我看过一些评论文章，说你是这些平庸之作的始作俑者，起了不好的示范作用。

杨红樱：这种言论对我来说，是很不公平的；对读者来说，是不负责任的。应该把我的作品与跟风作品和伪书区分开来。不能说因为我的作品受欢迎，出现了跟风作品和伪书，就是我的错。检验一部作品的优劣，是要看它能否经得住时间的考验和市场的考验。为什么那些跟风之作很快地烟消云散，为什么我的作品从2000年开始畅销，到现在还在畅销，成了常销的品牌书？这就是作品本质的高下之分。

乔世华：继"淘气包马小跳系列"法语版由法国Philippe Picquier（菲利浦·比基耶）出版社出版后，2007年8月，出版过《魔戒》等经典作品的英美跨国集团HarperCollins（哈珀·柯林斯）集团又购买了"淘气包马小跳系列"的全球发行版权，2008年以多语种大规模出版这一套书。有数字显示，2010年，"淘气包马小跳系列"6本图书的英文版，在英美地区销售已达10万册。哈珀·柯林斯的

CEO曾说过："我们发现，杨红樱已成为真正的国际性少儿作家。"能否谈一下马小跳在中国大陆以外地区读者群中的接受情况？

杨红樱：因为"淘气包马小跳系列"在中国孩子中的影响，引起了国外许多出版机构的关注。哈珀·柯林斯集团对这套书考察了三年，做了大量论证分析后才决定购买全球多语种版权。他们认为，马小跳虽然是一个典型的中国儿童形象，但马小跳身上的一些特质，比如充满活力，充满想象力，特别是马小跳的幽默感，都是他们所欣赏的。他们相信，马小跳能成为中国孩子的好朋友，也一定会成为世界各国孩子的好朋友。

"淘气包马小跳系列"是最早翻译到崇尚幽默的法国去的。它的法文版译者是一个当过小学老师的法国汉学家，他最初是坐在地铁里读的"马小跳"，当时他看得哈哈大笑。现在法文版已经多次再版，光是封面就换了三次。

至于英文版的外国读者，原来对中国的儿童文学了解不多，总以为是说教味很浓的，也不知道中国孩子在干什么，有时会问我一些挺幼稚的问题。但"马小跳"让他们很震撼，改变了原先的看法。他们觉得马小跳是一个非常国际化的孩子，那么聪明、幽默和富有想象力，从他身上看到的是一个生机勃勃的国家的儿童的生活状态。"马小跳"让他们了解到了中国的多样性，看到了中国的开放和文明。

乔世华：从这十几年时间上来看，"淘气包马小跳系列"的常销不衰也流露出了"经典"的某种迹象来。每一个作家或许都希望自己的作品成为经典，你是否也有这样的期待呢？

杨红樱：真正的经典，一定能经得起市场和时间的双重考验，也就是说，你的作品，有很多人来读，而且还能流传下去。我写的书是给孩子们看的，书中塑造的人物形象或者动物形象，比如马小跳，比如笑猫，还有书中的故事，能成为他们的童年记忆，书中的精神内涵能成为他们成长的力量，对我而言，这就是一部成功的作品。现在，有大学生在给我的来信中说到，"马小跳是我童年成长的精神伙伴"，"清理我的童年，一定有这样两个关键词：杨红樱，马小跳"。

1992 年

童话《寻找快活林》获海峡两岸童话小说征文优等奖第一名。

1993 年

童话《欢乐使者》获海峡两岸童话小说征文佳作奖。

1995 年

童话集《寻找快活林》获冰心儿童图书奖。

1997 年

童话《猫小花和鼠小灰》获海峡两岸童话征文一等奖。

1998 年

童话《三只老鼠三亩地》获全国少儿报刊联合征文佳作奖。

2001 年

童话《最好听的声音》获海峡两岸童话征文一等奖。

2002 年

小说《男生日记》获全国优秀畅销书奖。

小说《女生日记》获成都金芙蓉文学奖。

2003 年

小说《男生日记》获四川文学奖。

2004 年

小说《五·三班的坏小子》获全国优秀儿童读物二等奖。

小说《漂亮老师和坏小子》获第六届全国优秀儿童文学奖、全国优秀畅销书奖、成都金芙蓉文学奖。

2005 年

小说"淘气包马小跳系列"（十二册）获全国优秀畅销书奖。

童话集《杨红樱童话》获冰心儿童图书奖、全国优秀畅销书奖。

获奖记录

长篇童话《亲爱的笨笨猪》获全国优秀畅销书奖。

长篇童话《流浪狗和流浪猫》获全国优秀畅销书奖。

长篇童话《没有尾巴的狼》获全国优秀畅销书奖。

长篇童话《那个骑轮箱来的蜜儿》获全国优秀畅销书奖。

长篇童话《神秘的女老师》获全国优秀畅销书奖。

低幼童话《鼹鼠妈妈讲故事》获全国优秀幼儿读物奖。

低幼童话《骆驼爸爸讲故事》获全国优秀幼儿读物奖。

低幼童话"杨红樱亲子绘本故事"（五册）获全国优秀幼儿读物奖。

2006 年

小说《漂亮老师和坏小子》获全国第八届"五个一工程"优秀文化作品奖、四川文学特别荣誉奖。

小说《假小子戴安》获成都金芙蓉文学奖。

2007 年

"淘气包马小跳系列"获 2006 年度全国最佳少儿文学图书奖。

"笑猫日记系列"获 2006 年度全国最佳少儿文学图书奖。

小说《巨人的城堡》获全国第十届"五个一工程"入选作品奖、中国新闻出版总署首届中国出版政府奖提名奖。

2008 年

长篇童话《想变成人的猴子》获成都市"五个一工程"奖。

"淘气包马小跳系列"之《开甲壳虫车的女校长》入选第二届"三个一百"原创图书出版工程文艺少儿类图书。

"淘气包马小跳系列"、"笑猫日记系列"获 2007—2008 年度优秀少儿读物评选"年度优秀少儿文学"称号。

杨红樱纯美童话"桥梁书"系列获 2007—2008 年度优秀少儿读物评选"年度优秀多媒体图书"称号。

"淘气包马小跳系列"之《开甲壳虫车的女校长》、《名叫牛皮的插班生》获 2008 年度"全行业优秀畅销品种"称号。

"淘气包马小跳系列"之《侦探小组在行动》获2008年"中国图书榜中榜少儿类最佳图书营销奖"。

"笑猫日记系列"获第二届中华优秀出版物奖。

2009 年

大型偶形剧《巨人的城堡》获香港艺术节"评委会特别大奖"。

"淘气包马小跳系列"之《小英雄和芭蕾公主》入选2009年度新闻出版总署向全国青少年推荐的百种优秀图书。

大型卡通偶形剧《巨人的城堡》获全国儿童剧大赛三等奖。

大型卡通偶形剧《巨人的城堡》获四川省第十一届精神文明建设"五个一工程"奖。

"淘气包马小跳系列"之《小英雄和芭蕾公主》获中宣部第十一届精神文明建设"五个一工程"奖、四川省第十一届精神文明建设"五个一工程"奖。

2010 年

"淘气包马小跳系列"之《小英雄和芭蕾公主》获成都市精神文明建设第七届"五个一工程"奖、2009年度最佳少儿读物评选"年度最佳少儿文学"称号。

"淘气包马小跳系列"之《巨人的城堡》入选"2009年全国中小学生多媒体教育读物推荐目录"。

"笑猫日记系列"之《那个黑色的下午》获2010年新闻出版总署向全国青少年推荐的百种优秀图书、2009年度最佳少儿读物评选"年度最佳少儿文学"称号。

2011 年

"笑猫日记系列"之《那个黑色的下午》获第二届中国出版政府奖图书奖。

《寻找快活林》入选"中国小学生基础阅读书目"推荐书目。

获奖记录

1986 年

出版第一部作品、科学童话集《快乐天地》（四川科技出版社）。

1989 年

出版科学童话系列《蜗牛的小公馆》（四川少年儿童出版社）。

出版系列童话《胖猪罗罗》（四川少年儿童出版社）。

1992 年

出版第一部长篇童话《度假村的狗儿猫儿》（江苏少年儿童出版社）。

1993 年

出版短篇童话集《寻找快活林》（重庆出版社）。

1994 年

出版长篇童话《秃尾巴狼》（湖南少年儿童出版社）。

1995 年

出版长篇童话《胖猪笨笨》（四川少年儿童出版社）。

1998 年

出版长篇童话《那个骑轮箱来的蜜儿》（浙江少年儿童出版社）。

出版童话集《鼹鼠妈妈讲故事》（二十一世纪出版社）。

出版童话集《骆驼爸爸讲故事》（二十一世纪出版社）。

1999 年

出版系列童话《七个小淘气》（未来出版社）。

出版长篇科学童话《小蛙人游大海》（贵州人民出版社）。

出版长篇科学童话《再见野骆驼》（甘肃人民出版社）。

2000 年

出版系列童话《迷糊豆和小人精》（安徽教育出版社）。

出版长篇科学童话《神犬探长》（安徽教育出版社）。

出版第一部长篇儿童小说《女生日记》（作家出版社）。

2001 年

出版儿童小说《五·三班的坏小子》(作家出版社)。

出版系列童话《乖狐狸》(中国少年儿童出版社)。

2002 年

出版长篇儿童小说《男生日记》(作家出版社)。

出版长篇童话《神秘的女老师》(江苏少年儿童出版社)。

2003 年

出版长篇儿童小说《漂亮老师和坏小子》(作家出版社)。

出版儿童小说"淘气包马小跳系列"之一《贪玩老爸》、之二《轰隆隆老师》、之三《笨女孩安琪儿》、之四《四个调皮蛋》、之五《同桌冤家》、之六《暑假奇遇》(接力出版社)。

2004 年

出版"杨红樱童话系列"之一《那个骑轮箱来的蜜儿》、之二《神秘的女老师》、之三《亲爱的笨笨猪》(原版《胖猪罗罗》)、之四《流浪狗和流浪猫》(原版《度假村的猫儿狗儿》)、之五《没有尾巴的狼》(原版《秃尾巴狼》)(作家出版社)。

出版"淘气包马小跳系列"之七《天真妈妈》、之八《漂亮女孩夏林果》、之九《丁克舅舅》、之十《宠物集中营》、之十一《小大人丁文涛》、之十二《疯丫头杜真子》(接力出版社)。

出版童话集《杨红樱童话》(上、下)(中国少年儿童出版社)。

2005 年

出版长篇儿童小说《假小子戴安》(作家出版社)。

出版"淘气包马小跳系列"之十三《寻找大熊猫》、之十四《巨人的城堡》(接力出版社)。

出版亲子读本《鼹鼠妈妈讲故事》、《骆驼爸爸讲故事》(作家出版社)。

创作年表

出版"杨红樱文学精品赏析"之《优美童话卷》、《奥秘童话卷》、《校园小说卷》(北京少年儿童出版社)。

2006 年

出版"笑猫日记系列"之一《保姆狗的阴谋》、之二《塔顶上的猫》、之三《想变成人的猴子》(明天出版社)。

出版"淘气包马小跳系列"之十五《超级市长》、之十六《跳跳电视台》(接力出版社)。

出版"杨红樱科学童话系列"之《森林谜案》、《寻找美人鱼》、《猫头鹰开宴会》(作家出版社)。

2007 年

出版"笑猫日记系列"之四《能闻出孩子味儿的乌龟》、之五《幸福的鸭子》、之六《虎皮猫,你在哪里》(明天出版社)。

出版"淘气包马小跳系列"之十七《开甲壳虫车的女校长》、之十八《名叫牛皮的插班生》(接力出版社)。

出版《杨红樱作品好词好句好段》之一《写人篇》、之二《叙事篇》、之三《写景状物篇》、之四《写动物篇》(作家出版社)。

出版童话集《寻找快活林》"百年百部中国儿童文学经典书系"(湖北少年儿童出版社)。

2008 年

出版"笑猫日记系列"之七《蓝色的兔耳朵草》、之八《小猫出生在秘密山洞》(明天出版社)。

出版"杨红樱作品精选导读"之《科学童话系列》、《优美童话系列》、《校园小说系列》、《淘气包马小跳系列》、《笑猫日记系列》(浙江少年儿童出版社)。

出版"淘气包马小跳系列"之十九《侦探小组在行动》(接力出版社)。

出版"爱的童话"之《做梦的房子》(少儿双语版)、《乖狐狸的故事》(少儿双语版)、《鱼的天空》(少儿双语版)(安徽科学技术出版社)。

出版《我是你的朋友大熊猫》(明天出版社)。

2009 年

出版"淘气包马小跳系列"之二十《小英雄和芭蕾公主》(接力出版社)。

出版"笑猫日记系列"之九《樱桃沟的春天》、之十《那个黑色的下午》(明天出版社)。

出版"杨红樱校园小说"之《男生日记》(新版)、《女生日记》(新版)(作家出版社)。

出版"杨红樱童话珍藏版"之《一棵长着耳朵的树》、《小人精的黑夜故事》、《会走路的小房子》、《那个骑轮箱来的蜜儿》(明天出版社)。

2010 年

出版"笑猫日记系列"之十一《一头灵魂出窍的猪》、之十二《球球老老鼠》(明天出版社)。

出版"杨红樱童话手绘完全本"之《那个骑轮箱来的蜜儿》、《神秘的女老师》、《亲爱的笨笨猪》、《没有尾巴的狼》、《流浪狗和流浪猫》、《寻找美人鱼》、《森林谜案》、《猫头鹰开宴会》、《鼹鼠妈妈讲故事》、《骆驼爸爸讲故事》、《鸡蛋里的悄悄话》、《七个小淘气》(天天出版社)。

出版"樱桃园·杨红樱注音童书"之《亲爱的笨笨猪》、《一只会笑的猫》、《我是马小跳》、《仙女蜜儿》、《最美的一课》、《没有尾巴的狼》、《金瓜汤,银瓜汤》、《最后的晚餐》、《小蛙人游大海》、《森林谜案》、《沙漠运动会》、《流浪狗和流浪猫》(浙江少年儿童出版社)。

出版"杨红樱校园小说成长三部曲"之《漂亮老师和坏小子》(新版)、《五·三班的坏小子》(新版)、《假小子戴安》(新版)(作家出版社)。

出版"杨红樱优美童话"之《迷糊豆和小镇》、《七个小淘气》、

《小人精的黑夜故事》、《会走路的小房子》、《背着房子的蜗牛》（中国少年儿童出版社）。

出版"杨红樱校园小说"之《小男生杜歌飞》（注音版）、《小女生金贝贝》（注音版）（中国少年儿童出版社）。

2011 年

出版"笑猫日记系列"之十三《绿狗山庄》、之十四《小白的选择》（明天出版社）。

出版"杨红樱非常校园系列 最新版"之《非常男生》、《非常女生》、《非常小男生和小女生》、《非常爸爸》、《非常妈妈》、《非常老师》、《非常搭档》、《非常事件》（浙江少年儿童出版社）。

出版"杨红樱画本·科学童话系列"之《背着房子的蜗牛》、《寻找美人鱼》、《蚂蚁破案》、《穿救生衣的种子》、《猫头鹰开宴会》、《了不起的鱼爸爸》、《森林谜案》、《再见野骆驼》（湖北少年儿童出版社）。

出版"杨红樱画本·好性格系列"之《笨笨猪上学》、《一朵五彩的云》、《鸡妈妈孵鸭蛋》、《春天的野餐会》、《小骡子找妈妈》、《笨笨猪打呼噜》、《巧克力饼屋》、《天冷要盖房》、《七只淘气的小鸡》、《老鼠换脑袋》（湖北少年儿童出版社）。

出版"淘气包马小跳系列 升级版"之《贪玩老爸》、《轰隆隆老师》、《笨女孩安琪儿》、《四个调皮蛋》、《同桌冤家》、《暑假奇遇》、《天真妈妈》、《漂亮女孩夏林果》、《丁克舅舅》、《宠物集中营》、《小大人丁文涛》、《疯丫头杜真子》、《寻找大熊猫》、《巨人的城堡》、《超级市长》、《跳跳电视台》、《开甲壳虫车的女校长》、《名叫牛皮的插班生》、《侦探小组在行动》、《小英雄和芭蕾公主》（接力出版社）。

出版《小男生杜歌飞》、《小女生金贝贝》（明天出版社）。

出版"淘气包马小跳 漫画版"之《贪玩老爸》（上、下）、《轰隆隆老师》（上、下）、《笨女孩安琪儿》（上、下）、《四个调皮蛋》（上、下）（安徽少年儿童出版社）。

图书在版编目(CIP)数据

杨红樱作品精选导读品藏版 淘气包马小跳系列/
杨红樱著 . —杭州:浙江少年儿童出版社,2012.4
ISBN 978-7-5342-6800-7

Ⅰ.①杨… Ⅱ.①杨… Ⅲ.①儿童文学-文学评
论-中国-当代②儿童文学-长篇小说-小说评论-中国-
当代③儿童文学-长篇小说-小说集-中国-当代 Ⅳ.
①I207.8②I287.47

中国版本图书馆 CIP 数据核字(2012)第 016237 号

杨红樱作品精选导读 品藏版
淘气包马小跳系列

杨红樱/著
王泉根/主编 乔世华/导读

责任编辑 王宜清 龚小萍
美术编辑 周翔飞
装帧设计 小飞侠
内文插图 沈苑苑
责任校对 倪建中
责任印制 林百乐

浙江少年儿童出版社出版发行
地址:杭州市天目山路 40 号
网址:www.ses.zjcb.com
杭州杭新印务有限公司印刷
全国各地新华书店经销
开本 710×1000 1/16
印张 17.25
插页 6 字数 184000
印数 1—50000
2012 年 4 月第 1 版
2012 年 4 月第 1 次印刷
ISBN 978-7-5342-6800-7
定价:25.00 元
(如有印装质量问题,影响阅读,请与承印厂联系调换)

Disaster Recovery

EC-Council | Press

Volume 1 of 2 mapping to

E | C D R™   E | C V T™

EC-Council | **Certified DR Professional**   **EC-Council** | **Certified VT Professional**

Certification   Certification

COURSE TECHNOLOGY
CENGAGE Learning™

Australia • Brazil • Japan • Korea • Mexico • Singapore • Spain • United Kingdom • United States

COURSE TECHNOLOGY
CENGAGE Learning™

Disaster Recovery
EC-Council | Press

Course Technology/Cengage Learning
Staff:

Vice President, Career and Professional
Editorial: Dave Garza

Director of Learning Solutions:
Matthew Kane

Executive Editor: Stephen Helba

Managing Editor: Marah Bellegarde

Editorial Assistant: Meghan Orvis

Vice President, Career and Professional
Marketing: Jennifer Ann Baker

Marketing Director: Deborah Yarnell

Marketing Manager: Erin Coffin

Marketing Coordinator: Shanna Gibbs

Production Director: Carolyn Miller

Production Manager: Andrew Crouth

Content Project Manager:
Brooke Greenhouse

Senior Art Director: Jack Pendleton

EC-Council:

President | EC-Council: Sanjay Bavisi

Sr. Director US | EC-Council:
Steven Graham

For product information and technology assistance, contact us at
Cengage Learning Customer & Sales Support, 1-800-354-9706

For permission to use material from this text or product,
submit all requests online at **www.cengage.com/permissions**.
Further permissions questions can be e-mailed to
permissionrequest@cengage.com

Library of Congress Control Number: 2010928097

ISBN-13: 978-1-4354-8870-0

ISBN-10: 1-4354-8870-9

Cengage Learning
5 Maxwell Drive
Clifton Park, NY 12065-2919
USA

Cengage Learning is a leading provider of customized learning solutions with office locations around the globe, including Singapore, the United Kingdom, Australia, Mexico, Brazil, and Japan. Locate your local office at: **international.cengage.com/region**

Cengage Learning products are represented in Canada by
Nelson Education, Ltd.

For more learning solutions, please visit our corporate website at **www.cengage.com**

NOTICE TO THE READER

Cengage Learning and EC-Council do not warrant or guarantee any of the products described herein or perform any independent analysis in connection with any of the product information contained herein. Cengage Learning and EC-Council do not assume, and expressly disclaim, any obligation to obtain and include information other than that provided to it by the manufacturer. The reader is expressly warned to consider and adopt all safety precautions that might be indicated by the activities described herein and to avoid all potential hazards. By following the instructions contained herein, the reader willingly assumes all risks in connection with such instructions. Cengage Learning and EC-Council make no representations or warranties of any kind, including but not limited to, the warranties of fitness for particular purpose or merchantability, nor are any such representations implied with respect to the material set forth herein, and Cengage Learning and EC-Council take no responsibility with respect to such material. Cengage Learning and EC-Council shall not be liable for any special, consequential, or exemplary damages resulting, in whole or part, from the readers' use of, or reliance upon, this material.

Printed in the United States of America
1 2 3 4 5 6 7 12 11 10

Brief Table of Contents

Table of Contents

CHAPTER 3

Disaster Recovery Planning and Implementation **3-1**

CHAPTER 7
Data Storage Technologies **7-1**

CHAPTER 8
Disaster Recovery Services and Tools **8-1**

CHAPTER 9
Certification and Accreditation of Information Systems **9-1**

Preface

Hacking and electronic crimes sophistication has grown at an exponential rate in recent years. In fact, recent reports have indicated that cyber crime already surpasses the illegal drug trade! Unethical hackers better known as *black hats* are preying on information systems of government, corporate, public, and private networks and are constantly testing the security mechanisms of these organizations to the limit with the sole aim of exploiting it and profiting from the exercise. High profile crimes have proven that the traditional approach to computer security is simply not sufficient, even with the strongest perimeter, properly configured defense mechanisms like firewalls, intrusion detection, and prevention systems, strong end-to-end encryption standards, and anti-virus software. Hackers have proven their dedication and ability to systematically penetrate networks all over the world. In some cases *black hats* may be able to execute attacks so flawlessly that they can compromise a system, steal everything of value, and completely erase their tracks in less than 20 minutes!

The EC-Council Press is dedicated to stopping hackers in their tracks.

About EC-Council

The International Council of Electronic Commerce Consultants, better known as EC-Council was founded in late 2001 to address the need for well-educated and certified information security and e-business practitioners. EC-Council is a global, member-based organization comprised of industry and subject matter experts all working together to set the standards and raise the bar in information security certification and education.

EC-Council first developed the *Certified Ethical Hacker,* CIEH program. The goal of this program is to teach the methodologies, tools, and techniques used by hackers. Leveraging the collective knowledge from hundreds of subject matter experts, the CIEH program has rapidly gained popularity around the globe and is now delivered in over 70 countries by over 450 authorized training centers. Over 80,000 information security practitioners have been trained.

CIEH is the benchmark for many government entities and major corporations around the world. Shortly after CIEH was launched, EC-Council developed the *Certified Security Analyst,* EICSA. The goal of the EICSA program is to teach groundbreaking analysis methods that must be applied while conducting advanced penetration testing. EICSA leads to the *Licensed Penetration Tester,* LIPT status. The *Computer Hacking Forensic Investigator,* CIHFI was formed with the same design methodologies above and has become a global standard in certification for computer forensics. EC-Council through its impervious network of professionals, and huge industry following has developed various other programs in information security and e-business. EC-Council Certifications are viewed as the essential certifications needed where standard configuration and security policy courses fall short. Providing a true, hands-on, tactical approach to security, individuals armed with the knowledge disseminated by EC-Council programs are securing networks around the world and beating the hackers at their own game.

About the EC-Council I Press

The EC-Council I Press was formed in late 2008 as a result of a cutting edge partnership between global information security certification leader, EC-Council and leading global academic publisher, Cengage Learning. This partnership marks a revolution in academic textbooks and courses of study in Information Security, Computer Forensics, Disaster Recovery, and End-User Security. By identifying the essential topics and content of EC-Council professional certification programs, and repurposing this world class content to fit academic programs, the EC-Council I Press was formed. The academic community is now able to incorporate this powerful cutting edge content into new and existing Information Security programs. By closing the gap between academic study and professional certification, students and instructors are able to leverage the power of rigorous academic focus and high demand industry certification. The EC-Council I Press is set to revolutionize global information security programs and ultimately create a new breed of practitioners capable of combating the growing epidemic of cybercrime and the rising threat of cyber-war.

Disaster Recovery/Virtualization Security Series

Disaster recovery and business continuity are daunting challenges for any organization. With the rise in the number of threats, attacks, and competitive business landscape, it is important that an organization be prepared and have the ability to withstand a disaster. Using the disaster recovery process, an organization recovers the lost data and gains back the access to the software/hardware so that the performance of the business can return to normal. Virtualization technologies gives the advantage of additional flexibility as well as cost savings while deploying a disaster recovery solution. Virtualization lessens the usage of hardware at a disaster recovery site and makes recovery operations easier.

The *Disaster Recovery/Virtualization Series* introduces methods to identify vulnerabilities and takes appropriate countermeasures to prevent and mitigate failure risks for an organization. This series takes an enterprise-wide approach to developing a disaster recovery plan. Students will learn how to create a secure network by putting policies and procedures in place, and how to restore a network in the event of a disaster. It also provides the networking professional with a foundation in disaster recovery principles. This series explores virtualization products such as VMware, Microsoft Hyper- V, Citrix Xen Server and Client, Sun xVM, HP virtualization, NComputing, NoMachine etc. The series when used in its entirety helps prepare readers to take and succeed on the E|CDR-E|CVT certification exam, Disaster Recovery and Virtualization Technology certification exam from EC-Council. The EC-Council Certified Disaster Recovery and Virtualization Technology professional will have a better understanding of how to setup disaster recovery plans using traditional and virtual technologies to ensure business continuity in the event of a disaster.

Books in Series
- *Disaster Recovery*/1435488709
- *Virtualization Security*/1435488695

Disaster Recovery

This product provides an introduction to disaster recovery and business continuity, a discussion of the relevant laws and regulations, how to plan and implement a disaster recovery plan, how to manage, assess and evaluate risk, certification and accreditation of information systems and much more!

Chapter Contents

Chapter 1 *Introduction to Disaster Recovery and Business Continuity*, discusses the different types of disasters and how to recover from them and explains the difference between disaster recovery and business continuity. Chapter 2, *Laws and Acts*, familiarizes the reader with the laws and regulations relevant to disaster recovery, and serves as a reference for the full text of some of these laws and regulations. Chapter 3, *Disaster Recovery Planning and Implementation*, discusses system security, in order to prevent disasters in the first place, and planning for disaster recovery. Chapter 4, *Business Continuity Management*, introduces the fundamentals of business continuity management (BCM) including sample forms for business continuity plans, contingency plans, and virtualization data recovery. Chapter 5, *Managing, Assessing, and Evaluating Risks*, discusses the importance of risk management, various risk management methodologies including a list of responsibilities of an information systems security office (ISSO). Chapter 6, *Risk Control Policies and Countermeasures*, explains system security and change control policies and how to conduct configuration management. Chapter 7, *Data Storage Technologies*, introduces three different data storage technologies, network attached storage, direct attached storage, and storage area networks. Chapter 8, *Disaster Recovery Services and Tools*, explains the importance of backing up data and how to implement effective and efficient data backup procedures. Chapter 9, *Certification and Accreditation of Information Systems*, introduces the concepts of certification and accreditation including what is involved in the process and how threats and vulnerabilities are related to the certification and accreditation process.

Chapter Features

Many features are included in each chapter and all are designed to enhance the learner's learning experience. Features include:

- *Objectives* begin each chapter and focus the learner on the most important concepts in the chapter.
- *Key Terms* are designed to familiarize the learner with terms that will be used within the chapter.

- *Chapter Summary*, at the end of each chapter, serves as a review of the key concepts covered in the chapter.

- *Review Questions* allow the learner to test their comprehension of the chapter content.

- *Hands-On Projects* encourage the learner to apply the knowledge they have gained after finishing the chapter Center. Note: you will need your access code provided in your book to enter the site. Visit *www.cengage.com/community/eccouncil* for a link to the Student Resource Center or follow the directions on your access card.

Student Resource Center

The Student Resource Center contains all the files you need to complete the Hands-On Projects found at the end of the chapters. Access the Student Resource Center with the access code provided in your book. Visit *www.cengage.com/community/eccouncil* for a link to the Student Resource Center.

Additional Instructor Resources

Free to all instructors who adopt the *Disaster Recovery* book for their courses is a complete package of instructor resources. These resources are available from the Course Technology web site, *www.cengage.com/coursetechnology*, by going to the product page for this book in the online catalog, click on the Companion Site on the Faculty side; click on any of the Instructor Resources in the left navigation and login to access the files. Once you accept the license agreement, the selected files will be displayed.

Resources include:

- *Instructor Manual*: This manual includes course objectives and additional information to help your instruction.

- *ExamView Testbank*: This Windows-based testing software helps instructors design and administer tests and pre-tests. In addition to generating tests that can be printed and administered, this full-featured program has an online testing component that allows students to take tests at the computer and have their exams automatically graded.

- *PowerPoint Presentations*: This book comes with a set of Microsoft PowerPoint slides for each chapter. These slides are meant to be used as a teaching aid for classroom presentations, to be made available to students for chapter review, or to be printed for classroom distribution. Instructors are also at liberty to add their own slides.

- *Labs*: Additional Hands-on Activities to provide additional practice for your students.

- *Assessment Activities*: Additional assessment opportunities including discussion questions, writing assignments, internet research activities, and homework assignments along with a final cumulative project.

- *Final Exam*: Provides a comprehensive assessment of *Disaster Recovery* content.

Cengage Learning Information Security Community Site

This site was created for learners and instructors to find out about the latest in information security news and technology.

Visit *community.cengage.com/infosec* to:

- Learn what's new in information security through live news feeds, videos and podcasts.

- Connect with your peers and security experts through blogs and forums.

- Browse our online catalog.

How to Become ECDR-ECVT Certified

The EC-Council Disaster Recovery and Virtualization Technology certification will fortify the disaster recovery and virtualization technology knowledge of system administrators, systems engineers, enterprise system architects, hardware engineers, software engineers, technical support individuals, networking professionals, and any IT professional who is concerned about the integrity of the network infrastructure. This is an advanced course for experienced system administrators and system integrators scaling their organization's deployment of the virtualization technologies. The ECDR-ECVT Program certifies individuals and explores installation, configuration, and management of different virtualization products. A certified EC-Council Disaster Recovery and Virtualization Technology professional will better understand how to recover after a disaster so that there is proper business continuity.

To achieve the certification, you must pass the ECDR-ECVT Professional exam 312-55.

E|CDR-E|CVT Certification exam is available through Prometric Prime. To obtain your certification after your training, you must:

1. Purchase an exam voucher from the EC-Council Community Site at Cengage: *www.cengage.com/community/eccouncil.*

2. Speak with your Instructor or Professor about scheduling an exam session, or visit the EC-Council Community Site referenced above for more information.

3. Attempt and pass the E|CDR—E|CVT certification examination with a score of 70% or better.

About Our Other EC-Council Press Products

Ethical Hacking and Countermeasures Series

The EC-Council | Press *Ethical Hacking and Countermeasures* series is intended for those studying to become security officers, auditors, security professionals, site administrators, and anyone who is concerned about or responsible for the integrity of the network infrastructure. The series includes a broad base of topics in offensive network security, ethical hacking, as well as network defense and countermeasures. The content of this series is designed to immerse the learner into an interactive environment where they will be shown how to scan, test, hack and secure information systems. A wide variety of tools, viruses, and malware is presented in these books, providing a complete understanding of the tactics and tools used by hackers. By gaining a thorough understanding of how hackers operate, ethical hackers are able to set up strong countermeasures and defensive systems to protect their organization's critical infrastructure and information. The series when used in its entirety helps prepare readers to take and succeed on the C|EH certification exam from EC-Council.

Books in Series
- *Ethical Hacking and Countermeasures: Attack Phases*/143548360X
- *Ethical Hacking and Countermeasures: Threats and Defense Mechanisms*/1435483618
- *Ethical Hacking and Countermeasures: Web Applications and Data Servers*/1435483626
- *Ethical Hacking and Countermeasures: Linux, Macintosh and Mobile Systems*/1435483642
- *Ethical Hacking and Countermeasures: Secure Network Infrastructures*/1435483650

Computer Forensics Series

The EC-Council | Press *Computer Forensics* series, preparing learners for C|HFI certification, is intended for those studying to become police investigators and other law enforcement personnel, defense and military personnel, e-business security professionals, systems administrators, legal professionals, banking, insurance and other professionals, government agencies, and IT managers. The content of this program is designed to expose the learner to the process of detecting attacks and collecting evidence in a forensically sound manner with the intent to report crime and prevent future attacks. Advanced techniques in computer investigation and analysis with interest in generating potential legal evidence are included. In full, this series prepares the learner to identify evidence in computer related crime and abuse cases as well as track the intrusive hacker's path through client system.

Books in Series
- *Computer Forensics: Investigation Procedures and Response*/1435483499
- *Computer Forensics: Investigating Hard Disks, File and Operating Systems*/1435483502
- *Computer Forensics: Investigating Data and Image Files*/1435483510
- *Computer Forensics: Investigating Network Intrusions and Cybercrime*/1435483529
- *Computer Forensics: Investigating Wireless Networks and Devices*/1435483537

Network Defense Series

The EC-Council | Press *Network Defense* series, preparing learners for E|NSA certification, is intended for those studying to become system administrators, network administrators and anyone who is interested in network security technologies. This series is designed to educate learners, from a vendor neutral standpoint, how to defend the networks they manage. This series covers the fundamental skills in evaluating internal and external threats to network security, design, and how to enforce network level security policies, and ultimately protect an organization's information. Covering a broad range of topics from secure network fundamentals, protocols & analysis, standards and policy, hardening infrastructure, to configuring IPS, IDS and firewalls, bastion host and honeypots, among many other topics, learners completing this series will have a full understanding of defensive measures taken to secure their organizations information. The series when used in its entirety helps prepare readers to take and succeed on the EINSA, Network Security Administrator certification exam from EC-Council.

Books in Series
- *Network Defense: Fundamentals and Protocols*/1435483553
- *Network Defense: Security Policy and Threats*/1435483561
- *Network Defense: Perimeter Defense Mechanisms*/143548357X
- *Network Defense: Securing and Troubleshooting Network Operating Systems*/1435483588
- *Network Defense: Security and Vulnerability Assessment*/1435483596

Penetration Testing Series

The EC-Council I Press Security Analyst/Licensed *Penetration Tester* series, preparing learners for EICSA/LPT certification, is intended for those studying to become Network Server Administrators, Firewall Administrators, Security Testers, System Administrators and Risk Assessment professionals. This series covers a broad base of topics in advanced penetration testing and security analysis. The content of this program is designed to expose the learner to groundbreaking methodologies in conducting thorough security analysis, as well as advanced penetration testing techniques. Armed with the knowledge from the Security Analyst series, learners will be able to perform the intensive assessments required to effectively identify and mitigate risks to the security of the organization's infrastructure. The series when used in its entirety helps prepare readers to take and succeed on the EICSA, Certified Security Analyst certification exam.

Books in Series
- *Penetration Testing: Security Analysis*/1435483669
- *Penetration Testing: Procedures and Methodologies*/1435483677
- *Penetration Testing: Network and Perimeter Testing*/1435483685
- *Penetration Testing: Communication Media Testing*/1435483693
- *Penetration Testing: Network Threat Testing*/1435483707

Cyber Safety/1435483715

Cyber Safety is designed for anyone who is interested in learning computer networking and security basics. This product provides information cyber crime; security procedures; how to recognize security threats and attacks, incident response, and how to secure internet access. This book gives individuals the basic security literacy skills to begin high-end IT programs. The book also prepares readers to take and succeed on the SecurityI5 certification exam from EC-Council.

Wireless Safety/1435483766

Wireless Safety introduces the learner to the basics of wireless technologies and its practical adaptation. *WirelessI5* is tailored to cater to any individual's desire to learn more about wireless technology. It requires no pre-requisite knowledge and aims to educate the learner in simple applications of these technologies. Topics include wireless signal propagation, IEEE and ETSI Wireless Standards, WLANs and Operation, Wireless Protocols and Communication Languages, Wireless Devices, and Wireless Security Network. The book also prepares readers to take and succeed on the WirelessI5 certification exam from EC-Council.

Network Safety/1435483774

Network Safety provides the basic core knowledge on how infrastructure enables a working environment. Intended for those in an office environment and for the home user who wants to optimize resource utilization, share infrastructure and make the best of technology and the convenience it offers. Topics include foundations of networks, networking components, wireless networks, basic hardware components, the networking environment and connectivity as well as troubleshooting. The book also prepares readers to take and succeed on the NetworkI5 certification exam from EC-Council.

Acknowledgements

Michael H. Goldner is the Chair of the School of Information Technology for ITT Technical Institute in Norfolk Virginia, and also teaches bachelor level courses in computer network and information security systems. Michael has served on and chaired ITT Educational Services Inc. National Curriculum Committee on Information Security. He received his Juris Doctorate from Stetson University College of Law, his undergraduate degree from Miami University and has been working over fifteen years in the area of Information Technology. He is an active member of the American Bar Association, and has served on that organization's Cyber Law committee. He is a member of IEEE, ACM and ISSA, and is the holder of a number of industrially recognized certifications including, CISSP, CEH, CHFI, CEI, MCT, MCSE/Security, Security +, Network + and A+. Michael recently completed the design and creation of a computer forensic program for ITT Technical Institute, and has worked closely with both EC-Council and Delmar/Cengage Learning in the creation of this EC-Council Press series.

Chapter 1

Introduction to Disaster Recovery and Business Continuity

Objectives

After completing this chapter, you should be able to:

- Understand disaster recovery and types of disasters
- Perform disaster recovery
- Describe a disaster recovery team
- Enumerate the disaster recovery phases
- List the best practices of disaster recovery
- Understand business continuity
- Understand the difference between disaster recovery and business continuity
- Perform business continuity and disaster recovery planning
- Develop a security management plan

Key Terms

Business continuity   the ability of an organization to keep the business running even after a disaster strikes

Disaster   a natural or human-caused incident that negatively affects organizations or the environment

Disaster recovery   the processes, policies, and procedures necessary for the recovery of operations and the continuation of the critical functions of an organization after a disaster

Security management plan   a documented set of policies and procedures to ensure the security of an organization's operations and assets

Introduction to Disaster Recovery and Business Continuity

Developing plans for disaster recovery and business continuity is important for any organization. Disasters may happen at any time, often with little or no warning, so it is important for an organization to have these plans in place to ensure its ability to quickly recover from disasters. This chapter teaches you about the different types of disasters and how to recover from them. It goes through the different phases of the disaster recovery process and the best practices to use during this process. It also goes into business continuity and the difference between disaster recovery and business continuity. The chapter finishes with a discussion of security management planning.

Disaster

A *disaster* is a natural or human-caused incident that negatively affects organizations or the environment. It disrupts business continuity and may affect long-term business objectives. Disasters are often seen as the failure to effectively manage risks to different business entities.

In the present global economic scenario, organizations are more susceptible to natural, human, or technical problems. Any disaster, from floods and fires to viruses and cyber terrorism, can affect the accessibility, reliability, and privacy of major business resources.

Disasters can lead to the following:

- *Loss of life*: This is the most damaging and traumatic impact of any disaster. Individuals may lose their family members and colleagues, whereas organizations may lose their key personnel. Disasters often leave many with temporary and permanent disabilities. Epidemics after disasters leave many more people with diseases that affect their employability and economic conditions.

- *Loss of property*: Property loss is a consequence of many disasters. Disasters leave man-made structures collapsed and ruin necessary services such as communication and transportation systems.

- *Relocation or displacement*: Individuals or organizations may, at times, need to shift or completely relocate to a new site.

- *Disruptions in business continuity*: Disasters may cause disruptions in business activities due to failure in processes, machinery, and communication, and these disruptions ultimately result in loss of revenue or cessation of all business activity and closure.

Statistics: Different Sources of Disaster

The graph in Figure 1-1 indicates the major causes of disasters. It shows that human interference is the major cause of concern for protecting organizational resources from disastrous events. Human inference is also considered the most challenging aspect of information security controls.

Types of Disasters

Natural catastrophes, technical failures, manual errors, and malicious activities have led to an increased disruption in business operations. Enterprises should be aware of such happenings and accordingly plan and prepare themselves to avoid or face them. Disasters are broadly categorized into the following two categories (Figure 1-2):

1. *Natural disasters*: Natural disasters are sudden events caused by environmental factors, resulting in damage to life and property.

2. *Man-made disasters*: Man-made disasters are caused by human error, ignorance, negligence, or individuals with malicious intentions. These disasters are unpredictable and can spread across a wide area. They are sometimes unpreventable as well. System failures, power and telecommunication outages, terrorism, and cyber terrorism fall under this category.

Data Breach Investigations Report 2008/2009

Data breach incidents in which unauthorized people acquired access to or tampered with confidential data have been the main security concern for most of the top Fortune 500 companies over the last five years. Statistical analysis of various data breach reports highlights a worrying scenario for organizational

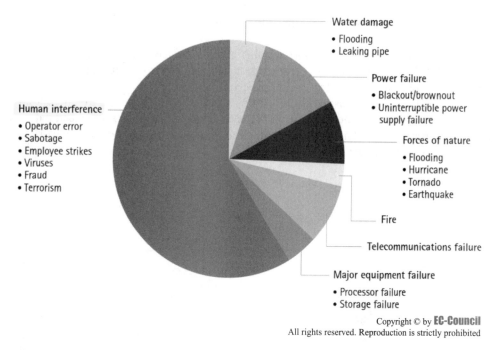

Figure 1-1 Human interference is a major cause of disastrous events.

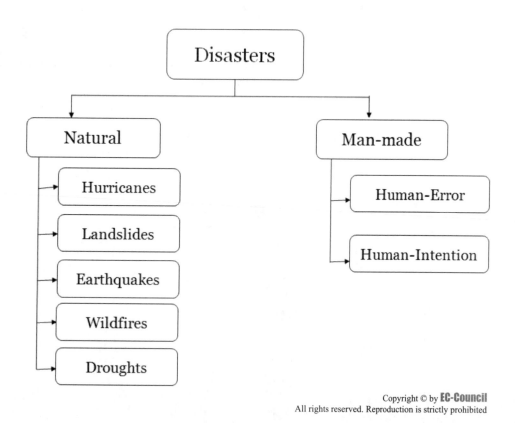

Figure 1-2 Disasters can be categorized as either natural or man-made disasters.

security and business competitiveness. According to Verizon's 2008 Data Breach Investigations Report, which analyzes the data breach incidents from more than 500 forensic engagements handled by its Business Investigative Response team over a four-year period, to the question "Who is behind data breaches?" almost 73% of responders answered that they resulted from external sources, whereas 18% of responders answered that they came from the inside. The graph in Figure 1-3 highlights the major perpetrators of data breach incidents.

Similar to the Verizon's 2008 report numbers, most data breaches continued to originate from external sources in 2009. The majority of total records lost still resulted from external sources. Additionally, 91% of all compromised records were linked to organized criminal groups.

The graph in Figure 1-4 illustrates the major causes of data breaches. To the question "How do breaches occur?" almost 62% of responders answered that their organizations experienced data breach incidents due to significant technical errors. This highlights the need for a well-trained and aware workforce that can effectively handle and respond to incidents.

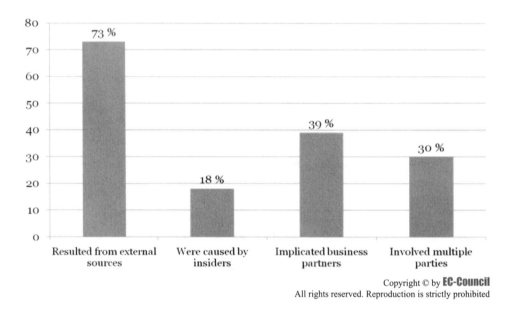

Figure 1-3 Most reported data breaches are caused by external sources.

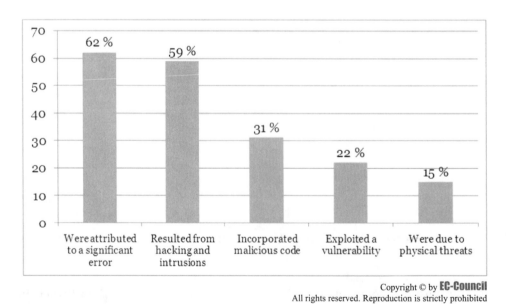

Figure 1-4 A great many data breach incidents were due to significant technical errors.

Disaster Recovery

Disaster recovery involves the processes, policies, and procedures necessary for the recovery of operations and the continuation of the critical functions of an organization after a disaster. Issues such as physical violence, hacking attempts, computer malware, and the rising incidences of information security emergencies have forced governments and corporations to focus on disaster recovery.

Disaster recovery strategies should consider the type of organization and the elements required to keep the organization running.

Disaster recovery is important to organizations for the following reasons:

- It returns the organizations to normal operating conditions.
- It limits the effects of the disaster on business functions.
- It minimizes the occurrence of certain types of disasters in the future.

Operational Cycle of Disaster Recovery

Disasters have various causes and origins, ranging from natural disasters to intentional man-made disasters, and lead to a certain period of business discontinuity. Disaster recovery efforts start as soon as there is an indication or report of an incident. Disaster recovery teams first verify the occurrence of the disaster and then execute disaster recovery plans to overcome disasters and restore operations to their normal state. Figure 1-5 presents an overview of a complete disaster recovery operations cycle.

Disaster Recovery Cost

As businesses are becoming increasingly dependent on technology, a serious failure or loss in technology will have a great impact on an organization. The disaster recovery statistics in Figure 1-6 show the relationship between cost of disruption and recovery time. As time goes on, the cost of disruption increases and the cost of recovery decreases.

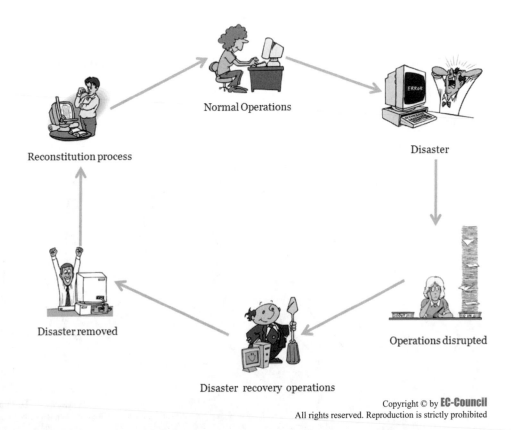

Normal Operations

Disaster

Reconstitution process

Operations disrupted

Disaster removed

Disaster recovery operations

Figure 1-5 This represents the cycle of disaster recovery.

Incidents That Required the Execution of Disaster Recovery Plans

Symantec's Global Disaster Recovery Survey highlights the importance of disaster recovery plans. Disaster recovery planning is a major driving force in business continuity planning and strategic business decisions. According to the survey (Figure 1-7), out of the organizations that executed disaster recovery (DR) plans, 59% of organizations were forced to execute DR plans to overcome incidents involving computer system failures. External computer threats and natural disasters were other major issues of concern.

Evaluating Disaster Recovery Methods

Evaluation of disaster recovery mechanisms is important for implementing any DR strategy effectively. Disaster recovery teams should analyze the available recovery mechanisms for all entities directly related to the organization's normal functioning and determine the appropriate recovery procedures according to need and feasibility.

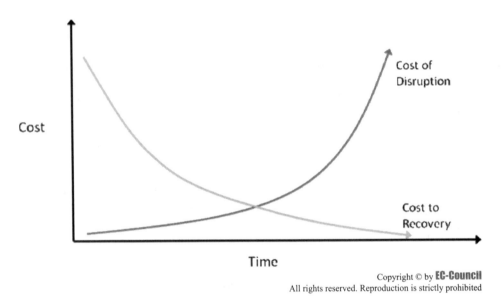

Figure 1-6   As time goes on, the cost of disruption increases and the cost of recovery decreases.

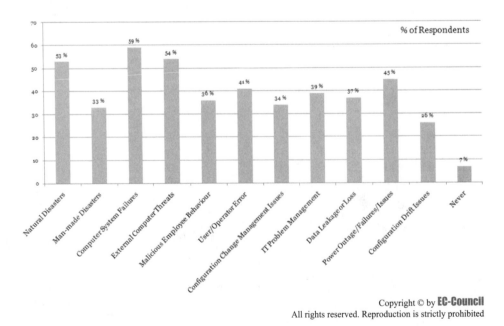

Figure 1-7   Computer system failures are a major cause of disaster for organizations.

Evaluation of DR mechanisms involves a careful consideration of the resources already employed in the recovery process. Recovery mechanisms vary according to different entities. Data storage and processing systems, power supplies, networking infrastructure, and telecommunication systems are some of the basic and most important organizational entities. There are one or more recovery mechanisms available for these entities.

Recovery mechanisms for critical information processing and storage systems may include data backup solutions. Organizations may opt for an off-site hot backup service, in which all the operational data are synchronized in real time, or a cold backup service, in which data are synchronized at regular intervals according to data criticality and synchronization medium. For less critical information systems, organizations may opt for local hardware and software redundancy. The redundancy in the organization may result in extra costs, but it can save organizational data in case of a limited disaster. Organizations decide on which disaster recovery mechanisms to implement by considering their budget, cost-benefit analysis, and availability of human resources to manage these solutions.

Similarly, to prepare for disasters related to power outage, organizations may arrange for multiple alternative sources of power, such as generator systems and UPSs. Selection of these solutions is also dependent on an organization's budget and feasibility.

Overall, selection of different disaster recovery mechanisms for an organization depends on the following:

- Acquisition, maintenance, and operation costs of the solutions
- Disaster recovery budget of the organization
- Desired recovery time
- Availability of human resources to operate and manage the solutions
- Availability of third-party solutions

Disaster Recovery Team

A disaster recovery team is responsible for developing and managing disaster recovery operations and procedures. The team includes representatives from different departments and third-party associates of the organization. The members of the team have predefined roles and responsibilities in different stages of the disaster recovery process. All departments in an organization—such as management, human resources, IT, customer service centers, security, and finance—should be adequately represented in the disaster recovery team.

The disaster recovery team builds, implements, and maintains the disaster recovery plan. It is also responsible for coordinating various disaster recovery processes between different organizational units, third parties, and public services such as police and legal systems.

The major roles and responsibilities of disaster recovery teams include the following:

- Developing, deploying, and monitoring the implementation of appropriate disaster recovery plans after analysis of business objectives and threats to organizations
- Notifying management, affected personnel, and third parties about the disaster
- Initiating the execution of the disaster recovery procedures
- Monitoring the execution of the disaster recovery plan and assessing the results
- Returning operations to normal conditions
- Modifying and updating the disaster recovery plan according to lessons learned from previous disaster recovery efforts
- Increasing the level of the organization's disaster recovery preparedness by conducting mock drills, regular DR systems testing, and threat analysis
- Creating awareness among various stakeholders of the organization by conducting training and awareness sessions

Organizations should consider the following points to develop an efficient disaster recovery team:

- Roles and responsibilities of each team member should be clearly defined and communicated.
- Reporting structure should be transparent and easy.
- Team members should be equipped with the required skills and tools.

Additional human resources should be designated to fill any vacancies in case the primary member is unavailable. Backup team members should be aware of their responsibilities and should be able to join disaster recovery efforts on short notice. Team development and skill enhancement trainings should also involve backup team members so that they are equally able to effectively handle incidents.

Management's decision concerning having backup disaster recovery team members is generally based on perceived level of risk, availability of human resources, and the organization's risk tolerance. Financial factors are also a major determinant in having backup teams. According to recent surveys by Verizon and Symantec, prevailing economic conditions are forcing organizations to cut their disaster recovery budget, which can reduce the organization's capability of having backup disaster recovery plans and teams.

Disaster Recovery Phases

Activation Phase

Immediate and proactive handling and response to disasters can reduce the impact on an organization to a large extent. The ability of disaster recovery teams to detect precursors of disasters on time may help the organization avoid the disasters altogether. In situations in which detection of disasters beforehand is not possible, a swift implementation of disaster recovery procedures and plans plays an important role in minimizing the impact of disasters. The activation phase is the first step after the symptoms of a disaster are detected. Disaster recovery teams need to verify the occurrence of a disaster before activating the disaster recovery process. The activation phase involves the following:

- Notifying the affected entities and other stakeholders that will be actively involved in the disaster recovery process
- Assessing the damage to ascertain the urgency level of response
- Making a decision concerning disaster recovery process activation

Notification

The notification makes all affected entities aware of a disaster in the organization. It puts the organization into a disaster mode of operations, and activates the disaster recovery mechanisms implemented in the organization. It gives a formal instruction to disaster recovery teams to shift to disaster recovery mode.

Disaster notifications can be communicated by different telecommunication systems such as e-mails, faxes, and telephone calls. Organizations should have a notification policy that clearly outlines the type of communication mediums to be used in different scenarios and details of personnel to be contacted and notified in different situations.

A call tree is a general notification technique that can be used in the activation phase. It documents the primary and alternate contact methods and includes procedures to be followed if the personnel could not be contacted.

Notification information consists of the following:

- Nature of the disaster and the damage it may cause
- Loss of life, injuries, and damage to critical infrastructures
- First-response details
- Estimation of recovery time
- Alternate arrangements to minimize the impact on life and property
- Information on the briefings, meetings, and discussions for further response instructions
- Information and instructions for relocation if there is a need for short-term or permanent relocation
- Instructions for whom to contact for further information and assistance if required

Damage Assessment

Damage assessment is important for initiating an appropriate disaster recovery response. It is necessary for determining the urgency level and implementing the appropriate disaster recovery solution. For example, if damage assessment results for a power-failure case show that the power supplies will be restored before the systems run out of battery power, disaster recovery team will not have to go into panic mode.

A proper damage assessment also helps in avoiding unnecessary alarms. Damage assessment procedures and outcomes after disaster differ depending on the following factors:

- Nature and cause of disaster
- Criticality of operations and systems affected by the disaster
- Possibility of further damage due to the disastrous event
- Nature of loss to critical infrastructures
- Expected recovery time for affected systems and operations

Decision on Disaster Recovery Process Activation

The decision to activate the disaster recovery process requires a careful consideration of various factors, such as whether the alarm is true, how people will react to the situation, and if there is a need to really activate a comprehensive disaster recovery procedure. The decision to activate the disaster recovery process should be based on the damage assessment findings. Before deciding to activate the process, disaster recovery teams should also decide which plan is appropriate for the situation.

Execution Phase

The execution phase involves the implementation of disaster recovery plans, procedures, and solutions. It starts after the disaster recovery activation phase, when disaster recovery teams are ready to implement specific solutions to contain and overcome disasters. The execution phase includes activities such as opening emergency doors, starting power generators, making arrangements for relocation, and contacting law enforcement agencies to help in the DR effort. The following are important aspects of this phase:

- *Prioritization of disaster recovery activities*: Prioritization of critical operations and systems to recover after a disaster is important to ensure that the most critical assets and operations are restored first. This helps in minimizing the impact of the disaster.
- *Recovery procedures*: A well-defined methodological approach to disaster recovery is important for the execution of disaster recovery procedures. Disaster recovery teams should be aware of the sequence of processes they need to perform under various circumstances.

Reconstitution Phase

In this phase, the affected operations and systems are restored to normal operating conditions. The affected systems that cannot be restored to original conditions are replaced with completely new systems. Disaster recovery teams should ensure that the systems are free from disaster aftereffects before restoring them to the original facilities.

The reconstitution phase also involves the periodic inspection of restored systems to check their performance. The execution team should be involved until the restoration and testing is complete. This terminates with the shutdown of the disaster recovery systems and processes.

Disaster Recovery Objectives

The following are the three different types of objectives for the disaster recovery process:

1. *Short-term recovery objectives*: After the occurrence of an emergency, the first few hours and days are spent restoring the required structural (facilities) and nonstructural (power, water, sanitation, telecommunications, etc.) functions. The DR team should provide the direction and the required operational support to achieve and manage these objectives.

2. *Medium-term recovery objectives*: During the first weeks after an emergency event, the primary goal is to restore all the preidentified business functions that are found to be critical to normal business operations.

3. *Long-term recovery objectives*: The main objective of a DR effort is to resume normal operations. The long-term objectives focus on the resumption of operations to predisaster conditions. A long-term recovery team may be employed to consider and coordinate strategic planning for long-term recovery efforts. The timeline to restore to normal operations is dependent on the level of the disrupted critical services. In case of a major disaster, the recovery efforts can last for months or even years.

Disaster Recovery Checklist

Table 1-1 shows a sample checklist for disaster recovery procedures.

Plan: Technology	Yes	No
Is a written disaster recovery plan available?		
Is the plan current?		
Has the plan been tested?		
Are the legal or regulatory compliance requirements addressed in the plan?		
Are all the critical data and applications (including e-mail) part of the plan?		
Is there a clear recovery time objective for each business requirement?		
Is that recovery time objective tiered based on criticality to the business?		
Is a designated recovery site present for data?		
Are hardware, software, facilities, and service vendors part of the plan?		
Are critical data backed up on a frequent and regular basis?		
Are backups located off-site?		
Are backups tested?		
Are you located in a mandatory evacuation zone?		
Plan: People	**Yes**	**No**
Does the plan include employees (with current contact info) critical to recovery?		
Do those employees know their roles in the plan?		
Do you have a designated recovery site for people?		
Will your staff relocate?		
Has your staff participated in an actual test of your disaster recovery plan?		
Does your staff have access to documentation online and offline?		
Do you have an alternative if your staff is not available during an actual disaster?		
Do you require contractors or business partners to be available?		
Do those contractors/partners know about your plan and expectations?		
Do you have an alternative if your contractors/partners are not available?		
Plan: Data Center	**Yes**	**No**
Is your platform for critical data and applications located in a secure data center (DC)?		
Is access to the DC secured with badge, PIN, or biometric?		
Do you have access to a second DC networked to/with the primary DC (hot or cold)?		
Does your DC monitor and ensure proper temperature and humidity?		
Does your DC have adequate fire suppression?		
Is your hardware adequately secured and monitored inside the DC (or cage)?		
Does your DC provide fully conditioned power to all hardware?		
Does your DC provide redundant power with a UPS and generator?		
Does your DC have a power plan and scheduled maintenance?		
Does your DC test on a regular basis?		
Plan: Network	**Yes**	**No**
Does your network have multiple fiber connections to a SONET-based network service provider?		
Do you have multiple carrier-class ISPs to the Internet?		
Is your network failover integrated into the network topography?		
Do you perform BGP routing to facilitate failover?		

Table 1-1 Sample disaster recovery checklist

(continues)

Plan: Data Protection and Support	Yes	No
Are your data automatically backed up daily?		
Do you secure backup data off-site?		
Do you have a comprehensive security strategy with policies and procedures in place?		
Do your data have virus protection?		
Do you perform intrusion detection?		
Is your firewall managed and monitored?		
Do you employ or have access to live engineers, 24 hours a day, 7 days a week, 365 days a year?		

Table 1-1   Sample checklist for disaster recovery (continued)

Best Practices for Disaster Recovery

The following are some best practices for disaster recovery:

- *Dedicate and empower staff*: There should be a separate team in the organization to manage the business continuity planning. The team members should have access to a set of resources required to perform their roles during disaster recovery. The staff should be given proper training and should be well prepared to counter any disaster.

- *Divide and conquer*: To ensure business involvement, the organization should divide the business continuity and disaster recovery plan into two initiatives. Both have their own governance and goals. In case of disaster recovery, the goal is technical recovery, and the plan is created and managed by developers and engineers. The goal of business continuity is business process stability.

- *Design an independent plan*: DR teams and strategic planners should ensure that the disaster recovery plan is effective, even without the help of other plans and the involvement of people from other organizational teams. The plan should be implemented even when the key personnel in the recovery plan are unavailable. Proper backups should be maintained to take on the responsibility of key personnel.

- *Provide facilities*: Organizations should determine the right staffing to be involved during a disaster. They should also provide the appropriate services that are required to recover from disasters.

- *Align disaster recovery with application development*: Organizations should develop an isolated test environment that allows for full-time access and testing of all systems and applications. This allows the functions to be updated and tested regularly in order to minimize the occurrence of a disaster. It is advantageous to test the DR functions before a disaster strikes.

- *Try (and test) before you buy*: Organizations should make sure to try the trial version of any disaster recovery solution product before purchasing it. As there are different types of disasters and disaster recovery solutions, it is advisable to test the most appropriate recovery solution for that particular disaster.

Business Continuity

Business continuity is the ability of an organization to keep the business running even after a disaster strikes. It ensures that critical activities are available for users who have access to those activities. Business continuity also helps to prevent or reduce the interruption of operations and services.

Business continuity is not implemented at the time of a disaster, as it refers to activities performed daily to maintain service, consistency, and recoverability. Business continuity plans and processes help an organization in the following ways:

- Ensure uninterrupted critical business services
- Minimize business losses
- Ensure that the business is able meet its short-term and long-term objectives

Disaster Recovery Versus Business Continuity

The following are characteristics of disaster recovery:

- Disaster recovery deals with recovering systems to their normal state in the event of a disaster.
- It tends to deal with systems and data affected by a disaster.
- It is reactive, as its focus is to restore the business after a disaster.
- It includes plans and procedures that enable businesses to deal with a crisis.
- It ensures that the business is out of the crisis.

The following are characteristics of business continuity:

- Business continuity involves prioritizing various business processes and recovering the most important ones first.
- It is concerned with the overall business operation.
- It is proactive, as it focuses on avoiding or mitigating risks.
- It guarantees the survival and functioning of the business during and after a crisis.
- It does not ensure that the business has completely recovered from the crisis.

Business Continuity and Disaster Recovery Planning

Disaster recovery plans enable organizations to analyze and identify the different ways to handle a disaster. Business continuity planning helps organizations to develop and document procedures that enable them to achieve predefined business objectives before, during, and after a disaster. Business continuity plans should be tailored according to the particular needs of the organization. The objectives of business continuity plans are to:

- Protect corporate assets
- Provide management control for risks associated with the organization
- Ensure the survival and continuity of the business after a disaster
- Ensure practical management control over any business interruption

The following are the basic steps in any BC/DR plan:

1. Project initiation
2. Risk assessment
3. Business impact analysis
4. Mitigation strategy development
5. Plan development
6. Training, testing, and auditing
7. Plan maintenance

Security Management Plan

A *security management plan* is a documented set of policies and procedures to ensure the security of an organization's operations and assets. It includes guidelines on the procedures to minimize the perceived risks to an acceptable level and provides appropriate response measures for disasters. The main objective of the security management plan is to establish a secured organizational environment by reducing the risks.

A security management plan enables organizations to effectively manage security issues. It educates the faculty, staff, and visitors about the basic security measures to be taken during an emergency. The plan also helps an organization coordinate its response to different security incidents.

A security management plan generally includes the following:

- List of identified threats or risks to the organization
- Description of different countermeasures for identified threats
- Guidelines for reporting incidents
- First-response strategies for different disasters
- Description of risk mitigation strategies
- Assignment of roles and responsibilities in case of emergencies
- Guidelines for auditing and updating established plans

Disaster recovery teams and senior management are responsible for developing, testing, implementing, and monitoring security management plans according to the organization's requirements and business objectives.

Natural Threats to Consider While Preparing a Security Management Plan

Natural disasters are often sudden, giving organizations only a small amount of time to deploy any security measures. They have a negative effect on the environment and people. These types of disasters include natural hazards such as volcanic eruptions, earthquakes, and landslides that result in loss of life, property, and economy.

Natural disasters can cause massive losses and may affect a large population and geographical area. With the advancement of meteorological science, it is now possible to forecast certain natural disasters with varying precision; however, it is still not possible to completely avoid their effects on life and property. Natural disasters may cost billions of dollars and cripple economies. Natural disasters may jeopardize the survival of organizations. The following are some of the natural threats that should be considered when preparing a security management plan:

- Fires
- Floods
- Earthquakes
- Volcanoes
- Hurricanes

Fires

Organizations need to build a security management plan that helps them effectively handle fire incidents. The security management plan should include the following measures:

- Emergency exit doors to provide a way out for employees, important systems, and files
- Fire extinguishers at different points on the organization's premises to minimize the extent of the fire or to completely extinguish the fire
- Free space around the premises to allow fire engines and firefighters to operate freely
- Provisions for backups of all important data and documents at a third-party site

Floods

Floods often hit areas where there are rivers or lakes or where the drainage facilities are poor. The security management plan should include the following measures:

- The organization should build its structures in a secured location where flooding problems are minimal. Before building on a site, the organization should check for the possibility of flooding in that area.
- The organization should avoid storing important documents, data, and valuable property on the ground floor. This can help prevent damage to important assets during a flood.
- The organization can develop proper drainage facilities to reduce the incidence of most flooding problems. Floods are generally caused by poor drainage facilities.

Earthquakes

Earthquakes can lead to the destruction of an organization's valuable assets. Earthquakes can take place any time without a warning, making planning and precaution the only ways to protect life and property and to minimize damage. A security management plan should include the following measures:

- Before building on a site, the organization should study the geographical location to discover the frequency of earthquakes in that area.
- The organization needs to provide proper emergency exit facilities for employees and valuable assets during an earthquake.
- The organization should maintain a backup of all important resources and data at a different location in case of an earthquake.
- The organization should maintain emergency phone numbers and have a safe evacuation plan.
- If the building is in an earthquake-prone area, it should incorporate all necessary structural elements to minimize damage during an earthquake.

Man-Made Threats as Part of a Security Management Plan

Man-made disasters generally occur due to intervention, ignorance, or malicious intentions. In intentional threats, individuals with the intent to damage an organization or personnel opt for different methods and techniques. Individuals without any malicious intentions unknowingly cause disasters. Man-made disasters can range from events such as system crashes to terrorism.

Man-made attacks are classified into the following general categories:

- Human error
- Intentional attacks

Human Error

Disasters caused by human error are those that are mostly the result of errors in carrying out certain operations or processes, ignorance, or negligence. Disasters caused by human error include the following:

- Accidents
- Power outages
- Telecommunication outages
- System or network crashes

Accidents An accident may be the result of a person's inexperience or carelessness, or it may be the result of equipment malfunction. The following are some examples of accidents:

- A user uses a system and accidentally modifies or deletes data
- A user deletes data that are linked to data in another file, making the other file inoperable
- A user shuts down a system while critical operations are running

The security management plan should consider the following measures:

- Store a backup of all important data
- Keep backup systems on hand to replace any damaged systems
- Train personnel in the proper use of systems or equipment
- Prepare a checklist regarding the typical mistakes that personnel make

Power Outages Power outages are caused by an interruption in the power supply. Power outages can be short term or long term. The following are human errors involved in power outages:

- Mechanical failure that includes failure at the power station, damage of a power line, or a short circuit
- Overuse of power by the organization

The security management plan should include the following measures:

- Have a regular backup of data and systems to avoid any loss of data
- Make use of power generators to minimize data losses and system crashes
- Implement measures to prevent any fluctuations of power that may result in system crashes
- Do not use more power than necessary, and do not overload the power infrastructure

Telecommunication Outages Telecommunication outages disrupt communications, making it more difficult for the organization to handle emergencies. These types of outages include failure of Internet connections; communication stations, such as radio and television; and other communication media.

Telecommunication outages can occur due to the following:

- Mechanical failure caused by faulty equipment or machinery
- Human error

The security management plan should include the following measures:

- Make use of emergency alarms or signals to communicate about threat situations
- Make use of risk management techniques to reduce the impact of outages

System or Network Crashes When a system or network crashes, it stops responding to other parts of the system or network. A system or network crash can be caused by the following:

- Application errors
- Power outages
- Threats from the external and internal environment
- User actions
- Hardware faults

The security management plan should include the following measures:

- Make sure there is a continuous power supply to all critical systems.
- All systems should be protected by an effective antivirus tool.
- Users should only be allowed to perform the actions necessary to do their work.

Intentional Attacks

Intentional disasters refer to incidents when a person attempts to damage an organization or person for financial gain or revenge. The following are some human intentions that can harm or damage an organization or personnel:

- Terrorism
- Hacking
- Data theft

Intentional attacks such as terrorism and hacking are generally used as tools to achieve socioeconomic objectives, whereas financial gain is a prime objective in cases involving data theft. Organizations can overcome these attacks by means of awareness, vigilance, and proper preparedness for a timely response.

Terrorism Terrorism can damage a country socially and economically. The main intentions of terrorism are loss of life and disturbing a country's financial system. The security management plan should include the following measures:

- Have a security system and perform security checks to allow only authorized personnel into the building.
- Install an emergency alarm signal to alert employees and security forces in case of any terrorist actions in the organization.
- Deploy security personnel outside the building to combat any terrorist action outside the building.

- Monitor the Web sites that employees access to make sure they are not visiting terrorism sites.
- Place security cameras at different places all over the building to provide the most coverage.

Hacking Attackers hack systems and networks to illegally gain information or to cause damage to an organization or personnel. Hacking involves infringement on the privacy of others or damage to computer-based property such as files, Web pages, and software. The security management plan should include the following measures:

- Provide proper authentication to the organization's data and Web sites so that only authorized users and employees have access.
- Perform regular audits on system logs, user accounts, and passwords.
- Use a variety of antihacking tools.
- Disable any unused network services or services with known vulnerabilities.
- Install up-to-date security updates and patches.
- Place valuable information in a secured place to which third parties do not have access.

Data Theft Attackers acquire an organization's valuable data for their own profit. Attackers illegally copy information from either a business or an individual. Stolen information typically includes user information such as passwords, Social Security numbers, credit card information, and other personal information, as well as confidential corporate information.

The security management plan should include the following measures:

- Prevent data from unnecessarily flowing out of the organization.
- Allow personnel to access only the data they need to do their jobs.
- Maintain strong password protection on important data to prevent illegitimate access.
- Do not store passwords and other personal data on paper in unsecured areas, such as on a user's desk or in a trash bin.
- Make use of different encryption tools to make data unreadable to outsiders.

Chapter Summary

- A disaster is a natural or human-caused incident that negatively affects organizations or the environment.
- *Disaster recovery* involves the processes, policies, and procedures necessary for the recovery of operations and the continuation of the critical functions of an organization after a disaster.
- Business continuity is the ability of an organization to keep the business running after a disaster.
- A disaster recovery plan enables an organization to analyze and identify different ways to handle a disaster.
- Business continuity is not implemented at the time of a disaster, as it refers to activities performed daily to maintain service, consistency, and recoverability.
- A security management plan enables an organization to effectively manage security issues.
- Natural threats typically come without much warning, giving organizations little time to deploy security measures.
- Man-made disasters are caused by intervention, ignorance, or malicious intent.
- Power outages are caused by interruptions in the power supply.

Review Questions

1. Define disaster recovery.

   _____

   _____

   _____

   _____

2. List the responsibilities of a disaster recovery team.

   _____

   _____

   _____

   _____

3. Explain the different phases of disaster recovery.

   _____

   _____

   _____

   _____

4. List the best practices for disaster recovery.

   _____

   _____

   _____

   _____

5. Define business continuity. Discuss different factors that affect business continuity.

   _____

   _____

   _____

   _____

6. Describe the difference between disaster recovery and business continuity.

   _____

   _____

   _____

   _____

7. Describe the purpose of a security management plan.

   _____

   _____

   _____

   _____

8. Describe what should be included in a security management plan to deal with fire incidents.

_____

_____

_____

_____

9. Describe what should be included in a security management plan to deal with earthquake incidents.

_____

_____

_____

_____

10. Describe the different components of a security management plan to deal with telecommunication outages.

_____

_____

_____

_____

Hands-On Projects

1. Navigate to Chapter 1 of the Student Resource Center. Open data_recovery.pdf. Read the following sections:
   - 1.1 Introduction
   - 1.2 Reasons for Disaster Recovery
   - 1.5 Business Continuity Planning

2. Navigate to Chapter 1 of the Student Resource Center. Open Disaster Recovery Plans.pdf. Read the following sections:
   - Chapter 1: Introduction
   - Chapter 2: Research Background Information
   - Chapter 3: The Disaster Recovery Plan

3. Navigate to Chapter 1 of the Student Resource Center. Open Disaster Recovery Plan-part. pdf. Read the following sections:
   - 1. Notification Process
   - 1.2. System Unavailability Notification
   - 2. Recovery Process

4. Navigate to Chapter 1 of the Student Resource Center. Open Disaster Recovery Best Practices.pdf. Read the following sections:
   - 1 Executive Summary
   - 2 Disaster Recovery Planning
   - 3 Disaster Recovery Phases
   - 4 The Disaster Recovery Plan Document

5. Navigate to Chapter 1 of the Student Resource Center. Open chapter-13.pdf. Read the following sections:

   - Introduction
   - Road Accidents and Stampede

6. Navigate to Chapter 1 of the Student Resource Center. Open doc12973-7a.pdf. Read the following sections:

   - Natural Disasters
   - Volcanic Eruptions

7. Navigate to Chapter 1 of the Student Resource Center. Open txt-sini.pdf. Read the following sections:

   - Principal Causes of Disasters
   - Disaster Plan

Chapter 2

Laws and Acts

Objectives

After completing this chapter, you should be able to:

- Understand various laws related to disaster recovery

Key Terms

Civil law   a set of rules that the state has established for itself, generally through common usage (common law), judicial decision, or statutory legislation, dealing with the private rights of individuals; in civil cases the defendant is never incarcerated and never executed, but if found liable, is usually fined for the damage caused by his or her action.

Criminal law   a set of rules and statutes that specifically defines conduct prohibited by the state to protect public safety and welfare; in criminal prosecutions, the defendant is presumed innocent, and the state must prove beyond a reasonable doubt that he or she has indeed violated the law. The defendant, if found guilty, is usually punished by incarceration, fines paid to the government, or, in capital cases, execution.

Introduction to Laws and Acts

Local, state, and federal governments develop and implement a complex variety of laws and regulations related to disasters, regulating land use, building practices, emergency response planning, and other actions. These laws define government and private liability during the process of disaster recovery. Generally, laws can be put into two categories:

1. *Civil law*: A set of rules that the state has established for itself, generally through common usage (common law), judicial decision, or statutory legislation, dealing with the private rights of individuals. In civil cases the defendant is never incarcerated and never executed, but if found liable, is usually fined for the damage caused by his or her action.

2. *Criminal law*: A set of rules and statutes that specifically defines conduct prohibited by the state to protect public safety and welfare. In criminal prosecutions, the defendant is presumed

innocent, and the state must prove beyond a reasonable doubt that he or she has indeed violated the law. The defendant, if found guilty, is usually punished by incarceration, fines paid to the government, or, in capital cases, execution.

Every business is governed by laws that dictate how it must conduct itself in the normal course of business. For a publicly traded company, regulations are likely to include financial reporting and corporate governance rules intended to protect investors. In the case of a disaster, the burden of the proof is on the company to prove that all reasonable measures had been taken to mitigate the harm caused by the disaster. Courts evaluate liability through the following:

- Probability of loss
- Magnitude of damage
- Balance against the cost of prevention

This chapter familiarizes you with the laws and regulations relevant to disaster recovery, and serves as a reference for the full text of some of these laws and regulations.

Types of Relevant Acts

Acts that influence disaster recovery policies, practices, and standards include the following:

- Business contingency planning acts
- Liability acts
- Life/safety acts
- Risk-reduction acts
- Security acts
- Vital records acts

United States of America Laws and Acts

Sarbanes-Oxley Act of 2002[1]

The Sarbanes-Oxley Act introduced significant legislative changes to financial practice and corporate governance regulation. It has the following stated objective: "To protect investors by improving the accuracy and reliability of corporate disclosures made pursuant to the securities laws."

All companies must comply with this act as of 2005. It is organized into eleven titles, although sections 302, 401, 404, 409, 802, and 906 are the most significant for disaster recovery. In addition, the act also created a public company accounting board. This is a very high profile act, so any company must be extremely careful to comply with it.

The act covers financial reporting to the Securities and Exchange Commission (SEC) and states that auditors must keep every document regarding clients for at least seven years.

Foreign Corrupt Practices Act (FCPA)[2]

U.S. firms seeking to do business in foreign markets must be familiar with the FCPA. In general, the FCPA prohibits corrupt payments made to foreign officials for the purpose of obtaining or maintaining business. In addition, other statutes such as the mail and wire fraud statutes, 18 U.S.C. § 1341, 1343, and the Travel Act, 18 U.S.C. § 1952, which provides for federal prosecution of violations of state commercial bribery statutes, may also apply to such conduct.

The Department of Justice is the chief enforcement agency, with a lesser role played by the Securities and Exchange Commission (SEC). The Office of General Counsel of the Department of Commerce also answers general questions from U.S. exporters concerning the FCPA's basic requirements and constraints.

Enforcement

The Department of Justice is responsible for all criminal enforcement and for civil enforcement of the antibribery provisions with respect to domestic concerns as well as foreign companies and nationals. The SEC is responsible for the civil enforcement of the antibribery provisions with respect to issuers.

Antibribery Provisions

The FCPA makes it unlawful to bribe foreign government officials to obtain or retain business. With respect to the basic prohibition, there are five elements that must be met to constitute a violation of the act. These are described below.

Who The FCPA potentially applies to any individual, firm, officer, director, employee, or agent of a firm and any stockholder acting on behalf of a firm. Individuals and firms may also be penalized if they order, authorize, or assist someone else to violate the antibribery provisions or if they conspire to violate those provisions.

Under the FCPA, U.S. jurisdiction over corrupt payments made to foreign officials depends upon whether the violator is an issuer, a domestic concern, or a foreign national or business.

An issuer is a corporation that has issued securities that have been registered in the United States or who are required to file periodic reports with the SEC. A domestic concern is any individual who is a citizen, national, or resident of the United States, or any corporation, partnership, association, joint-stock company, business trust, unincorporated organization, or sole proprietorship that has its principal place of business in the United States, or that is organized under the laws of a state, territory, possession, or commonwealth of the United States.

Issuers and domestic concerns may be held liable under the FCPA under either territorial or nationality jurisdiction principles. For acts taken within the territory of the United States, issuers and domestic concerns are liable if they take an act in furtherance of a corrupt payment made to a foreign official using the U.S. mails or other means or instrumentalities of interstate commerce. Such means or instrumentalities include telephone calls, fax transmissions, wire transfers, and interstate or international travel. In addition, issuers and domestic concerns may be held liable for any act in furtherance of a corrupt payment taken outside the United States. Thus, a U.S. company or national may be held liable for a corrupt payment authorized by employees or agents operating entirely outside the United States, using money from foreign bank accounts, and without any involvement by personnel located within the United States.

Prior to 1998, foreign companies, with the exception of those who qualified as issuers, and foreign nationals were not covered by the FCPA. The 1998 amendments expanded the FCPA to assert territorial jurisdiction over foreign companies and nationals. A foreign company or person is now subject to the FCPA if it causes, directly or through agents, an act in furtherance of the corrupt payment to take place within the territory of the United States. There is, however, no requirement that such act make use of the U.S. mails or other means or instrumentalities of interstate commerce.

Finally, U.S. parent corporations may be held liable for the acts of foreign subsidiaries where they authorize, direct, or control the activity in question, as can U.S. citizens or residents, themselves domestic concerns, who were employed by or acting on behalf of such foreign-incorporated subsidiaries.

Corrupt Intent The person making or authorizing the payment must have a corrupt intent, and the payment must be intended to induce the recipient to misuse his or her official position to direct business wrongfully to the payer or to any other person. The FCPA does not require that a corrupt act succeeds in its purpose. The offer or promise of a corrupt payment can constitute a violation of the statute. The FCPA prohibits any corrupt payment intended to influence any act or decision of a foreign official in his or her official capacity, to induce the official to do or omit any act in violation of his or her lawful duty, to obtain any improper advantage, or to induce a foreign official to use his or her influence improperly to affect or influence any act or decision.

Payment The FCPA prohibits paying, offering, promising to pay (or authorizing to pay or offer) money or anything of value.

Recipient The prohibition extends only to corrupt payments made to a foreign official, a foreign political party or party official, or any candidate for foreign political office. A foreign official means any officer or employee of a foreign government, a public international organization, or any department or agency thereof, or any person acting in an official capacity.

The FCPA applies to payments to any public official, regardless of rank or position. The FCPA focuses on the purpose of the payment instead of the particular duties of the official receiving the payment, offer, or promise of payment, and there are exceptions to the antibribery provision for "facilitating payments for routine governmental action."

Business Purpose Test The FCPA prohibits payments made in order to assist firms in obtaining or retaining business for or with, or directing business to, any person. The Department of Justice interprets "obtaining or retaining business" broadly, such that the phrase encompasses more than the mere award or renewal of a contract. It should be noted that the business to be obtained or retained does not need to be with a foreign government or foreign government instrumentality.

Sanctions Against Bribery

Criminal The following criminal penalties may be imposed for violations of the FCPA's antibribery provisions:

- Corporations and other business entities are subject to a fine of up to $2,000,000.
- Officers, directors, stockholders, employees, and agents are subject to a fine of up to $100,000 and imprisonment for up to five years.

Moreover, under the Alternative Fines Act, these fines may be actually quite higher—the actual fine may be up to twice the benefit that the defendant sought to obtain by making the corrupt payment. Fines imposed on individuals may not be paid by their employer or principal.

Civil The attorney general or the SEC, as appropriate, may bring a civil action for a fine of up to $10,000 against any firm as well as any officer, director, employee, or agent of a firm, or stockholder acting on behalf of the firm, who violates the antibribery provisions. In addition, in an SEC enforcement action, the court may impose an additional fine not to exceed the following:

- The gross amount of the pecuniary gain to the defendant as a result of the violation
- A specified dollar limitation

The specified dollar limitations are based on the egregiousness of the violation, ranging from $5,000 to $100,000 for a natural person and $50,000 to $500,000 for any other person.

The attorney general or the SEC, as appropriate, may also bring a civil action to enjoin any act or practice of a firm whenever it appears that the firm (or an officer, director, employee, agent, or stockholder acting on behalf of the firm) is in violation (or about to be) of the antibribery provisions.

Other Governmental Action Under guidelines issued by the Office of Management and Budget, a person or firm found in violation of the FCPA may be barred from doing business with the federal government. Indictment alone can lead to suspension of the right to do business with the government. The president has directed that no executive agency shall allow any party to participate in any procurement or nonprocurement activity if any agency has debarred, suspended, or otherwise excluded that party from participation in a procurement or nonprocurement activity.

In addition, a person or firm found guilty of violating the FCPA may be ruled ineligible to receive export licenses; the SEC may suspend or bar persons from the securities business and impose civil penalties on persons in the securities business for violations of the FCPA; the Commodity Futures Trading Commission and the Overseas Private Investment Corporation both provide for possible suspension or debarment from the agency programs for violation of the FCPA; and a payment made to a foreign government official that is unlawful under the FCPA cannot be deducted under the tax laws as a business expense.

Private Cause of Action Conduct that violates the antibribery provisions of the FCPA may also give rise to a private cause of action for treble damages under the Racketeer Influenced and Corrupt Organizations Act (RICO), or to actions under other federal or state laws. For example, an action might be brought under RICO by a competitor who alleges that the bribery caused the defendant to win a foreign contract.

Health Care: HIPAA Regulations[3,4]

Public Law 104-191 of the 104th Congress has the following stated purpose:

To amend the Internal Revenue Code of 1986 to improve portability and continuity of health insurance coverage in the group and individual markets; to combat waste, fraud, and abuse in health insurance and health care delivery; to promote the use of medical savings accounts; to improve access to the long-term care services and coverage; to simplify the administration of the health insurance; and for other purposes.

HIPAA Privacy and Disclosures in Emergency Situations

The HIPAA Privacy Rule allows the patient's information to be shared to assist in disaster relief efforts and to assist patients in receiving the care they need. Providers and health plans covered by the HIPAA Privacy Rule can share the patient's information in the following ways:

- *Treatment*: Health care providers can share patient information as necessary to provide treatment. Treatment includes the following:

  - Sharing information with other providers (including hospitals and clinics)

  - Referring patients for treatment (including linking patients with the available providers in areas where the patients have relocated)

  - Coordinating patient's care with others (such as emergency relief workers or others that can help patients obtain the appropriate health services)

  Providers can also share the patient's information to the extent necessary to seek payment for these health care services.

- *Notification*: Health care providers can share the patient's information as necessary to identify, locate, and notify family members, guardians, or anyone else responsible for the individual's care of the individual's location, general condition, or death. The health care provider should get verbal permission from individuals, when possible; however, if the individual is incapacitated or not available, providers may share information for these purposes if, in their professional judgment, doing so is in the patient's best interest.

  Thus, when necessary, the hospital may notify the police, the press, or the public at large to the extent necessary to help locate, identify, or otherwise notify the family members and others as to the location and general condition of their loved ones.

  In addition, when a health care provider is sharing information with disaster relief organizations that, like the American Red Cross, are authorized by law or by their charters to assist in disaster relief efforts, it is unnecessary to obtain the patient's permission to share the information if doing so would interfere with the organization's ability to respond to the emergency.

- *Imminent danger*: Providers can share the patient's information with anyone as necessary to prevent or lessen a serious and imminent threat to the health and safety of a person or the public, consistent with applicable law and the provider's standards of ethical conduct.

- *Facility directory*: Health care facilities maintaining a directory of patients can tell people who call or ask about individuals whether the individual is at the facility, his or her location in the facility, and his or her general condition.

The HIPAA Privacy Rule does not apply to disclosures if they are not made by entities covered by the Privacy Rule. Thus, for instance, the HIPAA Privacy Rule does not restrict the American Red Cross from sharing a patient's information.

Financial Institutions: Financial Modernization Act of 1999[5]

The Financial Modernization Act of 1999, also known as the Gramm-Leach-Bliley Act or GLB Act, includes provisions to protect consumers' personal financial information held by financial institutions. There are three main parts to the act's privacy requirements:

1. The Financial Privacy Rule
2. The Safeguards Rule
3. Pretexting provisions

The GLB Act gives authority to eight federal agencies and the states to administer and enforce the Financial Privacy Rule and the Safeguards Rule. These two regulations apply to financial institutions, which include not only banks, securities firms, and insurance companies, but also companies providing many other types of financial products and services to consumers. These services include the following:

- Lending, brokering, or servicing any type of consumer loan

- Transferring or safeguarding money

- Preparing individual tax returns

- Providing financial advice or credit counseling

- Providing residential real estate settlement services

- Collecting consumer debts

The Financial Privacy Rule governs the collection and disclosure of customers' personal financial information by financial institutions. It also applies to companies who receive such information, whether or not they are financial institutions.

The Safeguards Rule requires all financial institutions to design, implement, and maintain safeguards to protect the customer's information. The Safeguards Rule applies not only to the financial institutions that collect information from their own customers, but also to those that receive customer information from other financial institutions.

The pretexting provisions of the GLB Act protect consumers from individuals and companies that obtain their personal financial information under false pretenses, a practice known as pretexting.

Flood Disaster Protection Act of 1973[6]

The act's stated purpose is as follows:

To expand the national flood insurance program by substantially increasing the limits of the coverage and total amount of insurance authorized to be outstanding and by requiring known flood-prone communities to participate in the program, and for other purposes.[7]

Findings and Declaration of Purpose

SEC.2. (a) The Congress finds that—

- (1) annual losses throughout the Nation from floods and mudslides are increasing at an alarming rate, largely as a result of the accelerating development of, and concentration of population in, areas of flood and mudslide hazards;

- (2) the availability of Federal loans, grants, guaranties, insurance, and other forms of financial assistance are often the determining factors in the utilization of land and the location and construction of public and of private industrial, commercial, and residential facilities;

- (3) property acquired or constructed with grants or other Federal assistance may be exposed to risk of loss through floods, thus frustrating the purpose for which such assistance was extended;

- (4) Federal instrumentalities insure or otherwise provide financial protection to banking and credit institutions whose assets include a substantial number of mortgage loans and other indebtedness secured by property exposed to loss and damage from floods and mudslides;

- (5) the Nation cannot afford the tragic losses of life caused annually by flood occurrences, nor the increasing losses of property suffered by flood victims, most of whom are still inadequately compensated despite the provision of costly disaster relief benefits; and

- (6) it is in the public interest for persons already living in flood-prone areas to have both an opportunity to purchase flood insurance and access to more adequate limits of coverage, so that they will be indemnified for their losses in the event of future flood disasters.

SEC.2. (b) The purpose of this Act, therefore, is to—

- (1) substantially increase the limits of coverage authorized under the national flood insurance program;

- (2) provide for the expeditious identification of, and the dissemination of information concerning, flood-prone areas;

- (3) require State or local communities, as a condition of future Federal financial assistance, to participate in the flood insurance program and to adopt adequate flood plan ordinances with effective enforcement provisions consistent with Federal standards to reduce or avoid future flood losses; and

- (4) require the purchase of flood insurance by property owners who are being assisted by Federal programs or by federally supervised, regulated, or insured agencies or institutions in the acquisition or improvement of land or facilities located or to be located in identified areas having special flood hazards.

Robert T. Stafford Disaster Relief and Emergency Assistance Act[8]

Robert T. Stafford Disaster Relief and Emergency Assistance Act, also known as the Stafford Act, is amended by Public Law 106-390, October 30, 2000.[9]

SEC. 101. (b) It is the intent of the Congress, by this Act, to provide an orderly and continuing means of assistance by the Federal Government to State and local governments in carrying out their responsibilities to alleviate the suffering and damage which result from such disasters by—

- (1) revising and broadening the scope of existing disaster relief programs;

- (2) encouraging the development of comprehensive disaster preparedness and assistance plans, programs, capabilities, and organizations by the States and by local governments;

- (3) achieving greater coordination and responsiveness of disaster preparedness and relief programs;

- (4) encouraging individuals, States, and local governments to protect themselves by obtaining insurance coverage to supplement or replace governmental assistance;

- (5) encouraging hazard mitigation measures to reduce losses from disasters, including development of land use and construction regulations; and

- (6) providing Federal assistance programs for both public and private losses sustained in disasters

Overview of the Stafford Act[10]

The Stafford Act authorizes the president to issue major disaster declarations that authorize federal agencies to provide assistance to states overwhelmed by disasters. Through executive orders, the president has delegated to the Federal Emergency Management Agency (FEMA), within the Department of Homeland Security (DHS), responsibility for administering the major provisions of the Stafford Act. Assistance authorized by the statute is available to individuals, families, state and local governments, and certain nonprofit organizations.

Activities undertaken under authority of the Stafford Act are provided through funds appropriated to the Disaster Relief Fund (DRF). Federal assistance supported by DRF money is used by states, localities, and certain nonprofit organizations to provide mass care, restore damaged or destroyed facilities, clear debris, and aid individuals and families with uninsured needs, among other activities.

Presidential Declarations

Under Stafford Act authority, five types of actions may be taken, summarized as follows:

1. *Major disaster*: The president issues a major disaster declaration after receiving a request from the governor of the affected state. Major disaster declarations may be issued after a natural catastrophe or, "regardless of cause, fire, flood, or explosion." A declaration authorizes DHS to administer various federal disaster assistance programs for victims of the declared disasters. Each major disaster declaration specifies the type of incident covered, the time period covered, the types of disaster assistance available, the counties affected by the declaration, and the name of the federal coordinating officer.

2. *Emergency*: The declaration process for emergencies is similar to that used for major disasters; the president may, however, issue an emergency declaration without a gubernatorial request if primary responsibility rests with the federal government. An emergency declaration may be issued on "any occasion or instance" in which the president determines that federal assistance is required. Under an emergency declaration, the federal government funds and undertakes emergency response activities, debris removal, and individual assistance and housing programs. DRF expenditures for an emergency are limited to $5 million per declaration unless the president determines that there is a continuing need; Congress must be notified if the $5 million ceiling is breached.

3. *Fire suppression*: The Secretary of DHS is authorized to provide fire suppression assistance to supplement the resources of communities when fires threaten such destruction as would warrant a major disaster declaration.

4. *Defense emergency*: Upon request from the governor of an affected state, the president may authorize the Department of Defense (DOD) to carry out emergency work for a period not to exceed 10 days. DOD emergency work is limited to work essential for the preservation of life and property.

5. *Predeclaration activities*: When a situation threatens human health and safety, and a disaster is imminent but not yet declared, the Secretary of DHS may place agency employees on alert. DHS monitors the status of the situation, communicates with state emergency officials on potential assistance requirements, and deploys teams and resources to maximize the speed and effectiveness of the anticipated federal response and, when necessary, performs preparedness and preliminary damage assessment activities.

In considering a gubernatorial request for disaster relief, the president evaluates a number of factors, including the cause of the catastrophe, damages, needs, certification by state officials that state and local governments will comply with cost sharing and other requirements, and official requests for assistance. FEMA has established thresholds that are considered by the president and DHS officials in the process of determining whether a major disaster is to be declared. Neither the Stafford Act nor implementing regulations provide for a Congressional role in the declaration process.

Types of Assistance and Eligibility

FEMA has established three major categories of aid under the Stafford Act—individual and household, public, and hazard mitigation assistance. The persons and organizations eligible for assistance authorized by the Stafford Act may be summarized as follows:

1. *Individuals and households*: Immediate temporary shelter; cash grants (maximum of approximately $25,000, adjusted for inflation) for uninsured emergency personal needs; temporary housing assistance (rental and mortgage payments), generally for 18 months; home repair grants; unemployment assistance due to the disaster; debris removal from private property when deemed in the public interest; emergency food supplies; legal aid for low-income individuals; and crisis counseling

2. *State, tribal, and local governments and certain private nonprofit organizations*: Repair, reconstruction, or replacement of infrastructure and recreational facilities; emergency protective measures, emergency communications, and transportation systems; and loans to replace lost revenue or meet federal cost-sharing requirements

3. *State governments*: Hazard mitigation assistance to reduce future disaster losses

CAN-SPAM Act of 2003[11]

Public Law 108–187

Section 1: Short Title

This Act may be cited as the "Controlling the Assault of Non-Solicited Pornography and Marketing Act of 2003," or the "CAN-SPAM Act of 2003."

Section 2: Congressional Findings and Policy

(a) Findings.—The Congress finds the following:

(1) Electronic mail has become an important and popular means of communication, relied on by millions of Americans on a daily basis for personal and commercial purposes. Its low cost and global reach make it convenient and efficient, and offer unique opportunities for the development and growth of frictionless commerce.

(2) The convenience and efficiency of electronic mail are threatened by the extremely rapid growth in the volume of unsolicited commercial electronic mail. Unsolicited commercial electronic mail is currently estimated to account for over half of all electronic mail traffic, up from an estimated 7% in 2001, and the volume continues to rise. Most of these messages are fraudulent or deceptive in one or more respects.

(3) The receipt of unsolicited commercial electronic mail may result in costs to recipients who cannot refuse to accept such mail and who incur costs for the storage of such mail, or for the time spent accessing, reviewing, and discarding such mail, or for both.

(4) The receipt of a large number of unwanted messages also decreases the convenience of electronic mail and creates a risk that wanted electronic mail messages, both commercial and noncommercial, will be lost, overlooked, or discarded amidst the larger volume of unwanted messages, thus reducing the reliability and usefulness of electronic mail to the recipient.

(5) Some commercial electronic mail contains material that many recipients may consider vulgar or pornographic in nature.

(6) The growth in unsolicited commercial electronic mail imposes significant monetary costs on providers of Internet access services, businesses, and educational and nonprofit institutions that

carry and receive such mail, as there is a finite volume of mail that such providers, businesses, and institutions can handle without further investment in infrastructure.

(7) Many senders of unsolicited commercial electronic mail purposefully disguise the source of such mail.

(8) Many senders of unsolicited commercial electronic mail purposefully include misleading information in the messages' subject lines in order to induce the recipients to view the messages.

(9) While some senders of commercial electronic mail messages provide simple and reliable ways for recipients to reject (or "opt-out" of) receipt of commercial electronic mail from such senders in the future, other senders provide no such "opt-out" mechanism, or refuse to honor the requests of recipients not to receive electronic mail from such senders in the future, or both.

(10) Many senders of bulk unsolicited commercial electronic mail use computer programs to gather large numbers of electronic mail addresses on an automated basis from Internet Web sites or online services where users must post their addresses in order to make full use of the Web site or service.

(11) Many States have enacted legislation intended to regulate or reduce unsolicited commercial electronic mail, but these statutes impose different standards and requirements. As a result, they do not appear to have been successful in addressing the problems associated with unsolicited commercial electronic mail, in part because, since an electronic mail address does not specify a geographic location, it can be extremely difficult for law-abiding businesses to know with which of these disparate statutes they are required to comply.

(12) The problems associated with the rapid growth and abuse of unsolicited commercial electronic mail cannot be solved by Federal legislation alone. The development and adoption of technological approaches and the pursuit of cooperative efforts with other countries will be necessary as well.

(b) Congressional Determination of Public Policy.—On the basis of the findings in subsection (a), the Congress determines that—

(1) there is a substantial government interest in regulation of commercial electronic mail on a nationwide basis;

(2) senders of commercial electronic mail should not mislead recipients as to the source or content of such mail; and

(3) recipients of commercial electronic mail have a right to decline to receive additional commercial electronic mail from the same source.

Requirements for Commercial E-Mailers[12]

The CAN-SPAM Act of 2003 establishes requirements for those who send commercial e-mail, spells out penalties for spammers and companies whose products are advertised in spam if they violate the law, and gives consumers the right to ask e-mailers to stop spamming them.

The law covers e-mail whose primary purpose is advertising or promoting a commercial product or service, including content on a Web site. A "transactional or relationship message" e-mail that facilitates an agreed-upon transaction or updates a customer in an existing business relationship may not contain false or misleading routing information, but otherwise is exempt from most provisions of the CAN-SPAM Act.

The Federal Trade Commission (FTC) is authorized to enforce the CAN-SPAM Act. CAN-SPAM also gives the Department of Justice (DOJ) the authority to enforce its criminal sanctions. Other federal and state agencies can enforce the law against organizations under their jurisdiction, and companies that provide Internet access may sue violators as well.

The following are the law's main provisions:

- *Bans false or misleading header information*: Any e-mail's From header, To header, and routing information must be accurate, and the person who initiated the e-mail must be identified.

- *Prohibits deceptive subject lines*: The subject line cannot mislead the recipient about the contents or subject matter of the message.

- *Requires an opt-out method*: There must be a return e-mail address or another Internet-based response mechanism that allows a recipient to request that no future e-mail messages be sent to that e-mail address, and those requests must be honored. There may be a menu of choices allowing a recipient to opt out of certain types of messages, but there must also be an option to end any commercial messages from the sender.

- *Requires that commercial e-mail be identified as an advertisement and include the sender's valid physical postal address*: The message must contain clear and conspicuous notice that the message is an advertisement or solicitation and that the recipient can opt out of receiving more commercial e-mails from the sender. It also must include the sender's valid physical postal address.

Penalties

Each violation of the above provisions is subject to fines of up to $11,000. Deceptive commercial e-mail also is subject to laws banning false or misleading advertising.

Additional fines are provided for commercial e-mailers who not only violate the rules described above, but also do the following:

- Harvest e-mail addresses from Web sites or Web services that have published a notice prohibiting the transfer of e-mail addresses for the purpose of sending e-mail

- Generate e-mail addresses using a dictionary attack, combining names, letters, or numbers into multiple permutations

- Use scripts or other automated ways to register for multiple e-mail or user accounts to send commercial e-mail

- Relay e-mails through a computer or network without permission—for example, by taking advantage of open relays or open proxies without authorization

The law allows the DOJ to seek criminal penalties, including imprisonment, for commercial e-mailers who do or conspire to do the following:

- Use another computer without authorization and send commercial e-mail from or through it

- Use a computer to relay or retransmit multiple commercial e-mail messages to deceive or mislead recipients or an Internet access service about the origin of the message

- Falsify header information in multiple e-mail messages and initiate the transmission of such messages

- Register for multiple e-mail accounts or domain names using information that falsifies the identity of the actual registrant

- Falsely represent themselves as owners of the multiple Internet Protocol addresses that are used to send commercial e-mail messages

Financial Institutions Reform, Recovery, and Enforcement Act of 1989[13]

SEC. 951. CIVIL PENALTIES

(a) IN GENERAL—

Whoever violates any provision of law to which this section is made applicable by subsection (c) of this section shall be subject to a civil penalty in an amount assessed by the court in a civil action under this section.

(b) MAXIMUM AMOUNT OF PENALTY—

(1) GENERALLY—

The amount of the civil penalty shall not exceed $1,000,000.

(2) SPECIAL RULE FOR CONTINUING VIOLATIONS—

In the case of a continuing violation, the amount of the civil penalty may exceed the amount described in paragraph (1) but may not exceed the lesser of $1,000,000 per day or $5,000,000.

(3) SPECIAL RULE FOR VIOLATIONS CREATING GAIN OR LOSS—

(A) If any person derives pecuniary gain from the violation, or if the violation results in pecuniary loss to a person other than the violator, the amount of the civil penalty may exceed the amounts described in paragraphs (1) and (2) but may not exceed the amount of such gain or loss.

(B) As used in this paragraph, the term "person" includes the Bank Insurance Fund, the Savings Association Insurance Fund and after the merger of such funds, the Deposit Insurance Fund, and the National Credit Union Share Insurance Fund.

(c) VIOLATIONS TO WHICH PENALTY IS APPLICABLE

This section applies to a violation of, or a conspiracy to violate—

(1) section 215, 656, 657, 1005, 1006, 1007, 1014, or 1344 of Title 18; or

(2) section 287, 1001, 1032, 1341 or 1343 of Title 18 affecting a federally insured financial institution. This section shall apply to violations occurring on or after August 10, 1984.

(d) ATTORNEY GENERAL TO BRING ACTION—

A civil action to recover a civil penalty under this section shall be commenced by the Attorney General.

(e) BURDEN OF PROOF—

In a civil action to recover a civil penalty under this section, the Attorney General must establish the right to recovery by a preponderance of the evidence.

(f) ADMINISTRATIVE SUBPOENAS—

(1)IN GENERAL—

For the purpose of conducting a civil investigation in contemplation of a civil proceeding under this section, the Attorney General may—

(A) administer oaths and affirmations;

(B) take evidence; and

(C) by subpoena, summon witnesses and require the production of any books, papers, correspondence, memoranda, or other records which the Attorney General deems relevant or material to the inquiry. Such subpoena may require the attendance of witnesses and the production of any such records from any place in the United States at any place in the United States designated by the Attorney General.

(2) PROCEDURES APPLICABLE

The same procedures and limitations as are provided with respect to civil investigative demands in subsections (g), (h), and (j) of section 1968 of Title 18 apply with respect to a subpoena issued under this subsection. Process required by such subsections to be served upon the custodian shall be served on the Attorney General. Failure to comply with an order of the court to enforce such subpoena shall be punishable as contempt.

(3) LIMITATION—

In the case of a subpoena for which the return date is less than 5 days of service, no person shall be found in contempt for failure to comply by the return date if such person files a petition under paragraph (2) not later than 5 days after the date of service.

- (g) STATUTE OF LIMITATIONS—

A civil action under this section may not be commenced later than 10 years after the cause of action accrues.

Computer Security Act of 1987[14]

SEC. 2 PURPOSE

(a) IN GENERAL.-The Congress declares that improving the security and privacy of sensitive information in Federal computer systems is in the public interest, and hereby creates a means for establishing minimum acceptable security practices for such systems, without limiting the scope of security measures already planned or in use.

(b) SPECIFIC PURPOSES.-The purposes of this Act are—

1. by amending the Act of March 3, 1901, to assign to the National Bureau of Standards responsibility for developing standards and guidelines for Federal computer systems, including responsibility for developing standards and guidelines needed to assure the cost-effective security and privacy of sensitive information in Federal computer systems, drawing on the technical advice and assistance (including work products) of the National Security Agency, where appropriate;

2. to provide for promulgation of such standards and guidelines by amending section 111(d) of the Federal Property and Administrative Services Act of 1949;

3. to require establishment of security plans by all operators of Federal computer systems that contain sensitive information; and

4. to require mandatory periodic training for all persons involved in management, use, or operation of Federal computer systems that contain sensitive information.

Computer Fraud and Abuse Act of 1986[15]

Section 1030. Fraud and related activity in connection with computers

(a) Whoever—

1. knowingly accesses a computer without authorization or exceeds authorized access, and by means of such conduct obtains information that has been determined by the United States Government pursuant to an Executive order or statute to require protection against unauthorized disclosure for reasons of national defense or foreign relations, or any restricted data, as defined in paragraph r. of section 11 of the Atomic Energy Act of 1954, with the intent or reason to believe that such information so obtained is to be used to the injury of the United States, or to the advantage of any foreign nation;

2. intentionally accesses a computer without authorization or exceeds authorized access, and thereby obtains information contained in a financial record of a financial institution, or of a card issuer as defined in section 1602(n) of title 15, or contained in a file of a consumer reporting agency on a consumer, as such terms are defined in the Fair Credit Reporting Act (15 U.S.C. 1681 et seq.);

3. intentionally, without authorization to access any nonpublic computer of a department or agency of the United States, accesses such a computer of that department or agency that is exclusively for the use of the Government of the United States or, in the case of a computer not exclusively for such use, is used by or for the Government of the United States and such conduct affects the use of the Government's operation of such computer;

4. knowingly and with intent to defraud, accesses a Federal interest computer without authorization, or exceeds authorized access, and by means of such conduct furthers the intended fraud and obtains anything of value, unless the object of the fraud and the thing obtained consists only of the use of the computer;

5. intentionally accesses a Federal interest computer without authorization and by means of one or more instances of such conduct alters, damages, or destroys information in any such Federal interest computer, or prevents authorized use of any such computer or information, and thereby—

   (A) causes loss to one or more others of a value aggregating $1,000 or more during any one year period; or

   (B) modifies or impairs, or potentially modifies or impairs the medical examination, medical diagnosis, medical treatment, or medical care of one or more individuals; or

6. knowingly and with intent to defraud traffics (as defined in section 1029) in any password or similar information through which a computer may be accessed without authorization, if—

   (A) such trafficking affects interstate or foreign commerce; or

   (B) such computer is used by or for the Government of the United States; shall be punished as provided in subsection (c) of this section.

   (b) Whoever attempts to commit an offense under subsection (a) of this section shall be punished as provided in subsection (c) of this section.

   (c) The punishment for an offense under subsection (a) or (b) of this section is—

(1)(A) a fine under this title or imprisonment for not more than ten years, or both, in the case of an offense under subsection (a)(1) of this section which does not occur after a conviction for another offense under such subsection, or an attempt to commit an offense punishable under this subparagraph; and

   (B) a fine under this title or imprisonment for not more than twenty years, or both, in the case of an offense under subsection (a)(1) of this section which occurs after a conviction for another offense under such subsection, or an attempt to commit an offense punishable under this subparagraph; and

(2)(A) a fine under this title or imprisonment for not more than one year, or both, in the case of an offense under subsection (a)(2), (a)(3), or (a)(6) of this section which does not occur after a conviction for another offense under such subsection, or an attempt to commit an offense punishable under this subparagraph; and

   (B) a fine under this title or imprisonment for not more than ten years, or both, in the case of an offense under subsection (a)(2), (a)(3) or (a)(6) of this section which occurs after a conviction for another offense under such subsection, or an attempt to commit an offense punishable under this subparagraph; and

(3)(A) a fine under this title or imprisonment for not more than five years, or both, in the case of an offense under subsection (a)(4) or (a)(5) of this section which does not occur after a conviction for another offense under such subsection, or an attempt to commit an offense punishable under this subparagraph; and

(3)(B) a fine under this title or imprisonment for not more than ten years, or both, in the case of an offense under subsection (a)(4) or (a)(5) of this section which occurs after a conviction for another offense under such subsection, or an attempt to commit an offense punishable under this subparagraph.

(d) The United States Secret Service shall, in addition to any other agency having such authority, have the authority to investigate offenses under this section. Such authority of the United States Secret Service shall be exercised in accordance with an agreement which shall be entered into by the Secretary of the Treasury and the Attorney General.

Federal Financial Institutions Examination Council (FFIEC)[16]

The FFIEC is a formal interagency body empowered to prescribe uniform principles, standards, and report forms for the federal examination of financial institutions by the Board of Governors of the Federal Reserve System, the Federal Deposit Insurance Corporation (FDIC), the National Credit Union Administration (NCUA), the Office of the Comptroller of the Currency (OCC), and the Office of Thrift Supervision (OTS), and to make recommendations to promote uniformity in the supervision of financial institutions.

Federal Reserve System

The Federal Reserve System is the central bank of the United States. It was founded by Congress in 1913 to provide the nation with a safer, more flexible, and more stable monetary and financial system. Over the years, its role in banking and the economy has expanded.

Today, the Federal Reserve's duties fall into four general areas:

1. Conducting the nation's monetary policy by influencing the monetary and credit conditions in the economy in pursuit of maximum employment, stable prices, and moderate long-term interest rates

2. Supervising and regulating banking institutions to ensure the safety and soundness of the nation's banking and financial system, and to protect the credit rights of consumers

3. Maintaining the stability of the financial system and containing systemic risk that may arise in financial markets

4. Providing financial services to depository institutions, the U.S. government, and foreign official institutions, including playing a major role in operating the nation's payments system

Federal Deposit Insurance Corporation (FDIC)[17]

The Federal Deposit Insurance Corporation (FDIC) preserves and promotes public confidence in the U.S. financial system through the following:

- Insuring deposits in banks and thrift institutions for at least $100,000

- Identifying, monitoring, and addressing risks to the deposit insurance funds

- Limiting the effect on the economy and the financial system when a bank or thrift institution fails

An independent agency of the federal government, the FDIC was created in 1933 in response to the thousands of bank failures that occurred in the 1920s and early 1930s. Since the start of FDIC insurance on January 1, 1934, no depositor has lost a single cent of insured funds as a result of a failure.

The FDIC receives no congressional appropriations—it is funded by premiums that banks and thrift institutions pay for deposit insurance coverage and from earnings on investments in U.S. Treasury securities. With an insurance fund totaling more than $49 billion, the FDIC insures more than $3 trillion of deposits in U.S. banks and thrifts—deposits in virtually every bank and thrift in the country.

Savings, checking, and other deposit accounts, when combined, are generally insured to $250,000 per depositor in each bank or thrift the FDIC insures. Deposits held in different categories of ownership—such as single or joint accounts—may be separately insured. Also, the FDIC generally provides separate coverage for retirement accounts, such as individual retirement accounts (IRAs) and Keoghs, insured up to $250,000. The FDIC insures deposits only. It does not insure securities, mutual funds, or similar types of investments that banks and thrift institutions may offer.

The FDIC directly examines and supervises about 5,250 banks and savings banks, more than half of the institutions in the banking system. Banks can be chartered by the states or by the federal government. Banks chartered by states also have the choice of whether to join the Federal Reserve System. The FDIC is the primary federal regulator of banks that are chartered by states that do not join the Federal Reserve System. In addition, the FDIC is the backup supervisor for the remaining insured banks and thrift institutions.

To protect insured depositors, the FDIC responds immediately when a bank or thrift institution fails. Institutions generally are closed by their chartering authority—the state regulator, the Office of the Comptroller of the Currency, or the Office of Thrift Supervision. The FDIC has several options for resolving institution failures, but the one most used is to sell deposits and loans of the failed institution to another institution. Customers of the failed institution automatically become customers of the assuming institution. Most of the time, the transition is seamless from the customer's point of view.

The FDIC is managed by a five-person Board of Directors, all of whom are appointed by the president and confirmed by the Senate, with no more than three being from the same political party.

National Credit Union Administration (NCUA)[18]

The National Credit Union Administration (NCUA) is the federal agency that charters and supervises federal credit unions and insures savings in federal and most state-chartered credit unions across the country through the National Credit Union Share Insurance Fund (NCUSIF), a federal fund backed by the full faith and credit of the U.S. government.

The 1970s brought major changes in the products offered by financial institutions and credit unions found they too needed to expand their services. In 1977, legislation expanded services available to credit union members, including share certificates and mortgage lending. In 1979, a three-member board replaced the NCUA administrator. That same year Congress created the Central Liquidity Facility, the credit union lender of last resort. The 1970s were years of tremendous growth in credit unions. The number of credit union members more than doubled and assets in credit unions tripled to over $65 billion.

Deregulation, increased flexibility in merger and field-of-membership criteria, and expanded member services characterized the 1980s. High interest rates and unemployment in the early 1980s brought supervisory changes and insurance losses. With the Share Insurance Fund experiencing stress, the credit union community called on Congress to approve a plan to recapitalize the Fund.

In 1985, federally insured credit unions recapitalized the NCUSIF by depositing 1% of their shares into the Share Insurance Fund. Backed by the "full faith and credit of the United States Government," the fully capitalized National Credit Union Share Insurance Fund has "fail safe" features. Since recapitalization, the NCUA Board has only charged credit unions one premium when the Fund dropped to a 1.23% equity level in 1991.

During the 1990s and into the 21st century, credit unions have been healthy and growing. Credit union failures remain low, and the Share Insurance Fund maintains a healthy equity level.

Office of the Comptroller of the Currency (OCC)[19]

The Office of the Comptroller of the Currency (OCC) charters, regulates, and supervises all national banks. It also supervises the federal branches and agencies of foreign banks. Headquartered in Washington, D.C., the OCC has four district offices plus an office in London to supervise the international activities of national banks.

The OCC was established in 1863 as a bureau of the U.S. Department of the Treasury. The OCC is headed by the comptroller, who is appointed by the president, with the advice and consent of the Senate, for a five-year term. The comptroller also serves as a director of the Federal Deposit Insurance Corporation (FDIC) and a director of the Neighborhood Reinvestment Corporation.

The OCC's nationwide staff of examiners conducts on-site reviews of national banks and provides sustained supervision of bank operations. The agency issues rules, legal interpretations, and corporate decisions concerning banking, bank investments, bank community development activities, and other aspects of bank operations.

National bank examiners supervise domestic and international activities of national banks and perform corporate analyses. Examiners analyze a bank's loan and investment portfolios, funds management, capital, earnings, liquidity, sensitivity to market risk, and compliance with consumer banking laws, including the Community Reinvestment Act. They review the bank's internal controls, internal and external audits, and compliance with the law. They also evaluate bank management's ability to identify and control risk.

In regulating national banks, the OCC has the power to do the following:

- Examine the banks.

- Approve or deny applications for new charters, branches, capital, or other changes in corporate or banking structure.

- Take supervisory actions against banks that do not comply with laws and regulations or that otherwise engage in unsound banking practices. The agency can remove officers and directors, negotiate agreements to change banking practices, and issue cease-and-desist orders as well as civil money penalties.

- Issue rules and regulations governing bank investments, lending, and other practices.

Objectives The OCC's activities are predicated on four objectives that support the OCC's mission to ensure a stable and competitive national banking system. The following are the four objectives:

1. To ensure the safety and soundness of the national banking system

2. To foster competition by allowing banks to offer new products and services

3. To improve the efficiency and effectiveness of OCC supervision, including reducing regulatory burden

4. To ensure fair and equal access to financial services for all Americans

Office of Thrift Supervision (OTS)[20]

The Office of Thrift Supervision (OTS) is the primary federal regulator of federally chartered and state-chartered savings associations, their subsidiaries, and their registered savings and loan holding companies. OTS was established as a bureau of the U.S. Department of the Treasury on August 9, 1989, and has four regional offices located in Jersey City, Atlanta, Dallas, and San Francisco. OTS is funded by assessments and fees levied on the industry it regulates.

Canadian Laws and Acts

Personal Information Protection and Electronic Documents Act (PIPEDA)[21]

The Personal Information Protection and Electronic Documents Act (PIPEDA) is federal legislation passed in 2001 and fully implemented on January 1, 2004. Increasingly, organizations and businesses rely on personal information to connect with their customers and members. Respecting and protecting customers' and members' privacy is part of good customer and member relations.

The stated purpose of the Act is "to establish, in an era in which technology increasingly facilitates the circulation and exchange of information, rules to govern the collection, use and disclosure of personal information in a manner that recognizes the right of privacy of individuals with respect to their personal information and the need of organizations to collect, use or disclose personal information for purposes that a reasonable person would consider appropriate in the circumstances."

PIPEDA requires Canadians to:

- Obtain the clear consent of an individual before collecting, using, or disclosing personal information about that individual

- Use the information only for the purposes consented to

- Protect the information from unauthorized access and use

- Keep the information up to date and correctly filed so that decisions are based on correct information

- Destroy information when it is no longer needed for the original purpose

- Implement accountability mechanisms in their organizations to ensure compliance with the above

What Is Personal Information?

The act aims to protect information about an individual, including information such as:

- Age, name, income, ethnic origin, religion, and blood type

- Opinions, evaluations, comments, social status, and disciplinary actions

- Credit records, employment history, and medical records

Personal information does not include the name, title, business address, or telephone number of an employee of an organization. For many organizations, this means that the information collected to establish eligibility for membership, programs, donor histories, personnel files of staff, and volunteers may be considered personal information.

Principles of PIPEDA

The act is based on the following ten principles that are applied to an organization's activities:

- *Accountability*: An organization is responsible for the personal information under its control and shall designate an individual who is responsible for the organization's compliance. This chief privacy officer will understand the policies and procedures, and deal with complaints.

- *Identifying purposes*: The purposes for which the information is collected should be identified on or at the time of collection. Organizations should develop "purpose statements."

- *Consent*: The knowledge and consent of the individual are required for collection, use, or disclosure of personal information in a commercial activity. Consent can be expressed or implied. Some examples of expressed consent are:

  - An individual completes and signs a form giving consent to the collection of information for specified purposes, its use, and if it is to be disclosed.

  - A check-off box allows individuals to request their personal information not be given.

- *Limiting collection*: Information is to be collected for specific purposes and can only be used for those purposes. Information cannot be collected by misleading or deceiving individuals about the purpose for which it is intended.

- *Limiting use, disclosure, and retention of personal information*: Organizations can only use, disclose, and retain personal information for the specific purposes it was collected for and must not retain it longer than needed for those specific purposes.

- *Accuracy*: Personal information shall be accurate, complete, and up to date.

- *Safeguards*: The organization must protect personal information against loss or theft as well as unauthorized access, disclosure, copying, use, or modification. The level of security should be appropriate to the sensitivity of the information. People with access should sign confidentiality agreements. The organization should ensure the security of its computers and paper files.

- *Openness*: The organization's privacy policies must be readily available to anyone.

- *Individual access*: Individuals have the right to know what personal information about them has been collected, how it is being used, and to whom it has been disclosed, and to challenge the accuracy and completeness and have errors corrected.

- *Challenging compliance*: Individuals should be able to address any challenges concerning compliance to the organization's chief privacy officer.

European Laws and Acts

U.K.: The Civil Contingencies Act[22]

The Civil Contingencies Act, and accompanying nonlegislative measures, delivers a single framework for civil protection in the event of a major emergency in the United Kingdom. The act is separated into two parts: local arrangements for civil protection (Part 1) and emergency powers (Part 2).

Part 1

Part 1 of the act and supporting regulations establish a clear set of roles and responsibilities for those involved in emergency preparation and response at the local level. The act divides local responders into two categories, imposing a different set of duties on each.

Category 1 includes organizations at the core of the response to most emergencies, such as emergency services, local authorities, and NHS bodies. Category 1 responders are subject to the full set of civil protection duties. They are required to do the following:

- Assess the risk of emergencies occurring and use this to inform contingency planning
- Put in place emergency plans
- Put in place business continuity management arrangements
- Put in place arrangements to make information available to the public about civil protection matters and maintain arrangements to warn, inform, and advise the public in the event of an emergency
- Share information with other local responders to enhance coordination
- Cooperate with other local responders to enhance coordination and efficiency
- Provide advice and assistance to businesses and voluntary organizations about business continuity management (local authorities only)

Category 2 organizations, such as health and safety executives and transport and utility companies, are cooperating bodies less likely to be involved in the heart of planning work but will be heavily involved in incidents that affect their sector. Category 2 responders have a lesser set of duties—cooperating and sharing relevant information with other Category 1 and 2 responders.

Category 1 and 2 organizations will come together to form local resilience forums (based on police areas), which will help coordination and cooperation between responders at the local level.

Part 2

Part 2 of the act updates the 1920 Emergency Powers Act to reflect the developments in the intervening years and the current and future risk profile. It allows for the making of temporary special legislation (emergency regulations) to help deal with the most serious of emergencies. The use of emergency powers is a last-resort option, and planning arrangements at the local level should not assume that emergency powers will be made available. Their use is subject to a robust set of safeguards; they can only be deployed in exceptional circumstances.

U.K.: Data Protection Act 1998[23]

The Data Protection Act 1998 gives legal rights to individuals (data subjects) with respect to personal data processed about them by others. The act promotes a culture of openness and fairness in those who process personal data (data controllers).

According to the act, U.K. citizens have the right to:

- Ask any data controller if it holds personal information
- Ask what the information is used for
- Ask to be given a copy of the information held
- Ask whether the data controller discloses the information to others and if so to whom
- Ask the data controller to correct, erase, or destroy any incorrect data
- Ask the data controller not to use personal information for direct marketing purposes
- Ask the data controller to stop processing that causes unwarranted damage or distress
- Seek compensation if the data controller has failed to uphold this act

EU: Directive 2002/58/EC[24]

Directive 2002/58/EC forms part of the Telecoms Package, a legislative framework designed to regulate the electronic communications sector and replace the existing regulations governing the telecommunications sector.

This directive tackles a number of issues of varying degrees of sensitivity, such as the retention of connection data by the member states for police surveillance purposes (data retention), the sending of unsolicited electronic messages, the use of cookies, and the inclusion of personal data in public directories.

- *Confidentiality of communications*: The directive reiterates the basic principle that member states must, through national legislation, ensure the confidentiality of communications made over a public electronic communications network. They must in particular prohibit the listening into, tapping, and storage of communications by persons other than users without the consent of the users concerned.
- *Data retention*: On the sensitive issue of data retention, the directive stipulates that member states may withdraw the protection of data only to allow criminal investigations or to safeguard national security,

defense, and public security. Such action may be taken only where it constitutes a "necessary, appropriate and proportionate measure within a democratic society."

- *Unsolicited electronic messages (spam)*: The directive takes an "opt-in" approach to unsolicited commercial electronic communications: users must have given their prior consent before such messages are addressed to them. This opt-in system also covers SMS text messages and other electronic messages received on any fixed or mobile terminal.

- *Cookies*: Cookies are hidden information exchanged between an Internet user and a Web server, and are stored in a file on the user's hard disk. Their original purpose was to retain information between sessions. They are also a useful and much-decried tool for monitoring a user's activity. The directive stipulates that users should have the opportunity to refuse to have a cookie or similar device stored on their terminal equipment. To that end, users must also be provided with clear and precise information on the purposes and role of cookies.

- *Public directories*: European citizens will have to give prior consent in order for their telephone numbers (landline or mobile), e-mail addresses, and postal addresses to appear in public directories.

EU: Directive 95/46/EC[25]

The directive contains definitions of basic terms pertaining to the field of personal data. It stipulates rules on collection, storage, and disclosure of personal data. It also determines rules and conditions of lawful personal data processing and rights of data subjects.

Article 1

In accordance with this directive, member states shall protect the fundamental rights and freedoms of natural persons and in particular their right to privacy with respect to the processing of personal data.

Article 2

For the purposes of this directive, "personal data" shall mean any information relating to an identified or identifiable natural person ("data subject"); an identifiable person is one who can be identified, directly or indirectly, in particular by reference to an identification number or to one or more factors specific to his or her physical, physiological, mental, economic, cultural, or social identity.

Article 6

Member states shall provide that personal data must be:

- Processed fairly and lawfully
- Collected for specified, explicit, and legitimate purposes and not further processed in a way incompatible with those purposes. Further processing of data for historical, statistical, or scientific purposes shall not be considered as incompatible provided that member states provide appropriate safeguards.
- Adequate, relevant, and not excessive in relation to the purposes for which they are collected and/or further processed
- Accurate and, where necessary, kept up to date; every reasonable step must be taken to ensure that data that are inaccurate or incomplete, having regard to the purposes for which they were collected or for which they are further processed, are erased or rectified
- Kept in a form that permits identification of data subjects for no longer than is necessary for the purposes for which the data were collected or for which they are further processed. Member states shall lay down appropriate safeguards for personal data stored for longer periods for historical, statistical, or scientific use.

EU: Financial Groups Directive (FGD)[26]

The Financial Groups Directive, referenced as 2002/87/EC, has resulted in two main areas of change:

1. First, the directive requires supervisors and groups to measure the prudential soundness of groups with significant business in both the banking/investment and the insurance sectors. This helps them better assess whether the group is a prudential source of weakness to the individual firms within in it. The directive

also makes some progress toward consistency of treatment between the sectors by amending the respective banking/investment and insurance sectoral group directives.

2. The directive also introduces new requirements for conglomerates with non-EEA parents, as well as non-EEA banking and investment groups (as a result of an amendment to the Banking Consolidation Directive). For each of these third-country groups, EEA authorities must work together as appropriate to determine whether the group is subject to equivalent groupwide supervision in its home country. Where this is not the case, the FGD/BCD requires that organizations undertake worldwide group supervision themselves or apply other methods that achieve the objectives of the relevant directive.

The Foundation of Personal Data Security Law: OECD Principles

The OECD Principles state that "personal data should be protected by reasonable security safeguards against such risks as loss of unauthorized access, destruction, use, modification, or disclosure of data."

Purpose Specification Principle

When personal data are collected in a justice system, the system's purpose should be specified in writing, not later than at the time of data collection. The subsequent use must be limited to the fulfillment of those stated purposes (or other compatible purposes that are specified on each occasion of change of purpose). As well, the personal data collected should be pertinent to the stated purposes for which the information is to be used.

The purpose statements also need to address various third-party and private-sector partnerships or relationships where personal data are or will be disclosed.

For example, each component of a justice system (law enforcement/investigative systems, prosecutorial systems, defense systems, court systems, correction systems, and probation and parole systems) has a set of stated purposes for collecting information. These purposes need to be articulated and harmonized prior to the technology design and prior to the outset of data collection. With an integrated system, data can be easily reused in the future. However, the purposes for collection, by each component of a justice system, should be relatively stable.

Generally, the purpose statements should directly relate to the mandate of the relevant sector of the justice system. For example, the purpose of law enforcement agencies for collecting personal information is to investigate (suspected) criminal activity to bring suspects to trial, whereas the purpose of the court system is to process cases, provide accurate and complete information for judicial decisions, and produce dispositions for complete criminal history records. The purposes of these systems should be harmonized to provide a privacy framework governing collection, use, and reuse of personal information.

Collection Limitation Principle

There should be some limits placed on the collection of personal data. Personal data should be obtained by lawful and fair means and, where appropriate, with the knowledge or consent of the data subject. It is important to remember that the knowledge and consent rights of individuals will vary depending on their relationship (e.g., suspect, offender, victim, witness, juror, offender's family) to the justice system.

A test of relevance should also be applied (e.g., by an independent third party or as authorized in legislation) when collecting personal data on individuals without their knowledge or consent, or when the individual is not charged with a crime, i.e., under investigation, or when an investigative body is information gathering.

This principle differentiates between the knowledge and consent rights of an offender, arrestee, victim, witness, juror, offender's family, or victim's family. Special consideration must be made to limit collection of personal information on victims, witnesses, and jurors (e.g., to test their credibility). For suspects or accused persons, although broader, the collection limits should be set by the legislative framework and legal precedent. However, obtaining a person's consent to collect their personal information is generally not applicable during case investigation or prosecution.

The collector of personal information varies. In the criminal justice system, the collector is generally law enforcement. In the civil justice system, it is the court. In the criminal justice system, personal information is collected by the investigative arm on suspects and those associated with the suspects, including victims, witnesses, and family members. In addition, most parts of the justice system collect personal information on offenders and those convicted, if only as a result of the actions, utterances, and changing condition of the convicted offender. As well, personal information is generated by the workings of the justice system itself as the offender moves through the various components of the justice system.

Data Quality Principle

Personal information, to the extent necessary for stated purposes, should be accurate, complete, current, and verified. This normally assumes that the person has some means of accessing the information to ensure it is accurate and up to date.

However, in the justice system other methods are needed to ensure that the data held are accurate and up to date. Those methods can involve passive data analysis, including cross-referencing, that identifies anomalies, plus authorized human correction that could involve the data subject. Separate from privacy concerns, data management and record retention need to be addressed as part of data quality. Inaccurate personal information can have a devastating impact on the person and the integrity of proceedings within the justice system. The accountability for data quality lies with the system's information steward.

Use Limitation Principle

Personal data should not be used or disclosed for purposes other than those specified in accordance with the purpose specification principle except:

- With the consent of the data subject
- By the authority of law
- For the safety of the community, including victims and witnesses

Generally, personal information should be retained as necessary, but its use must be limited to its original purpose for collection. Use limitation, generally, is more applicable where information is disclosed outside the justice system where issues of safety, risk, and the right to know by victims are factors applied in the use limitation principle. Within the criminal justice system, with the purpose for collection stipulated in the collection limitation principle, the use limitation principle is also applicable under the exception of the authority of law, and in an integrated justice system, where various components' system use purposes have been harmonized.

A general pattern of the use of personal information suggests that within the justice system, use is determined by access authorization and by assuming the doctrine of consistent use. Compilations of legal data prepared by the private sector may result in unintended consequences for citizens exercising their right to participate in the judicial system. For example, it is not uncommon for rental or housing associations to develop databases of persons who have filed an unlawful detainer claim. These legal actions are likely to be based on a valid claim by the renter or home owner, i.e., for lack of repair. The information in the database, however, follows an individual forever and may result in denial of housing.

A third area of concern is information sharing between "closed record" states and "open record" states, where the information not available to the public in the closed record state becomes publicly available once it is shared with the open record state. This type of availability has created a market for private information gatherers to use justice system access in one state to provide nonaccessible information to parties in their home state.

These types of data gathering have privacy implications that need to be addressed up front in integrated justice systems. Managing the sale and access to justice information may be difficult given the legislative framework in some states. Ideally, the sale of information in bulk should be limited to recognized justice system purposes, and contracts for the sale of bulk information should require compliance with privacy principles.

Through a privacy impact assessment, a justice system can be reviewed by the government for the impacts of information-handling practices. Ongoing reviews are necessary as future changes increase the ability to gather and use information and as market forces control these processes.

Security Safeguards Principle

Reasonable security safeguards against risks should protect personal data against loss or unauthorized access, destruction, use, modification, or disclosure of data. These safeguards should be provided according to the sensitivity of the information and risks to all involved parties. This principle recognizes that personal information collected by the justice system is highly sensitive and a natural target for compromise.

Openness Principle

There should be a general policy of openness about developments, practices, and policies with respect to the management of personal data (apart from the actual data). Openness includes public access to the management practices of the data, except where it directly relates to an investigation or a pending or open case, or where it involves safety concerns and other factors that a government determines as necessary exemptions. Barring these exceptions, the public should be able to establish the existence and nature of personal data (apart from the actual data), and the main purposes of the data's use, as well as the identity and office of the data controller responsible for that data.

In an investigation or prosecution of an offense, established precedent and evidentiary rules will determine the openness principle or exceptions to it.

The openness principle also requires clear communication to affected individuals where justice records are requested, sold, or released to third parties. The public should be informed of when information is sold in bulk for commercial purposes.

Individual Participation Principle

Given the unique environment of the justice system. an individual, or an agent for an individual or for victims and witnesses, should have the right, except as it would compromise an investigation, case, or court proceeding:

- To obtain confirmation of whether or not the data collector has data relating to him or her
- To have communicated to him or her data relating to him or her
  - Within a reasonable time
  - At a charge, if any, that is not excessive
  - In a reasonable manner
  - In a form that is readily intelligible to him or her
- To be given reasons if a request is denied and to be able to challenge such denial
- To challenge data relating to him or her and, if the challenge is successful, to have the data erased, rectified, completed, or amended
- To provide an annotation to data where an organization decides not to amend information as requested by an individual or an agent for an individual or for victims and witnesses

Accountability Principle

Accountability should be established within each information system to ensure the development and compliance with procedures that give effect to the principles stated above. The accountable party (information steward) is an individual or a body that must preserve the meaning and integrity of the other design principles and assess their effectiveness throughout the operation of the integrated system. Roles and responsibilities of the information steward should be established by the system's key partners at the development stages of an integrated justice information system.

The accountability principle is the "due process" mechanism of the privacy design principles. An individual or his or her proxy should be able to challenge the system's compliance with any one of the privacy design principles through administrative procedures designed, implemented, and enforced by the information steward. The information steward should assure that procedures are in places that guarantee a timely, fair response to inquiries.[27]

Dutch Personal Data Protection Act

Article 2

1. This Act applies to the fully or partly automated processing of personal data, and the no automated processing of personal data entered in a file or intended to be entered therein.
2. This Act does not apply to the processing of personal data:
   a. in the course of a purely personal or household activity;
   b. by or on behalf of the intelligence or security services referred to in the Intelligence and Security Services Act;
   c. for the purposes of implementing the police tasks defined in Article 2 of the Police Act 1993;
   d. governed by or under the Municipal Database (Personal Records) Act;
   e. for the purposes of implementing the Judicial Documentation Act;
   f. for the purposes of implementing the Electoral Provisions Act;
3. This Act does not apply to the processing of personal data by the armed forces where Our Defense Minister so decides with a view to deploying or making available the armed forces to maintain or promote

the international legal order. Such a decision shall be communicated to the Data Protection Commission as quickly as possible.

Article 3

1. This Act does not apply to the processing of personal data for exclusively journalistic, artistic or literary purposes, except where otherwise provided in this Chapter and in Articles 6 to 11, 13 to 15, 25, and 49.

2. The prohibition on processing personal data referred to in Article 16 does not apply where this is necessary for the purposes referred to under (1).

Article 4

1. This Act applies to the processing of personal data carried out in the context of the activities of an establishment of a responsible party in the Netherlands.

2. This Act applies to the processing of personal data by or for responsible parties who are not established in the European Union, whereby use is made of automated or nonautomated means situated in the Netherlands, unless these means are used only for forwarding personal data.

3. The responsible parties referred to under (2) are prohibited from processing personal data, unless they designate a person or body in the Netherlands to act on their behalf in accordance with the provisions of this Act. For the purposes of application of this Act and the provisions based upon it, the said person or body shall be deemed to be the responsible party.

Article 5

1. In the case that the data subjects are minors and have not yet reached the age of sixteen, or have been placed under legal restraint or the care of a mentor, instead of the consent of the data subjects, that of their legal representative is required.

    The data subjects or their legal representative may withdraw consent at any time.

Article 6

Personal data shall be processed in accordance with the law and in a proper and careful manner.

Article 7

Personal data shall be collected for specific, explicitly defined, and legitimate purposes.

Article 8

Personal data may only be processed where:

    a. the data subject has unambiguously given his consent for the processing;

    b. the processing is necessary for the performance of a contract to which the data subject is party, or for actions to be carried out at the request of the data subject and which are necessary for the conclusion of a contract;

    c. the processing is necessary in order to comply with a legal obligation to which the responsible party is subject;

    d. the processing is necessary in order to protect a vital interest of the data subject;

    e. the processing is necessary for the proper performance of a public law duty by the administrative body concerned or by the administrative body to which the data are provided, or

    f. the processing is necessary for upholding the legitimate interests of the responsible party or of a third party, to whom the data are supplied, except where the interests or fundamental rights and freedoms of the data subject, in particular the right to protection of individual privacy, prevail.

Article 9

1. Personal data shall not be further processed in a way incompatible with the purposes for which they have been obtained.

2. For the purposes of assessing whether processing is incompatible, as referred to under (1), the responsible party shall in any case take account of the following:

   a. the relationship between the purpose of the intended processing and the purpose for which the data have been obtained;

   b. the nature of the data concerned;

   c. the consequences of the intended processing for the data subject;

   d. the manner in which the data have been obtained, and

   e. the extent to which appropriate guarantees have been put in place with respect to the data subject.

3. The further processing of personal data for historical, statistical, or scientific purposes shall not be regarded as incompatible where the responsible party has made the necessary arrangements to ensure that the further processing is carried out solely for these specific purposes.

4. The processing of personal data shall not take place where this is precluded by an obligation of confidentiality by virtue of office, profession, or legal provision.

Article 10

1. Personal data shall not be kept in a form which allows the data subject to be identified for any longer than is necessary for achieving the purposes for which they were collected or subsequently processed.

2. Personal data may be kept for longer than provided under (1), where this is for historical, statistical, or scientific purposes, and where the responsible party has made the necessary arrangements to ensure that the data concerned are used solely for these specific purposes.

Article 11

1. Personal data shall only be processed where, given the purposes for which they are collected or subsequently processed, they are adequate, relevant, and not excessive.

2. The responsible party shall take the necessary steps to ensure that personal data, given the purposes for which they are collected or subsequently processed, are correct and accurate.

Article 12

1. Anyone acting under the authority of the responsible party or the processor, as well as the processor himself, where they have access to personal data, shall only process such data on the orders of the responsible party, except where otherwise required by law.

2. The persons referred to under (1), who are not subject to an obligation of confidentiality by virtue of office, profession, or legal provision, are required to treat as confidential the personal data which comes to their knowledge, except where the communication of such data is required by a legal provision or the proper performance of their duties. Article 272(2) of the Penal Code is not applicable.

Article 13

The responsible party shall implement appropriate technical and organizational measures to secure personal data against loss or against any form of unlawful processing. These measures shall guarantee an appropriate level of security, taking into account the state of the art and the costs of implementation, and having regard to the risks associated with the processing and the nature of the data to be protected. These measures shall also aim at preventing unnecessary collection and further processing of personal data.

Article 14

1. Where responsible parties have personal data processed for their purposes by a processor, these responsible parties shall make sure that the processor provides adequate guarantees concerning the technical and organizational security measures for the processing to be carried out. The responsible parties shall make sure that these measures are complied with.

2. The carrying out of processing by a processor shall be governed by an agreement or another legal act whereby an obligation is created between the processor and the responsible party.

3. The responsible party shall make sure that the processor:

   a. processes the personal data in accordance with Article 12(l) and

   b. complies with the obligations incumbent upon the responsible party under Article 13.

4. Where the processor is established in another country of the European Union, the responsible party shall make sure that the processor complies with the laws of that other country, notwithstanding the provisions of (3)(b).

5. With a view to the keeping of proof, the parts of the agreement or legal act relating to personal data protection and the security measures referred to in Article 13, shall be set down in writing or in another equivalent form.

Article 15

The responsible party shall make sure that the obligations referred to in Articles 6 to 12 and 14(2) and (5) of this Chapter are complied with.

Article 16

It is prohibited to process personal data concerning a person's religion or philosophy of life, race, political persuasion, health and sexual life, or personal data concerning trade union membership, except as otherwise provided in this Section. This prohibition also applies to personal data concerning a person's criminal behavior, or unlawful or objectionable conduct connected with a ban imposed with regard to such conduct.

Article 17

1. The prohibition on processing personal data concerning a person's religion or philosophy of life, as referred to in Article 16, does not apply where the processing is carried out by:

   a. church associations, independent sections thereof or other associations founded on spiritual principles, provided that the data concerns persons belonging thereto;

   b. institutions founded on religious or philosophical principles, provided that this is necessary to the aims of the institutions and for the achievement of their principles, or

   c. other institutions provided that this is necessary to the spiritual welfare of the data subjects, unless they have indicated their objection thereto in writing.

2. In the cases referred to under (1)(a), the prohibition also does not apply to personal data concerning the religion or philosophy of life of family members of the data subjects provided that:

   a. the association concerned maintains regular contacts with these family members in connection with its aims, and

   b. the family members have not indicated any objection thereto in writing.

3. In the cases referred to under (1) and (2), no personal data may be supplied to third parties without the consent of the data subject.

Article 18

1. The prohibition on processing personal data concerning a person's race, as referred to in Article 16, does not apply where the processing is carried out:

   a. with a view to identifying data subjects and only where this is essential for that purpose;

   b. for the purpose of assigning a preferential status to persons from a particular ethnic or cultural minority group with a view to eradicating or reducing actual inequalities, provided that:

      i this is necessary for that purpose;

      ii the data only relate to the country of birth of the data subjects, their parents or grandparents, or to other criteria laid down by law, allowing an objective determination whether a person belongs to a minority group as referred to under (b), and

      iii the data subjects have not indicated any objection thereto in writing.

Article 19

1. The prohibition on processing personal data concerning a person's political persuasion, as referred to in Article 16, does not apply where the processing is carried out:

   a. by institutions founded on political principles with respect to their members or employees or other persons belonging to the institution, provided that this is necessary to the aims of the institutions and for the achievement of their principles, or

   b. with a view to the requirements concerning political persuasion that can reasonably be applied in connection with the performance of duties in administrative and advisory bodies.

2. In the cases referred to under (1)(a), no personal data may be supplied to third parties without the consent of the data subject.

Article 20

1. The prohibition on processing personal data concerning a person's trade union membership, as referred to in Article 16, does not apply where the processing is carried out by the trade union concerned or the trade union federation to which this trade union belongs, provided that this is necessary to the aims of the trade union or trade union federation;

2. In the cases referred to under (1), no personal data may be supplied to third parties without the consent of the data subject.

Article 21

1. The prohibition on processing personal data concerning a person's health, as referred to in Article 16, does not apply where the processing is carried out by:

   a. medical professionals, health care institutions or facilities or social services, provided that this is necessary for the proper treatment and care of the data subject, or for the administration of the institution or professional practice concerned;

   b. insurance companies as referred to in Article 1(1)(h) of the Insurance Supervision Act 1993, insurance companies as referred to in Article 1(c) of the Funeral Insurance Supervision Act, and intermediaries and subagents as referred to in Article 1(b) and (c) of the Insurance Mediation Act, provided that this is necessary for:

      i assessing the risk to be insured by the insurance company and the data subject has not indicated any objection thereto, or

      ii the performance of the insurance agreement;

   c. schools, provided that this is necessary with a view to providing special support for pupils or making special arrangements in connection with their state of health;

   d. institutions for probation, child protection or guardianship, provided that this is necessary for the performance of their legal duties;

   e. Our Minister of Justice, provided that this is necessary in connection with the implementation of prison sentences or detention measures, or

   f. administrative bodies, pension funds, employers or institutions working for them, provided that this is necessary for:

      i the proper implementation of the provisions of laws, pension regulations, or collective agreements that create rights dependent on the state of health of the data subject, or

      ii the reintegration of or support for workers or persons entitled to benefit in connection with sickness or work incapacity.

2. In the cases referred to under (1), the data may only be processed by persons subject to an obligation of confidentiality by virtue of office, profession, or legal provision, or under an agreement. Where responsible parties personally process data and are not already subject to an obligation of confidentiality by virtue of office, profession, or legal provision, they are required to treat the data as confidential, except where they are required by law or in connection with their duties to communicate such data to other parties who are authorized to process such data in accordance with (1).

3. The prohibition on processing other personal data, as referred to in Article 16, does not apply where this is necessary to supplement the processing of personal data concerning a person's health, as referred to under (1)(a), with a view to the proper treatment or care of the data subject.

4. Personal data concerning inherited characteristics may only be processed, where this processing takes place with respect to the data subject from whom the data concerned have been obtained, unless:

   a. a serious medical interest prevails, or

   b. the processing is necessary for the purpose of scientific research or statistics.

   In the case referred to under (b), Article 23(l)(a) and (2) shall likewise be applicable.

5. More detailed rules may be issued by general administrative regulation concerning the application of (1)(b) and (e).

Article 22

1. The prohibition on processing personal data concerning a person's criminal behavior, as referred to in Article 16, does not apply where the processing is carried out by bodies, charged by law with applying criminal law and by responsible parties who have obtained these data in accordance with the Police Registers Act or the Judicial Documentation Act.

2. The prohibition does not apply to responsible parties who process these data for their own purposes with a view to:

   a. assessing an application by data subjects in order to make a decision about them or provide a service to them, or

   b. protecting their interests, provided that this concerns criminal offenses that have been or, as indicated by certain facts and circumstances, can be expected to be committed against them or against persons in their service.

3. The processing of these data concerning personnel in the service of the responsible party shall take place in accordance with the rules established in compliance with the procedure referred to in the Works Councils Act.

4. The prohibition does not apply where these data are processed for the account of third parties:

   a. by responsible parties acting in accordance with a license issued under the Private Security Organizations and Investigation Bureaus Act;

   b. where these third parties are legal persons forming part of the same group, as referred to in Article 2:24(b) of the Civil Code, or

   c. where appropriate and specific guarantees have been provided and the procedure referred to in Article 31 has been followed.

5. The prohibition on processing other personal data, as referred to in Article 16, does not apply where this is necessary to supplement the processing of data on criminal behavior, for the purposes for which these data are being processed.

6. The provisions of (2) to (5) are likewise applicable to personal data relating to a ban imposed by a court concerning unlawful or objectionable conduct.

7. Rules may be issued by general administrative regulation concerning the appropriate and specific guarantees referred to under (4)(c).

Article 23

1. Without prejudice to Articles 17 to 22, the prohibition on processing personal data referred to in Article 16 does not apply where:

   a. this is carried out with the express consent of the data subject;

   b. the data have manifestly been made public by the data subject;

   c. this is necessary for the establishment, exercise, or defense of a right in law;

d. this is necessary to comply with an obligation of international public law, or

e. this is necessary with a view to an important public interest, where appropriate guarantees have been put in place to protect individual privacy and this is provided for by law or else the Data Protection Commission has granted an exemption. When granting an exemption, the Commission can impose rules and restrictions.

2. The prohibition on the processing of personal data referred to in Article 16 for the purpose of scientific research or statistics does not apply where:

a. the research serves a public interest,

b. the processing is necessary for the research or statistics concerned,

c. it appears to be impossible or would involve a disproportionate effort to ask for express consent, and

d. sufficient guarantees are provided to ensure that the processing does not adversely affect the individual privacy of the data subject to a disproportionate extent.

3. Processing referred to under (1)(e) must be notified to the European Commission. This notification shall be made by Our Minister concerned where the processing is provided for by law. The Data Protection Commission shall make the notification in the case that it has granted an exemption for the processing.

Article 24

1. A number that is required by law for the purposes of identifying a person may only be used for the processing of personal data in execution of the said law or for purposes stipulated by the law.

2. Cases other than those referred to under (1) can be designated by general administrative regulation in which a number to be indicated in this connection, as referred to under (1), can be used. More detailed rules may be laid down in this connection concerning the use of such a number.[28]

Austrian Federal Act Concerning the Protection of Personal Data

Section 1: Fundamental Right to Data Protection

1. Everybody shall have the right to secrecy for the personal data concerning him, especially with regard to his private and family life, insofar as he has an interest deserving such protection. Such an interest is precluded when data cannot be subject to the right to secrecy due to their general availability or because they cannot be traced back to the data subject.

2. Insofar as personal data is not used in the vital interest of the data subject or with his consent, restrictions to the right to secrecy are only permitted to safeguard overriding legitimate interests of another, namely in case of an intervention by a public authority the restriction shall only be permitted based on laws necessary for the reasons stated in Art. 8, Para. 2 of the European Convention on Human Rights (Federal Law Gazette No. 210/1958). Such laws may provide for the use of data that deserve special protection only in order to safeguard substantial public interests and shall provide suitable safeguards for the protection of the data subjects' interest in secrecy. Even in the case of permitted restrictions the intervention with the fundamental right shall be carried out using only the least intrusive of all effective methods.

3. Everybody shall have, insofar as personal data concerning him are destined for automated processing or manual processing, i.e. in filing systems without automated processing, as provided for by law,

a the right to obtain information as to who processes what data concerning him, where the data originated, for which purpose they are used, as well as to whom the data are transmitted;

b the right to rectification of incorrect data and the right to erasure of illegally processed data.

4. Restrictions of the rights according to para. 3 are only permitted under the conditions laid out in para. 2.

5. The fundamental right to data protection, except the right to information, shall be asserted before the civil courts against organizations that are established according to private law, as long as they do not act in execution of laws. In all other cases the Data Protection Commission shall be competent to render the decision, unless an act of Parliament or a judicial decision is concerned.

Section 2: Legislative Power and Enforcement

1. The Federation shall have power to pass laws concerning the protection of personal data that are automatically processed.

2. The Federation shall have power to execute such federal laws. Insofar as such data are used by a State, on behalf of a State, by or on behalf of legal persons established by law within the powers of the States these Federal Acts shall be executed by the States unless the execution has been entrusted by federal law to the Data Protection Commission, the Data Protection Council, or the courts.

Section 3: Territorial Jurisdiction

1. The provisions of this Federal Act shall be applied to the use of personal data in Austria. This Federal Act shall also be applied to the use of data outside of Austria, insofar as the data is used in other Member States of the European Union for purposes of a main establishment or branch establishment (sect. 4 subpara. 15) in Austria of the controller (sect. 4 subpara. 4).

2. Deviating from para. 1 the law of the state where the controller has its seat applies, when a controller of the private sector (sect. 5 para. 3), whose seat is in another Member State of the European Union, uses personal data in Austria for a purpose that cannot be ascribed to any of the controller's establishments in Austria.

3. Furthermore, this law shall not be applied insofar as data are only transmitted through Austrian territory.

4. Legal provisions deviating from paras. 1 to 3 shall be permissible only in matters not subject to the jurisdiction of the European Union.

Section 5: Public and Private Sector

1. Data applications shall be imputed to the public sector according to this Federal Act if they are undertaken for purposes of a controller of the public sector (p. 2).

2. Public sector controllers are all those controllers who

   a. Are established according to public law legal structures, in particular also as an organ of a territorial corporate body, or

   b. As far as they execute laws despite having been incorporated according to private law.

3. Controllers not within the scope of para. 2 are considered controllers of the private sector according to this Federal Act.

Section 14: Data Security Measures

1. Measures to ensure data security shall be taken by all organizational units of a controller or processor that use data. Depending on the kind of data used as well as the extent and purpose of the use and considering the state of technical possibilities and economic justifiability it shall be ensured that the data are protected against accidental or intentional destruction or loss, that they are properly used and are not accessible to unauthorized persons.

2. In particular, the following measures are to be taken insofar as this is necessary with regard to the last sentence of para. 1:

   a. the distribution of functions between the organizational units as well as the operatives regarding the use of data shall be laid down expressly,

   b. the use of data must be tied to valid orders of the authorized organizational units or operatives,

   c. every operative is to be instructed about his duties according to this Federal Act and the internal data protection regulations, including data security regulations,

   d. the right of access to the premises of the data controller or processor is to be regulated,

   e. the right of access to data and programs is to be regulated as well as the protection of storage media against access and use by unauthorized persons,

   f. the right to operate the data processing equipment is to be laid down and every device is to be secured against unauthorized operation by taking precautions for the machines and programs used,

g. logs shall be kept in order that the processing steps that were actually performed, in particular modifications, consultations and transmissions, can be traced to the extent necessary with regard to their permissibility,

h. documentation shall be kept on the measures taken pursuant to subparas. 1 to 7 to facilitate control and conservation of evidence.

These measures must, taking into account the technological state of the art and the cost incurred in their execution, safeguard a level of data protection appropriate with regard to the risks arising from the use and the type of data to be protected.

3. Unregistered transmissions from data applications subject to an obligation to grant information pursuant to sect. 26 shall be logged in such a manner that the right of information can be granted to the subject pursuant to sect. 26. Transmissions provided for in the standard ordinance (sect. 17 para. 2 lit. 6) and the model ordinance (sect. 19 para. 2) do not require logging.

4. Logs and documentation data may not be used for purposes that are incompatible with the purpose of the collection - viz., monitoring the legitimacy of the use of the logged and documented data files. In particular, any further use for the purpose of supervising the data subjects whose data is contained in the logged data files, as well as for the purpose of monitoring the persons who have accessed the logged data files, or for any purpose other than checking access rights shall be considered incompatible, unless the data is used is for the purpose of preventing or prosecuting a crime according to sect. 278a StGB13 (criminal organization) or a crime punishable with a maximum sentence of more than five years imprisonment.

5. Unless expressly provided for otherwise by law, logs and documentation data shall be kept for three years. Deviations from this rule shall be permitted to the same extent that the logged or documented data files may legitimately be erased earlier or kept longer.

6. Data security regulations are to be issued and kept available in such a manner that the operatives can inform themselves about the regulations to which they are subject at any time.

Section 15: Confidentiality of Data

1. Controllers, processors and their operatives—these being the employees and persons comparable to employees—shall keep data from uses of data confidential that have been entrusted or made accessible to them solely for professional reasons, without prejudice to other professional obligations of confidentiality, unless a legitimate reason exists for the transmission of the entrusted or accessed data (confidentiality of data).

2. Operatives shall transmit data only if expressly ordered to do so by their employer. Controllers and processors shall oblige their operatives by contract, insofar as they are not already obliged by law, to transmit data from uses of data only if so ordered and to adhere to the confidentiality of data even after the end of their professional relationship with the controller or processor.

3. Controllers and processors may only issue orders for the transmission of data if this is permitted pursuant to the provisions of this Federal Act. They shall inform the operatives affected by these orders about the transmission orders in force and about the consequences of a violation of data confidentiality.

4. Without prejudice to the constitutional right to issue instructions, a refusal to follow an order to transmit data on the grounds that it violates the provisions of this Federal Act shall not be to the operatives' detriment.[29]

German Federal Data Protection Act

Section 1: Purpose and Scope

1. The purpose of this Act is to protect the individual against his right to privacy being impaired through the handling of his personal data.

2. This Act shall apply to the collection, processing, and use of personal data by

   1. public bodies of the Federation,

2. public bodies of the Lander insofar as data protection is not governed by Land legislation and insofar as they:

   a. execute federal law or

   b. act as bodies of the judicature and are not dealing with administrative matters,

3. private bodies insofar as they process or use data in or from data files in the normal course of business or for professional or commercial purposes.

   3. There shall be the following restrictions to the application of this Act:

      1. Sections 5 and 9 only of this Act shall apply to automated data files that are temporarily set up exclusively for reasons of processing and are automatically erased after processing.

      2. Sections 5, 9, 39, and 40 only of this Act shall apply to nonautomated data files in which the personal data are not intended for communication to third parties. Furthermore, the regulations on the processing and use of personal data in records shall apply to the data files of public bodies. If personal data are communicated in a particular case, the provisions of this Act shall apply without restriction.

4. Insofar as other legal provisions of the Federation are applicable to personal data, including their publication, such provisions shall take precedence over the provisions of this Act. This shall not affect the duty to observe the legal obligation of maintaining secrecy, or professional or special official confidentiality not based on legal provisions.

5. The provisions of this Act shall take precedence over those of the Administrative Procedures Act insofar as personal data are processed in ascertaining the facts.

Section 2: Public and Private Bodies

1. "Public bodies of the Federation" mean the authorities, the bodies of the judicature, and other public-law institutions of the Federation, of the federal corporations, establishments, and foundations under public law as well as of their associations irrespective of their legal structure. The enterprises established by law out of the Special Fund of the German Federal Postal Administration are to be considered as public bodies, as long as they have an exclusive right according to the Postal Administration Law or the Telecommunication Installations Act.

2. "Public bodies of the Lander" means the authorities, the bodies of the judicature and other public-law institutions of a Land, of a municipality, an association of municipalities or other legal persons under public law subject to Land supervision as well as of their associations irrespective of their legal structure.

3. Private-law associations of public bodies of the Federation and the Lander performing public administration duties shall be regarded as public bodies of the Federation, irrespective of private shareholdings, if

   1. they operate beyond the territory of a Land or

   2. the Federation possesses the absolute majority of shares or votes.

   Otherwise they shall be regarded as public bodies of the Lander.

4. "Private bodies" means natural or legal persons, companies and other private-law associations insofar as they are not covered by paragraphs 1 to 3 above. To the extent that a private body performs sovereign public administration duties, it shall be treated as a public body for the purposes of this Act.

Section 4: Admissibility of Data Processing and Use

1. The processing and use of personal data shall be admissible only if this Act or any other legal provision permits or prescribes them or if the data subject has consented.

2. When consent is obtained from the data subject, he shall be informed of the purpose of storage and of any envisaged communication of his data and, at his request, of the consequences of withholding consent. Consent shall be given in writing unless special circumstances warrant any other form. If consent is to be given together with other written declarations, the declaration of consent shall be made distinguishable in its appearance.

3. In the field of scientific research, a special circumstance pursuant to the second sentence of paragraph 2 above shall also be deemed to exist where the defined purpose of research would be impaired considerably

if consent were obtained in writing. In such case the information pursuant to the first sentence of paragraph 2 above and the reasons from which considerable impairment of the defined purpose of research would arise shall be recorded in writing.

Section 5: Confidentiality

Persons employed in data processing shall not process or use personal data without authorization (confidentiality). On taking up their duties such persons, insofar as they work for private bodies, shall be required to give an undertaking to maintain such confidentiality. This undertaking shall continue to be valid after termination of their activity.

Section 7: Compensation by Public Bodies

1. Where a public body causes harm to the data subject through automated processing of his personal data that is inadmissible or incorrect under the provisions of this Act or other data protection provisions, such body is obliged to compensate the data subject for the harm thus caused, irrespective of any fault.

2. In grave cases of violation of privacy, the data subject shall receive adequate pecuniary compensation for the immaterial harm caused.

3. The claims under paragraphs 1 and 2 above shall be limited to a total amount of DM 250,000. Where, due to the same occurrence, compensation has to be paid to several persons and exceeds the maximum amount of DM 250,000, the compensation paid to each of them shall be reduced in proportion to the maximum amount.

4. If, in the case of a data file, several bodies are entitled to store the data and the injured person is unable to ascertain the controller of the data file, each body shall be liable.

5. Where several parties are responsible they shall be jointly and severally liable.

6. Sections 254 and 852 of the Civil Code shall apply mutatis mutandis to contributory negligence on the part of the data subject and to statutory limitation.

7. Provisions according to which a party responsible is liable to a greater extent than under this provision or according to which another person is responsible for the harm shall remain unaffected.

8. Recourse may be had to ordinary courts of law.

Section 8: Compensation by Private Bodies

If a data subject asserts a claim against a private body for compensation because of automated data processing that is inadmissible or incorrect under this Act or other data protection provisions and if it is disputed whether the harm caused results from a circumstance for which the controller of the data file is responsible, the burden of proof shall rest with the controller of the data file.

Section 9: Technical and Organizational Measures

Public and private bodies processing personal data either on their own behalf or on behalf of others shall take the technical and organizational measures necessary to ensure the implementation of the provisions of this Act, in particular the requirements set out in the annex to this Act. Measures shall be required only if the effort involved is reasonable in relation to the desired level of protection.

Section 14: Storage, Modification, and Use of Data

1. The storage, modification, or use of personal data shall be admissible where it is necessary for the performance of the duties of the controller of the data file and if it serves the purposes for which the data were collected. If there has been no preceding collection, the data may be modified or used only for the purposes for which they were stored.

2. Storage, modification, or use for other purposes shall be admissible only if

   1. a legal provision prescribes or peremptorily presupposes this,

   2. the data subject has consented,

   3. it is evident that this is in the interest of the data subject and there is no reason to assume that he would withhold consent if he knew of such other purpose,

4. particulars supplied by the data subject have to be checked because there are actual indications that they are incorrect,

5. the data can be taken from generally accessible sources or the controller of the data file would be entitled to publish them, unless the data subject clearly has an overriding legitimate interest in excluding the change of purpose,

6. this is necessary to avert substantial detriment to the common weal or any other immediate threat to public safety,

7. this is necessary to prosecute criminal or administrative offences, to implement sentences or measures as defined in section 11 (1), No. 8 of the Penal Code or reformatory or disciplinary measures as defined in the Youth Courts Act, or to execute decisions imposing administrative fines,

8. this is necessary to avert a grave infringement of another person's rights, or

9. this is necessary for the conduct of scientific research; scientific interest in conduct of the research project substantially outweighs the interest of the data subject in excluding the change of purpose, and the research purpose cannot be attained by other means or can be attained thus only with disproportionate effort.

3. Processing or use for other purposes shall not be deemed to occur if this serves the exercise of powers of supervision or control, the execution of auditing or the conduct of organizational studies for the controller of the data file. This shall also apply to processing or use for training and examination purposes by the controller of the data file, unless the data subject has overriding legitimate interests.

4. Personal data stored exclusively for the purpose of monitoring data protection, safeguarding data, or ensuring proper operation of a data processing system may be used exclusively for such purposes.

Section 16: Communication of Data to Private Bodies

1. The communication of personal data to private bodies shall be admissible if

   1. this is necessary for the performance of the duties of the communicating body and the requirements of section 14 of this Act are met or

   2. the recipient credibly proves a justified interest in knowledge of the data to be communicated and the data subject does not have a legitimate interest in excluding their communication.

2. Responsibility for the admissibility of communication shall rest with the communicating body.

3. In cases of communication under paragraph 1, No. 2 above, the communicating body shall inform the data subject of the communication of his data. This shall not apply if it can be assumed that he will acquire knowledge of such communication in another manner or if such information would jeopardize public safety or otherwise be detrimental to the Federation or a Land.

4. The recipient may process or use the communicated data only for the purpose for which they were communicated to him. The communicating body shall point this out to the recipient. Processing or use for other purposes shall be admissible if communication under paragraph 1 above would be admissible and the communicating body has consented.

Section 24: Monitoring by the Federal Commissioner for Data Protection

1. The Federal Commissioner for Data Protection shall monitor compliance with the provisions of this Act and other data Protection provisions by public bodies of the Federation. Where personal data in records are processed or used, the Federal Commissioner shall monitor their collection, processing, or use if the data subject adequately indicates that his rights have been infringed in this respect or if the Federal Commissioner has in his possession adequate indications of such infringement.

2. Monitoring by the Federal Commissioner shall also extend to personal data subject to professional or special official secrecy, especially tax secrecy under section 30 of the Tax Code. In the case of the Federal Authorities within the meaning of section 2 para. (1) Sentence 2, the mail and telecommunication secrecy (Section 10 Basic Law) shall be restricted, as long as it is necessary for the exercise of supervision of the controller of the data file. Except as provided in No. 1 below, the right of monitoring shall not extend to the contents of posts and telecommunications. The following shall not be subject to monitoring by the Federal Commissioner:

1. personal data subject to monitoring by the commission set up under section 9 of the Act Implementing Article 10 of the Basic Law, unless the commission requests the Federal Commissioner to monitor compliance with data protection provisions in connection, with specific procedures or in specific areas and to report thereon exclusively to it, and

   a. personal data subject to privacy of posts and telecommunications under article 10 of the Basic Law,

   b. personal data subject to medical privacy, and

   c. personal data in personnel or vetting records.

   If the data subject objects in a particular case vis-à-vis the Federal Commissioner for Data Protection to the monitoring of data relating to him. Without prejudice to the Federal Commissioner's right of monitoring, the public body shall inform data subjects in a general form of their right of objection.

3. Federal courts shall be subject to monitoring by the Federal Commissioner only where they deal with administrative matters.

4. Public bodies of the Federation shall be obliged to support the Federal Commissioner and his assistants in the performance of their duties. In particular they shall be granted

   1. information in reply to their questions as well as the opportunity to inspect all documents and records, especially stored data and data processing programs, connected with the monitoring referred to in paragraph 1 above,

   2. access to all official premises at any time.

   The authorities referred to in sections 6 (2) and 19 (3) of this Act shall afford support exclusively to the Federal Commissioner himself and the assistants appointed by him in writing. The second sentence above shall not apply to such authorities where the supreme federal authority establishes in a particular case that such information or inspection would jeopardize the security of the Federation or a Land.

5. The Federal Commissioner shall inform the public body of the results of his monitoring. He may combine them with proposals for improving data protection, especially for rectifying irregularities discovered in the processing or use of personal data. Section 25 of this Act shall remain unaffected.

6. Paragraph 2 above shall apply mutatis mutandis to public bodies responsible for monitoring compliance with data protection provisions in the Lander.

Section 28: Storage, Communication, and Use of Data for Own Purposes

1. The storage, modification, or communication of personal data or their use as a means of fulfilling one's own business purposes shall be admissible

   1. in accordance with the purposes of a contract or a quasicontractual fiduciary relationship with the data subject,

   2. insofar as this is necessary to safeguard justified interests of the controller of the data file and there is no reason to assume that the data subject has an overriding legitimate interest in his data being excluded from processing or use,

   3. if the data can be taken from generally accessible sources or the controller of the data file would be entitled to publish them, unless the data subject clearly has an overriding legitimate interest in his data being excluded from processing or use,

   4. if this is necessary in the interest of the controller of the data file for the conduct of scientific research, if scientific interest in conduct of the research project substantially outweighs the interest of the data subject in excluding the change of purpose and if the research purpose cannot be attained by other means or can be attained thus only with disproportionate effort.

   The data must be obtained fairly and lawfully.

2. Communication or use shall also be admissible

   1. insofar as this is necessary to safeguard justified interests of a third party or public interests or

   2. if the data, compiled in lists or otherwise combined, concern members of a group of persons and are restricted to

      - the data subject's membership of this group of persons,

      - occupation or type of business,

- name,
- title,
- academic degrees,
- address,
- year of birth

And if there is no reason to assume that the data subject has a legitimate interest in his data being excluded from communication. In the cases under (b) above it can generally be assumed that such interest exists where data are to be communicated which were stored for the purposes of a contract or a quasi-contractual fiduciary relationship and which concern

- health matters,
- criminal offences,
- administrative offences,
- religious or political views and
- when communicated by the employer, to the legal status under labor law or if this is necessary in the interest of a research institute for the conduct of scientific research, if scientific interest in conduct of the research project substantially outweighs the interest of the data subject in excluding the change of purpose and if the research purpose cannot be attained by other means or can be attained thus only with disproportionate effort.

3. If the data subject objects vis-à-vis the controller of the data file to the use or communication of his data for purposes of advertising or of market or opinion research, use or communication for such purposes shall be inadmissible. Where the data subject objects vis-à-vis the recipient of data communicated under paragraph 2 above to processing or use for purposes of advertising or of market or opinion research, the recipient shall block the data for such purposes.

4. The recipient may process or use the communicated data for the purpose for which they were communicated to him. Processing or use for other purposes shall be admissible only if the requirements of paragraphs 1 and 2 above are met. The communicating body shall point this out to the recipient.

Section 29: Storage of Data in the Normal Course of Business for the Purpose of Communication

1. The storage or modification of personal data in the normal course of business for the purpose of communication shall be admissible if

    1. there is no reason to assume that the data subject has a legitimate interest in his data being excluded from storage or modification or

    2. the data can be taken from generally accessible sources or the controller of the data file would be entitled to publish them, unless the data subject clearly has an overriding legitimate interest in his data being excluded from use or processing.
    The second sentence of section 28 (1) of this Act shall apply.

2. Communication shall be admissible if

    a the recipient credibly proves a justified interest in knowledge of the data or

    b the data pursuant to Section 28 (2), No. 1 (b) of this Act have been compiled in lists or otherwise combined and are to be communicated for purposes of advertising or of market or opinion research and

    c there is no reason to assume that the data subject has a legitimate interest in his data being excluded from communication.
    The second sentence of Section 28 (2), No. 1 of this Act shall apply mutatis mutandis. In the case of communication under No. 1 (a) above, the reasons for the existence of a justified interest and the means of credibly presenting them shall be recorded by the communicating body. In the case of communication through automated retrieval, such recording shall be required of the recipient.

3. Section 28 (3) and (4) of this Act shall apply to the processing or use of communicated data.

Section 30: Storage of Data in the Normal Course of Business for the Purpose of Communication in Depersonalized Form

1. If personal data are stored in the normal course of business in order to communicate them in depersonalized form, the characteristics enabling information concerning personal or material circumstances to be attributed to an identified or identifiable individual shall be stored separately. Such characteristics may be combined with the information only where necessary for storage or scientific purposes.

2. The modification of personal data shall be admissible if

   1. there is no reason to assume that the data subject has a legitimate interest in his data being excluded from modification or

   2. the data can be taken from generally accessible sources or the controller of the data file would be entitled to publish them, unless the data subject clearly has an overriding legitimate interest in his data being excluded from modification.

3. Personal data shall be erased if their storage is inadmissible.

4. Sections 29, 33 to 35 of this Act shall not apply.

Section 32: Obligatory Registration

1. Bodies which in the normal course of business

   1. store personal data for the purpose of communication,

   2. store personal data for the purpose of depersonalized communication, or

   3. are commissioned to process or use personal data as a service enterprise

   As well as their branches and dependent offices shall notify the commencement and termination of their activities to the relevant supervisory authority within one month.

2. Upon registration, the following particulars shall be supplied for the register kept by the supervisory authority:

   1. name or title of the body,

   2. owners, managing boards, managing directors, or other lawfully, or Constitutionally appointed managers and the persons placed in charge of data processing,

   3. address,

   4. business purposes of the body and of data processing,

   5. name of the data protection officer,

   6. general description of the type of personal data stored. This information shall not be required in the case of paragraph 1, No. 3, above.

3. Upon registration, the following particulars that shall not be included in the register shall also be supplied:

   1. type of data processing systems used,

   2. in the event of regular communication of personal data, the recipients and type of data communicated.

4. Paragraph 1 above shall apply mutatis mutandis to the change of particulars supplied in accordance with paragraphs 2 and 3 above.

5. The supervisory authority may determine in a particular case which particulars have to be supplied in accordance with paragraph 2, Nos. 4 and 6, paragraph 3 and paragraph 4 above. The effort connected with the supply of these particulars must be in reasonable proportion to their significance for monitoring by the supervisory authority.

Section 33: Notification of the Data Subject

1. If personal data are stored for the first time for one's own purposes, the data subject shall be notified of such storage and of the type of data. If personal data are stored in the normal course of business for the purpose of communication, the data subject shall be notified of their initial communication and of the type of data communicated.

2. Notification shall not be required if

   1. the data subject has received knowledge by other means of the storage or communication of the data,

   2. the data are stored merely because they may not be erased due to legal, statutory, or contractual provisions on their preservation or exclusively serve purposes of data security or data protection control,

   3. the data must be kept secret in accordance with a legal provision or by virtue of their nature, in particular on account of an overriding legal interest of a third party,

   4. the relevant public body has stated to the controller of the data file that publication of the data would jeopardize public safety or order or would otherwise be detrimental to the Federation or a Land,

   5. the data are stored in a data file which is kept only temporarily and is erased within three months of being set up,

   6. the data are stored for one's own purposes

      a. are taken from generally accessible sources or

      b. notification would considerably impair the business purposes of the controller of the data file, unless the interest in notification outweighs such impairment, or

   7. the data are stored in the normal course of business for the purpose of communication and

      a. are taken from generally accessible sources insofar as they relate to those persons who published these data or

      b. the data are compiled in lists or otherwise combined (section 29 (2), No. 1 (b) of this Act).

Section 35: Correction, Erasure, and Blocking of Data

1. Incorrect personal data shall be corrected.

2. Apart from the cases mentioned in paragraph 3, Nos. 1 and 2, below, personal data may be erased at any time. They shall be erased if

   1. their storage is inadmissible,

   2. they relate to health matters, criminal offences, administrative offences as well as religious or political views and the controller of the data file cannot prove that they are correct,

   3. they are processed for one's own purposes, as soon as knowledge of them is no longer needed for fulfilling the purpose for which they are stored, or

   4. they are processed in the normal course of business for the purpose of communication and an examination five calendar years after their first being stored shows that further storage is not necessary.

3. Instead of erasure, personal data shall be blocked insofar as

   1. in the case of paragraph 2, No. 3 or 4 above, preservation periods prescribed by law, statutes, or contracts rule out any erasure,

   2. there is reason to assume that erasure would impair legitimate interests of the data subject, or

   3. erasure is not possible or is only possible with disproportionate effort due to the specific type of storage.

4. Personal data shall also be blocked if the data subject disputes that they are correct and it cannot be ascertained whether they are correct or incorrect.

5. Where they are stored in the normal course of business for the purpose of communication, personal data which are incorrect or whose correctness is disputed need not be corrected, blocked, or erased except in the cases mentioned in paragraph 2, No. 2 above, if they are taken from generally accessible sources and are stored for documentation purposes. At the request of the data subject, his counterstatement shall be added to the data for the duration of their storage. The data may not be communicated without this counterstatement.

6. If necessary to protect legitimate interests of the data subject, the correction of incorrect data, the blocking of disputed data, and the erasure or blocking of data due to inadmissible storage shall be notified to the bodies to which these data are transmitted for storage within the framework of regular data communication.

7. Blocked data may be communicated or used without the consent of the data subject only if

1. this is indispensable for scientific purposes, for use as evidence, or for other reasons in the overriding interests of the controller of the data file or a third party and

2. communication or use of the data for this purpose would be admissible if they were not blocked.

Section 36: Appointment of a Data Protection Officer

1. Private bodies which process personal data automatically and regularly employ at least five permanent employees for this purpose shall appoint in writing a data protection officer within one month of the commencement of their activities. The same shall apply where personal data are processed by other means and at least 20 persons are permanently employed for this purpose.

2. Only persons who possess the specialized knowledge and demonstrate the reliability necessary for the performance of the duties concerned may be appointed data protection officer.

3. The data protection officer shall be directly subordinate to the owner, managing board, managing director, or other lawfully or Constitutionally appointed manager. He shall be free to use his specialized knowledge in the area of data protection at his own discretion. He shall suffer no disadvantage through the performance of his duties. The appointment of a data protection officer may only be revoked at the request of the supervisory authority or by section 626 of the Civil Code being applied mutatis mutandis.

4. The data protection officer shall be bound to maintain secrecy on the identity of the data subject and on circumstances permitting conclusions to be drawn about the data subject, unless he is released from this obligation by the data subject.

5. The private body shall support the data protection officer in the performance of his duties and in particular, to the extent needed for such performance, make available assistants as well as premises, furnishings, equipment, and other resources.

Section 37: Duties of the Data Protection Officer

1. The data protection officer shall be responsible for ensuring that this Act and other provisions concerning data protection are observed. For this purpose he may apply to the supervisory authority in cases of doubt. In particular he shall

1. monitor the proper use of data processing programs with the aid of which personal data are to be processed; for this purpose he shall be informed in good time of projects for automatic processing of personal data;

2. take suitable steps to familiarize the persons employed in the processing of personal data with the provisions of this Act and other provisions concerning data protection, with particular reference to the situation prevailing in this area and the special data protection requirements arising therefrom;

3. assist and advise in the selection of persons to be employed in the processing of personal data.

2. The data protection officer shall receive from the private body a list on

1. data processing systems used,

2. designation and type of data files,

3. type of data stored,

4. business purposes, the fulfillments of which necessitate knowledge of these data,

5. their regular recipients,

6. groups of persons entitled to access or persons exclusively entitled to access.

3. Paragraph 2, Nos. 2 to 6 above shall not apply to data files that are kept only temporarily and are erased within three months of being set up.

Section 38: Supervisory Authority

1. The supervisory authority shall check in a particular case that this Act and other data protection provisions governing the processing or use of personal data in or from data files are observed if it possesses sufficient indications that any such provision has been violated by private bodies, especially if the data subject himself submits evidence to this effect.

2. If personal data are in the normal course of business

   1. stored for the purpose of communication,

   2. stored for the purpose of depersonalized communication or

   3. processed by service enterprises commissioned to do so,

   The supervisory authority shall monitor observance of this Act or other data protection provisions governing the processing or use of personal data in or from data files. The supervisory authority shall keep a register in accordance with section 32 (2) of this Act. The register shall be open to inspection by any person.

3. The bodies subject to monitoring and the persons responsible for their management shall provide the supervisory authority on request and without delay with the information necessary for the performance of its duties. A person obliged to provide information may refuse to do so where he would expose himself or one of the persons designated in section 383 (1), Nos. 1 to 3, of the Code of Civil Procedure to the danger of criminal prosecution or of proceedings under the Administrative Offenses Act. This shall be pointed out to the person obliged to provide information.

4. The persons appointed by the supervisory authority to exercise monitoring shall be authorized, insofar as necessary for the performance of the duties of the supervisory authority, to enter the property and premises of the body during business hours and to carry out checks and inspections there. They may inspect business documents, especially the list under section 37 (2) of this Act as well as the stored personal data and the data processing programs. Section 24 (6) of this Act shall apply mutatis mutandis. The person obliged to provide information shall permit such measures.

5. To guarantee data protection under this Act and other data protection provisions governing the processing or use of personal data in or from data files, the supervisory authority may instruct that, within the scope of the requirements set out in section 9 of this Act, measures be taken to rectify technical or organizational irregularities discovered. In the event of grave irregularities of this kind, especially where they are connected with a specific impairment of privacy, the supervisory authority may prohibit the use of particular procedures if the irregularities are not rectified within a reasonable period contrary to the instruction pursuant to the first sentence above and despite the imposition of a fine. The supervisory authority may demand the dismissal of the data protection officer if he does not possess the specialized knowledge and demonstrate the reliability necessary for the performance of his duties.

6. The Land governments or the bodies authorized by them shall designate the supervisory authorities responsible for monitoring the implementation of data protection within the area of application of this Part.

7. The Industrial Code shall continue to apply to commercial firms subject to the provisions of this Part.

Section 39: Limited Use of Personal Data Subject to Professional or Special Official Secrecy

1. Personal data that are subject to professional or special official secrecy and that have been supplied by the body bound to secrecy in the performance of its professional or official duties may be processed or used by the controller of the data file only for the purpose for which he has received them. In the event of communication to a private body, the body bound to secrecy must give its consent.

2. The data may be processed or used for another purpose only if the change of purpose is permitted by special legislation.

Section 40: Processing and Use of Personal Data by Research Institutes

1. Personal data collected or stored for scientific research purposes may be processed or used only for such purposes.

2. The communication of personal data to other than public bodies for scientific research purposes shall be admissible only if these undertake not to process or use the communicated data for other purposes and to comply with the provisions of paragraph 3 below.

3. The personal data shall be depersonalized as soon as the research purpose permits this. Until such time the characteristics enabling information concerning personal or material circumstances to be attributed to an identified or identifiable individual shall be stored separately. They may be combined with the information only to the extent required by the research purpose.

4. Bodies conducting scientific research may publish personal data only if

    1. the data subject has consented or

    2. this is indispensable for the presentation of research findings on contemporary events.

Section 43: Criminal Offenses

1. Anyone who, without authorization,

    1. stores, modifies, or communicates,

    2. makes available for automatic retrieval, or

    3. retrieves or obtains for himself or for others from data files

    Any personal data protected by this Act that are not common knowledge shall be punished by imprisonment for up to one year or by a fine.

2. Likewise punishable shall be anyone who

    1. obtains by means of incorrect information the communication of personal data protected by this Act which are not common knowledge,

    2. contrary to the first sentence of section 16 (4), the first sentence of section 28 (4), also in conjunction with section 29 (3), the first sentence of section 39 (1) or section 40 (1) of this Act, uses the communicated data for other purposes by transmitting them to third parties, or

    3. contrary to the second sentence of section 30 (1) of this Act, combines the characteristics mentioned in the first sentence of section 30 (1) with the information or, contrary to the third sentence of section 40 (3), combines the characteristics mentioned in the second sentence of section 40 (3) with the information.

3. Where the offender commits the offence in exchange for payment or with the intention of enriching himself or another person or of harming another person, he shall be liable to imprisonment for up to two years or to a fine.

4. Such offenses shall be prosecuted only if a complaint is filed.

Section 44: Administrative Offenses

1. An administrative offense shall be deemed to have been committed by anyone who, whether intentionally or through negligence,

    1. contrary to the third or fourth sentence of section 29 (2) of this Act, fails to record the reasons described there or the means of credibly presenting them,

    2. contrary to section 32 (1), also in conjunction with section 32 (4) of this Act, fails to submit a notification or fails to do so within the prescribed time limit or, contrary to section 32 (2), also in conjunction with section 32 (4) of this Act, falls, when registering, to provide the required particulars or to provide correct or complete particulars,

    3. contrary to section 33 (1) of this Act, fails to notify the data subject or fails to do so correctly or completely,

    4. contrary to the third sentence of section 35 (5) of this Act, communicates data without a counterstatement,

    5. contrary to section 36 (1) of this Act, fails to appoint a data protection officer or fails to do so within the prescribed time limit,

    6. contrary to the first sentence of section 38 (3) of this Act, fails to provide information or fails to do so correctly, completely, or within the prescribed time limit or, contrary to the fourth sentence of section 38 (4) of this Act, refuses to grant access to property or premises, or refuses to permit checks or inspections or the inspection of business documents, or

7. fails to comply with an executable instruction under the first sentence of section 38 (5) of this Act.

2. Such administrative offences shall be punishable by a fine of up to DM 50,000.

Annex to the First Sentence of Section 9 of This Act

Where personal data are processed automatically, measures suited to the type of personal data to be protected shall be taken

1. to prevent unauthorized persons from gaining access to data processing systems with which personal data are processed (access control);

2. to prevent storage media from being read, copied, modified, or removed without authorization (storage media control);

3. to prevent unauthorized input into the memory and the unauthorized examination, modification, or erasure of stored personal data (memory control);

4. to prevent data processing systems from being used by unauthorized persons with the aid of data transmission facilities (user control);

5. to ensure that persons entitled to use a data processing system have access only to the data to which they have a right of access (access control);

6. to ensure that it is possible to check and establish to which bodies personal data can be communicated by means of data transmission facilities (communication control);

7. to ensure that it is possible to check and establish which personal data have been input into data processing systems by whom and at what time (input control);

8. to ensure that, in the case of commissioned processing of personal data, the data are processed strictly in accordance with the instructions of the principal (job control);

9. to prevent data from being read, copied, modified, or erased without authorization during the transmission of personal data or the transport of storage media (transfer control);

10. to arrange the internal organization of authorities or enterprises in such a way that it meets the specific requirements of data protection (organizational control).

Australian Laws and Acts

Health Records and Information Privacy Act (HRIP)[30]

The HRIP Act governs the handling of health information in both the public and private sectors in New South Wales. This includes hospitals (public and private), doctors, and other health care organizations. It also includes all other organizations that have any type of health information, including such places as a university that undertakes research or a gymnasium that records information about a person's health and injuries.

The HRIP Act contains 15 health privacy principles (HPPs) outlining how health information must be collected, stored, used, and disclosed. The health privacy principles can be grouped into seven main headings:

- Collection
- Storage
- Access and accuracy
- Use
- Disclosure
- Identifiers and anonymity
- Transferals and linkage

These are legal obligations that must be followed, although the HRIP Act provides for a number of legal exemptions from these principles. The HRIP Act also sets out how to handle complaints regarding the handling of health information.

Financial Transactions Reporting (FTR) Act 1988[31]

Australia's anti–money laundering program places obligations on financial institutions and other financial intermediaries. Those obligations are contained in the Financial Transaction Reporting Act 1988 (the FTR Act). The FTR Act requires cash dealers, as defined in the act, to report to the Director of AUSTRAC (Australian Transaction Reports and Analysis Centre):

- Suspicious transactions

- Cash transactions of AUS $10,000 or more or the foreign currency equivalent

- International funds transfer instructions

The FTR Act also requires cash dealers to verify the identity of persons who are signatories to accounts, and also prohibits accounts being opened or operated under a false name.

Cash dealers as defined in the FTR Act include the following:

- Banks, building societies, and credit unions

- Financial corporations

- Insurance companies and insurance intermediaries

- Securities dealers and futures brokers

- Cash carriers

- Managers and trustees of unit trusts

- Firms that deal in travelers checks, money orders, and the like

- Persons who collect, hold, exchange, or remit currency on behalf of other persons

- Currency and bullion dealers

- Casinos and gambling houses

- Totalisators

The legislation provides penalties for avoiding the reporting requirements and presenting false or incomplete information. It also has penalties for persons who facilitate or assist in these activities.

The reporting and identification requirements, backed by penalties for offenses, provide a strong deterrent to money launderers and facilitators of money laundering. These provisions increase the level of risk associated with abuse of the Australian financial system by tax evaders and organized crime groups. It also adds to their costs of doing business and, in particular, in laundering their illicit profits.

The legislation also sets a standard that must be met by cash dealers. Failure to meet the standard places the cash dealer at risk of being used in the process of money laundering and thus subject to consequential penalties when detected. Penalties include pecuniary penalties and imprisonment.

Spam Act 2003

The Spam Act 2003 prohibits the sending of spam, which is identified as a commercial electronic message sent without the consent of the addressee via e-mail, short message service (SMS), multimedia message service (MMS), or instant messaging.

Chapter Summary

- Public safety is a major responsibility of local, state, and federal governments.

- A variety of laws define government and private liability in the process of disaster recovery.

- The Sarbanes-Oxley Act introduced significant legislative changes to financial practice and corporate governance regulation.

- In Australia, the Spam Act 2003 prohibits the sending of spam, which is identified as a commercial electronic message sent without the consent of the addressee via e-mail, short message service (SMS), multimedia message service (MMS), or instant messaging.

Review Questions

1. What is the Sarbanes-Oxley Act?

   _____

   _____

   _____

   _____

2. What is the FCPA?

   _____

   _____

   _____

   _____

3. What is HIPAA?

   _____

   _____

   _____

   _____

4. What is the Gramm-Leach-Bliley Act?

   _____

   _____

   _____

   _____

5. What is the Flood Disaster Prevention Act of 1973?

   _____

   _____

   _____

   _____

6. What is PIPEDA?

   _____

   _____

   _____

   _____

7. What is the Data Protection Act of 1998?

   _____

   _____

   _____

   _____

8. What are the OECD Principles of Corporate Governance?

   _____

   _____

   _____

   _____

9. What is the FTR Act of 1988?

_____

_____

_____

_____

Hands-On Projects

1. Read about several U.S. laws and acts.

    ■ Navigate to Chapter 2 of the Student Resource Center.

    ■ Open 01ccma.pdf and read the content.

2. Read about the Data Protection Act of 1998.

    ■ Navigate to Chapter 2 of the Student Resource Center.

    ■ Open data_protection_-_when_and_how_to_complain.pdf and read the content.

3. Read about the Sarbanes-Oxley Act.

    ■ Navigate to Chapter 2 of the Student Resource Center.

    ■ Open Zhang_Ivy_Economic_Consequences_of_S_O.pdf and read the content.

    ■ 3-68

Endnotes

[1] http://www.sarbanes-oxley-forum.com/

[2] http://www.usdoj.gov/

[3] http://www.cms.hhs.gov/

[4] http://www.hhs.gov/

[5] http://www.ftc.gov/

[6] http://www.fdic.gov/

[7] http://www.fdic.gov/regulations/laws/rules/6500-3600.html.

[8] http://www.fema.gov/

[9] http://www.fema.gov/pdf/about/stafford_act.pdf.

[10] http://fpc.state.gov/

[11] http://www.google.com/url?sa=t&source=web&ct=res&cd=5&ved=0CCAQFjAE&url=http%3A%2F%2Ffrwebgate.access.gpo.gov%2Fcgibin%2Fgetdoc.cgi%3Fdbname%3D108_cong_public_laws%26docid%3Df%3Apubl187.108.pdf&ei=XN4nS7inM9SWlAfGrIipDQ&usg=AFQjCNEXwLhZeBD_o5G0mrHO7AsiEiFmGQ&sig2=X4ziBrmpb0Br95j83aSmBg.

[12] http://www.ftc.gov/

[13] http://www.fdic.gov/regulations/laws/rules/8000-3100.html.

[14] http://epic.org/

[15] http://www.cnrc.navy.mil/sandiego/Security_Notice/Computer_Fraud_and_Abuse_Act/computer_fraud_and_abuse_act.htm.

[16] http://www.ffiec.gov/

[17] http://www.federalreserve.gov/

[18] http://www.ncua.gov

[19] http://www.occ.treas.gov/

[20] http://www.ots.treas.gov/

[21] http://www.omafra.gov.on.ca/

[22] http://www.cabinetoffice.gov.uk/

[23] http://www.ne-derbyshire.gov.uk/

[24]http://europa.eu/
[25]http://www.giodo.gov.pl/
[26]http://www.fsa.gov.uk/
[27]http://www.dutchdpa.nl/indexen/en_ind_wetten_wbp_wbp.shtml
[28]http://www.ris.bka.gv.at/Dokumente/Erv/ERV_1999_1_165/ERV_1999_1_165.html.
[29]http://www.bdd.de/Download/bdsg_eng.pdf
[30]http://www.lawlink.nsw.gov.au/
[31]Source: http://www.austrac.gov.au/

Chapter 3

Disaster Recovery Planning and Implementation

Objectives

After completing this chapter, you should be able to:

- Secure computer systems
- Develop, test, and implement a disaster recovery plan

Key Terms

Degaussing the process of thoroughly deleting data from magnetic media

Functional verification a process in which a tester creates conditions to which a security measure should respond and then notes the effects of that measure

Introduction to Disaster Recovery Planning and Implementation

When a disaster strikes, there is little time to react. The longer it takes to get critical systems up and running, the greater the potential loss. It is extremely important to be prepared to take action immediately. Therefore, the first steps in disaster recovery are planning and prevention. This chapter teaches you about system security, in order to prevent disasters in the first place, and planning for disaster recovery.

Aspects of Security

There are five primary aspects of security:

1. *Confidentiality*: Confidentiality is the prevention of unauthorized access, disclosure, and use of information. Loss of confidential information may lead to both tangible and intangible losses.

2. *Integrity*: This refers to the reliability and trustworthiness of information, and the quality of a system itself. Integrity means that there has been no unauthorized data manipulation and that the information received is the same as the information sent. Loss of information integrity could be a result of intentional attack or an error in the underlying information processing and communication system.

3. *Availability*: Availability is the ability to access necessary services and resources. This is, of course, critical for organizations that depend on these services and resources.

4. *Authentication*: Authentication provides the ability to confirm the identity of a person or the origin of an artifact, or to ensure that a computer program is a trusted one. Access control systems use various authentication mechanisms including passwords and biometrics.

5. *Nonrepudiation*: This guarantees that the sender has sent the message and the receiver has received the message, eliminating the possibility of denial on both ends. This is achieved through the use of digital signatures, time stamps, and confirmation services.

Application Security

In addition to the previously mentioned primary aspects of security, the following factors are critical for application security:

- *Access control*: Access to an application requires certain rights. Access control ensures that in the event of a disaster, investigators can determine who accessed the application. Methods of managing access control include:
  - Read, write, and execute permissions
  - Role-based access control performed by the administrator
  - Control access depending on the IP address
  - Control access based on the object level
- *Authorization*: Who is authorized to do what, when, and how
- *Confidentiality/privacy*: Often, sensitive data is treated the same as other data, which leads to threats related to confidentiality and privacy. Applications should be developed to keep confidential and private information secret.
- *Encryption*: Encryption changes data, preventing, attackers from reading the data after intercepting them. In order to read the data, the recipient must know the decryption procedure. Encryption algorithms can be asymmetric or symmetric. Asymmetric algorithms use separate keys for encryption and decryption, while symmetric algorithms use a single key for both encryption and decryption.
- *Segregation of data and privileges*: Data should be segregated through access control mechanisms. Only components that require access to the data should have access. Centralizing sensitive data helps the application designer better organize security functionality.
- *Error-handling*: Error-handling refers to the behavior of an application when something unexpected occurs. Error-handling components include:
  - Defining the type of error, such as processing error, runtime error, violation of security, or bug in a program
  - Defining the severity level of an error
  - Auditing different logging components, such as files, e-mail messages, or SMS messages
  - Responding to the error in ways such as issuing a warning, stopping the component's activities, restarting the service, shutting down the application, and informing the administrator
- *Testing for security*: Security measures must be tested to confirm their effectiveness. The most common method is **functional verification**, in which the tester creates conditions to which a security measure should respond and then notes the effects of that measure.

Security Issues with Commercial Off-The-Shelf (COTS) Products

By using commercial off-the-shelf (COTS) products, an organization can save the time and effort of creating their own programs and services by purchasing these products from a third-party vendor. This can speed up and reduce the cost of system construction, but it can also introduce the following issues:

- *Integration*: COTS products must be integrated with existing systems and may contain incompatibilities with existing programs and services.

- *Dependency on the third-party vendor*: Because COTS products require little effort by the organization, it becomes increasingly dependent on the third-party vendor. This can cause a risk if the vendor goes out of business or fails to produce products that meet the organization's changing requirements.

- *Failure to meet individual requirements*: Because COTS products are designed for general use, they may not meet all of the organization's specific requirements. Organizations then have to give up some of their requirements or build new products in addition to the COTS products.

- *Threats of failure*: If the COTS products do not perform as expected, projects may turn out poorly or fail entirely.

Database Security

Confidentiality, integrity, and availability, known as the *Information Security Triad*, are the most important elements of all information security. Databases implement various design and logical components to achieve these security elements.

System and Object Privileges

A particular user can connect to a database when the system grants the user the necessary privileges, or authorizations, to do so. There are several types of privileges, including the following:

- *System privileges*: System privileges permit the user to implement a systemwide action. Administrators and system developers are usually the only ones allowed to access system privilege configuration and information.

- *Schema object privileges*: Through schema object privileges, users are assigned privileges to a particular object or piece of data. Schema object privileges provide table security to data manipulation language (DML) and data dictionary language (DDL) operations. These privileges can only be granted by the object owner or the administrator. The owner can also give permission to a user, so that the user can give access to others.

Managing System and Object Privileges

The user must provide an authentic username and password to access the database or specific database tables. The following are different ways to manage these privileges:

- *Role-based privilege management*: Roles can be assigned to a single person or to a group of people. The following are some types of roles:

  - *Database roles*: Database roles can be used to provide privileges relating to accessing and modifying data in the database. These roles are assigned to users based on their job functions.

  - *Global roles*: A global role applies to an entire database.

  - *Enterprise roles*: These roles are assigned to enterprise users who have global roles on multiple databases.

  - *Secure application roles*: With secure application roles, users can be prevented from bypassing security measures in order to access data.

- *Managing privileges using stored procedures*: Users can be prevented from performing operations on the database by using stored procedures.

- *Managing privileges using network facilities*: Database roles can help manage and administer privileges from external services for all network resources.

- *Managing privileges by providing access to views*: Users can be given access to a particular view of a table, thus eliminating the possibility of accessing the entire table.

Row-Level Security

Access to particular rows of a table gives users the information they need without showing them information they should not see. Ways to achieve row-level security include the following:

- *Complex and dynamic views*: An application designer defines complex views by making user security tables. These security tables are then joined with the application tables depending on the application user's username.
- *Virtual private database*: In a virtual private database, or VPD, the users create row-level security by performing query modification based on a security policy.
- *Label-based access control*: In this type of access control, organizations provide sensitivity labels to data rows, and restrict and control the access to data based on those labels.

Encrypting Data on the Server

Encryption makes data unusable by unauthorized users. There are many industry standard encryption algorithms, including Data Encryption Standard (DES) and the more secure Triple DES (3DES) and Advanced Encryption Standard (AES)

Database Integrity Mechanisms

Database integrity ensures that the data present in a database are accurate and consistent.

System Availability Factors

Data must be accessible to authorized users at all times. System availability depends on the following factors:

- *Storage quotas*: The administrator should maintain a policy limiting each user to a specific amount of disk space in the database.
- *Resource limits*: Users should be restricted to only the resources necessary for their jobs.
- *Hot backups*: The administrator should always maintain a backup of critical data in case of an unexpected data loss or application error.
- *Resistance to attack*: Developers should write software based on secure coding standards.
- *Secure configuration*: Administrators should configure systems to prevent as many known vulnerabilities as possible.

Database Security Checklist

The following is a checklist for ensuring database security:

- Build a baseline for future database security by assessing the present level of security.
- Regularly check the database for vulnerabilities. Types of database vulnerabilities include the following:
  - *Vendor bugs* are any buffer overflow or programming errors caused when the user executes commands. These bugs can usually be eliminated by applying patches.
  - *Poor database architecture* can cause security issues. These vulnerabilities are difficult to fix because they require major reworking by the vendor.
  - Database security can be compromised if the database is configured incorrectly. This vulnerability is called a *misconfiguration*.
  - *Incorrect usage* is when attackers can use developer tools to break into a system.
- Regularly assess the database permissions granted to users.
- Apply patches to the database regularly.
- Perform frequent audits to test the accuracy of the security policies and discover any irregularities.

- Use security auditing tools to monitor and record the functions of the database and alerts in the case of undesired actions. Use an alert system that provides real-time security awareness.

- If the security audits do not succeed in securing the database, encryption is the most effective tool to protect critical data.

- Change default passwords immediately, and regularly change all passwords.

- Disable any user accounts that are not in use.

Distributed System Security

A distributed system is a collection of processors connected through a communication network. These systems make use of both local and remote resources, and can be used for:

- Resource sharing
- Increased computation speed
- Increased reliability through redundancy
- Communication

Distributed systems have four layers: host, infrastructure, application, and service. All of these layers must be secured.

1. Host-based vulnerabilities

   - *Malware*: Malware is software intended to perform undesired activities, often without the user's knowledge. Malware includes viruses, rootkits, Trojans, and other unwanted software.

   - *Eavesdropping*: Electronic eavesdropping is the use of an electronic device to monitor communications without the consent of the involved parties. A person can eavesdrop over almost any communication medium, including telephone lines, e-mail, and instant messaging.

   - *Resource starvation*: Here, the attacker consumes a particular resource until it is exhausted. For example, an attacker can continuously issue requests to a Web site to create shopping carts or users.

   - *Privilege escalation*: This is any attack that gives a user unauthorized access to resources.

2. Infrastructure-level vulnerabilities

   - *Network-level threats and vulnerabilities*: Common vulnerabilities at the network level include poor installation settings and outdated security patches. Network-level attacks include spoofing, denial of service (DoS), and packet sniffing.

   - *Grid computing threats and vulnerabilities*: Grid computing threats are related to many computers acting together to solve a single problem. Administrators must ensure that all computers in the grid are secure.

   - *Storage threats and vulnerabilities*: Storage devices must be protected from unauthorized external access using security software.

3. Application-level vulnerabilities

   - Individual applications are prone to different vulnerabilities, such as viruses, Trojans, and buffer overflows.

4. Service-level vulnerabilities

   - *Service-level threats and vulnerabilities*: These include software service-level problems, software error events such as memory errors, buffer overflows due to poor programming, and critical errors caused by improper implementation of software systems.

   - *Service-level security requirements*: Organizations should implement application service-level vulnerability assessment tests to detect software service-level vulnerabilities and software error events as part of an enterprise-level security test program. They should provide real-time assessment of software service-level problems, real-time software error events, and automatic alerts of critical errors.

   - *Service-level attacks*: Denial-of-service (DoS) and distributed denial-of-service (DDoS) attacks are the most common, followed by buffer overflow attacks, leading to systemwide compromise.

Firmware Security

Firmware is the fixed, small program that resides inside various electronic devices. This controls the basic, low-level operations in the device. Firmware is stored in computer chips such as ROM, PROM, and EPROM. Firmware security features include the following:

- *Power-on password*: Power-on password authentication is a form of preboot security. When the system is powered on, it tells the user to enter the stored password in order to continue with the boot process. When the password is entered incorrectly a certain number of times, the system is restarted. This is only effective on a single-user system, because the computer can only have one password.

- *Smart-card authentication*: With smart-card authentication, the user must provide the correct smart card and PIN to boot the system. That way, the user only needs to remember a small PIN instead of a strong password.

- *Embedded security chip authentication*: On computers that contain an embedded security chip, users are required to enter a key passphrase before the machine will boot. If the given key passphrase is authentic, the BIOS proceeds to boot the operating system. If the authentication is unsuccessful after a certain number of retries, the system halts or shuts down.

- *DriveLock hard drive protection*: DriveLock integrates with a power-on password and protects hard drive access with a password. DriveLock provides protection to a hard drive even if the hard drive is placed in another system.

- *Disk Sanitizer*: Information stored on a hard drive can still pose a security threat when the system is recycled or disposed. A data removal program, such as Disk Sanitizer, completely removes and destroys the data from the hard drive. That way, the data is impossible to retrieve, even using advanced tools.

Industrial Security

Industrial security is achieved through proper system design, effective monitoring, and comprehensive management of industrial functions. Measures taken for industrial security include the following:

- Make sure that security functions are working properly. Perform regular audits of these functions.

- Train employees about security measures. Employees should be able to handle sudden, undesired events.

- Clearly define the measures to be taken in the event of a disaster.

- Have specialized personnel for specific security functions.

- Protect important assets and documents in a secure location, such as a third-party site. Storing data off-site ensures that it will be available after even the most devastating disaster.

Vulnerabilities in Network Security Software and Services

Although network security software is used to protect the network from undesired events and threats, these programs contain their own vulnerabilities. The following are some common vulnerabilities in network security software:

- Firewalls
  - Misconfiguration
  - Trusting some IP addresses
  - Availability of extra and unnecessary services on the firewall
  - Unnecessarily opened TCP and UDP ports
- IPSec VPN
  - Most VPN servers can be fingerprinted by different fingerprinting methods
  - Insecure default settings
  - Insecure storage of authentication data by VPN clients
  - Offline password cracking

- Man-in-the-middle attacks
- Denial-of-service attacks
- Voice over IP (VoIP)
  - Low bandwidth
  - Minimal resources
  - Insufficient data verification
  - File/resource manipulation flaws
  - Authentication and certificate errors
  - Homogeneous network
  - Physical connection quality and packet collision

Remanence

Even after data are supposedly deleted from a medium, like a hard drive or memory card, a trace of the data usually remains. This is called remanence. There are two types of remanence: optical remanence and magnetic remanence.

1. In *optical remanence*, some information remains after data are removed from optical storage media, such as a CD-ROM or DVD-ROM. The best way to completely remove these data is to destroy the disc. Shredders strong enough to handle these discs are inexpensive and convenient.

2. *Magnetic remanence* is the residual magnetic information stored on hard drives, floppy disks, or magnetic tapes. This can be removed with a degausser device. *Degaussing* is the process of thoroughly deleting data from magnetic media.

When traces of data are present in storage devices, there is always a threat of those data being recovered by a third party. This leads to data theft and loss of valuable information such as passwords and crucial files.

Disaster Recovery Plan (DRP)

A disaster recovery plan, or DRP, aids and supports an organization in restoring information technology functions after a disaster. The DRP describes the framework and procedures to be followed in the case of a disaster. The DRP should address the following areas:

- *Prevention (predisaster)*: The organization should first secure vulnerable systems, protect systems containing important data, and train the disaster recovery team. This planning will make it significantly easier to quickly recover from a disaster.

- *Continuity (during a disaster)*: In this phase, the primary objective is to maintain and continue the critical operations that allow the organization to function properly. It includes maintaining the critical systems and resources, as well as moving systems and resources to secondary sites during a disaster.

- *Recovery (postdisaster)*: This phase includes restoring all systems and resources to their regular and fully operational state. All systems and resources present at secondary locations are brought back to the original site.

The main objectives of the DRP are as follows:

- Reducing the disruptions to normal operations
- Building alternate means of operation
- Educating the disaster recovery team about the emergency procedures
- Minimizing the system's downtime and recovery time
- Reducing the potential losses of core assets
- Defining clear procedures, reducing the need to make on-the-spot decisions
- Simulating several disaster recovery scenarios
- Ensuring system dependability before storing backups

When developing a DRP, an organization should be sure to meet these points:

- Defining the DRP's structure, elements, and phases
- Training personnel effectively
- Testing the DRP to be sure it functions properly
- Preparing an emergency response team to handle the disaster situation immediately
- Backing up data off-site
- Ensuring backup computers can handle the increased data load
- Circulating a contact list of all relevant staff
- Defining a prearranged disaster recovery site

Business Impact Analysis (BIA)

Organizations should perform a business impact analysis, or BIA, to identify the business and operational impact of a disaster. It should include the time frames within which systems must be restored and the time required to recover these systems. The BIA's objectives are as follows:

- Identifying the full business process
- Determining all potential financial, legal, and regulatory impacts
- Setting up time frames for recovery of all business-related processes
- Defining the key inner and outer dealings and dependencies of each process
- Identifying the required resources for all processes to recover and their related recovery time frames
- Training personnel in the recovery process
- Making management aware of the continuity plans

Table 3-1 shows a sample BIA form.

Business Impact Analysis	
Site Name:	System Name:
Date BIA Completed:	BIA Contact:
Assessment Date:	Functional Area:
System Information:	Information regarding the functions of the system and the system architecture.
Internal System Contacts	Responsibilities
Contact #1	Identify the personnel or offices in the organization that depend on or support the system.
Contact #2	
Contact #3	
External System Contacts	Responsibilities
Contact #1	Identify the individuals, positions, or offices outside the organization that depend on or support the system; specify their relationship to the system.
Contact #2	
Contact #3	
Hardware Resources	Identify the specific hardware used by the system.
Hardware	
Hardware	
Hardware	
Software Resources	Identify the software used by the system, including quantity and type.

Table 3-1   This is a sample business impact analysis form   *(continues)*

Software	
Software	
Software	
Critical Role	Critical Resources
Identify critical role	List the IT resources required for accomplishing the roles.
Identify critical role	
Identify critical role	

Table 3-1 This is a sample business impact analysis form *continued*

Disaster Recovery Roles and Responsibilities

When creating a disaster recovery plan, it is important to specify roles and responsibilities. Everyone involved in the plan should have a very clear idea of what is expected. The following sections detail the responsibilities of various personnel.

Operations Recovery Director

- Predisaster
  - Approving the final DRP and procedures
  - Maintaining the DRP and procedures
  - Conducting DR training
  - Authorizing the periodic testing of the DRP
- Postdisaster
  - Declaring the occurrence of a disaster
  - Defining the implementation of strategy if more than one strategy exists
  - Authorizing the travel and housing arrangements for team members
  - Managing and monitoring the overall recovery process
  - Providing updates on the status of disaster recovery efforts to the senior and user management
  - Coordinating media and press releases

Operations Recovery Manager and Teams

- Predisaster
  - Developing, maintaining, and updating the DRP
  - Appointing recovery personnel
  - Assigning parts of the DRP to the individual recovery teams and their members
  - Coordinating plan testing
  - Training disaster recovery team members on plan implementation
- Postdisaster
  - Obtaining the required approvals to activate the disaster recovery plan and the recovery teams
  - Informing all the recovery team leaders or alternates about the disaster declaration
  - Determining the degree of outage due to the disaster
  - Coordinating and summarizing the damage reports from all teams
  - Informing the organization's directors of the disaster's severity
  - Conducting briefings with all recovery teams
  - Coordinating all recovery teams
  - Requesting remote data backup, documentation, and required resources from the IT technical team

- Authorizing purchases and expenditures for required resources
- Reporting the recovery effort status to the operations recovery management director
- Coordinating media press releases

Facility Recovery Team

- Predisaster
  - Preparing the alternate site with hardware and supplies
  - Creating a complete layout and recovery procedure for the alternate site
- Postdisaster
  - Repairing and rebuilding the primary site

Network Recovery Team

- Predisaster
  - Installs networking equipment at the alternate site
- Postdisaster
  - Providing network connections at the alternate site
  - Restoring network connections at the primary site

Platform Recovery Team

- Predisaster
  - Maintaining lists of equipment needed in the restoration process
- Postdisaster
  - Installing hardware equipment
  - Restoring data and systems from remote backups

Application Recovery Team

- Predisaster
  - Testing applications for vulnerabilities
- Postdisaster
  - Restoring the database
  - Addressing specific application-related issues

Damage Assessment and Salvage Team

- Predisaster
  - Understanding the DR roles and responsibilities
  - Working closely with disaster recovery teams to minimize the occurrence of a disaster in the data center
  - Training employees to be well prepared in the case of emergencies
  - Participating in the DRP testing as needed
- Postdisaster
  - Determining damage and accessibility to the organization's resources
  - Determining the level of the damage to the data center in the organization
  - Assessing the need for physical security
  - Estimating the recovery time according to the damage assessment
  - Identifying the hardware and other equipment that can be repaired
  - Explaining to the disaster recovery team the extent of damages, estimated recovery time, physical safety, and repairable equipment

- Maintaining a repairable hardware and equipment log
- Coordinating with vendors and suppliers to restore, repair, or replace equipment
- Coordinating the transportation of salvaged equipment to a recovery site, if necessary
- Providing support to clean up the data center after a disaster

Physical Security Team

- Predisaster
  - Understanding the DR roles and responsibilities
  - Working closely with the DR team to ensure the physical safety of the existing systems and resources
  - Training employees
  - Becoming familiar with emergency contact numbers
  - Participating in DRP testing as needed
  - Maintaining the list of members allowed to enter the disaster site and recovery site
- Postdisaster
  - Assessing damage at the disaster site
  - Blocking the data center from illegal access
  - Scheduling security for transporting files, reports, and equipment
  - Providing assistance for investigations of the damaged site

Communications Teams

- Predisaster
  - Understanding DR roles and responsibilities
  - Working closely with the DR team to ensure the physical safety of existing systems and resources
  - Training employees
  - Participating in disaster recovery plan testing as required
  - Establishing and maintaining the communications equipment at the alternate site
- Postdisaster
  - Assessing communication equipment requirements by coordinating with other teams
  - Retrieving the communication configuration from off-site storage units
  - Planning, coordinating, and installing communication equipment at the alternate site
  - Planning, coordinating, and installing network cabling at the alternate site

Hardware Installation Teams

- Predisaster
  - Understanding the disaster recovery roles and responsibilities
  - Coordinating with the DR team to minimize the impact of a disaster in the data center
  - Training employees
  - Participating in DRP testing as needed
  - Maintaining the current system and LAN configuration in off-site storage
- Postdisaster
  - Verifying hardware requirements at the alternate location
  - Inspecting the alternate location for the required physical space
  - Notifying the alternate site of the impending occupancy
  - Interfacing with the IT technical and operation teams about the space configuration of the alternate location
  - Coordinating the transportation of repairable equipment to the alternate location

- Informing the administration team regarding the need for equipment repair and new equipment
- Ensuring the installation of temporary terminals connecting to the alternate location mainframe
- Planning and installing the hardware at the alternate location
- Planning, transporting, and installing hardware at the permanent location, when available
- Setting and operating a sign-in/sign-out method for all resources at the alternate location

IT Operations Teams

- Predisaster
  - Understanding disaster recovery roles and responsibilities
  - Coordinating with the DR team to ensure the physical safety of existing systems and resources
  - Training employees to be well prepared in case of emergencies
  - Ensuring complete backups as per the schedule
  - Ensuring backups are sent to the remote location as per the schedule
  - Participating in DRP testing as needed
- Postdisaster
  - Supporting the IT technical team as needed
  - Sending and receiving off-site storage containers
  - Ensuring backup tapes are sent to off-site storage
  - Maintaining a sign-in/sign-out method for all resources at the alternate location
  - Checking the alternate site's floor configuration to aid in the communication team's installation plans
  - Checking the security of the alternate location and its LAN network
  - Coordinating the transfer of systems, resources, and people to the alternate location

IT Technical Teams

- Predisaster
  - Understanding the disaster recovery roles and responsibilities
  - Working closely with disaster recovery teams to minimize the occurrence of a disaster in the data center
  - Training employees
  - Participating in DRP testing as needed
- Postdisaster
  - Restoring system resources from the backup media
  - Initializing new tapes as required in the DR process
  - Conducting backups at the remote location
  - Testing and verifying operating systems
  - Modifying the LAN configuration to connect with the alternate location's configuration

Administration Teams

- Predisaster
  - Understanding disaster recovery roles and responsibilities
  - Training employees
  - Ensuring the maintenance of the required business interruption insurance
  - Ensuring the adequate availability of emergency funds throughout the DR process
  - Assessing the alternative communication required if telephone services become unavailable
  - Participating in DRP testing as needed

- Postdisaster
  - Preparing, coordinating, and obtaining proper sanctions for all procurement requests
  - Maintaining logs of all procurements in process and scheduled deliveries
  - Processing the payment requests for all invoices related to the recovery procedure
  - Arranging travel and lodging for the recovery teams
  - Providing alternative communications for recovery team members if normal telephone service is not available
  - Performing provisional clerical and managerial duties as needed by the DR teams

Disaster Recovery Planning Steps

When putting together a disaster recovery plan, an organization should follow these steps:

1. *Identify and assess the risks*: Identify and list serious incidents that can affect the normal operations of the organization. Prioritize the list according to severity level.

2. *Prioritize business processes*: In case resources are limited, use those resources efficiently to provide an effective disaster recovery plan. Prioritize the business processes that are:
   - Most essential to the organization's mission
   - Most and least needed during a disaster

3. *Prioritize technology services*: After determining critical business processes, map the processes to the technology components that make those processes possible. This information is useful in identifying critical technology environment components and prioritizing each component accordingly.

4. *Define recovery strategy*: The recovery time objective (RTO) is the acceptable amount of time for returning the services or information availability to an organization after a disaster occurs. The recovery point objective (RPO) is the amount of data loss that can be considered acceptable when a disaster occurs. Implementing RTO and RPO for each critical information system helps in developing a plan that reflects the priorities of the organization. They also function as tools to check the success of the chosen strategies when a disaster recovery plan is tested.

5. *Secure facilities*: Having efficient technology facilities is useful when a disaster strikes. The technology facilities should be constructed so that they are secured and protected from any disruptive events. There are many inexpensive facility tools that can be used to minimize disaster situations, including electrical surge protectors, power conditioning units, and fire suppression systems.

6. *Identify alternate sites*: Maintain an alternate site for temporarily relocating required systems and resources. This site should be able to function when the primary location cannot. The alternate site should contain accurate and current technology environment documentation.

7. *Use redundancy and failover*: An extensive variety of technology solutions can be used for maintaining application and data continuity when a disaster occurs. Combining these technologies with a strategy of geographically dispersed technology resources will help in protecting data.

8. *Document the plan*: The disaster recovery plan should be documented in sequential milestones to allow the organization to return to normal operations. The first milestone should document the process of dealing with the immediate aftermath of the disaster. This includes notifying key employees, emergency services, and others who are required to respond to the disaster. The plan should then include resuming the operation of the technology services based on the business process priorities. The roles and responsibilities of all individuals should be described in the plan. The disaster recovery team should be able to access the plan even if the primary site is unavailable. Store multiple copies of the plan off-site.

9. *Test the plan*: Perform regular tests on the disaster recovery plan in order to ensure its effectiveness. The tests should be performed on the complete plan process. A useful testing technique is to develop a test scenario based on a disaster situation. After completing the testing, review the results with the team members to determine any possible improvements and update the plan accordingly.

10. *Update the recovery plan*: To make the disaster recovery plan effective, keep it up to date and applicable to current technology and business processes. Changes made to the plan should be communicated to all personnel affected by those changes.

Disaster Preparedness

To be adequately prepared for a disaster, it is essential to determine and assign responsibilities. The following are steps an organization should take:

1. Include the role names and the responsibilities of each role in the disaster recovery plan.
2. The person in charge should make policy decisions.
3. The person in charge should make critical IT-related decisions only after consulting with IT personnel.
4. Offer disaster recovery training for key (or all) staff members.
5. Set up a clear chain of command.

Strategies used in disaster preparedness include:

- Storing important data off-site and including information on how to access those data in the disaster recovery plan
- Maintaining hard copies of important data (including the disaster recovery plan)
- Maintaining current information regarding contacts and system resources
- Employing malware removal programs
- Utilizing and frequently examining devices such as UPS, fire and smoke sensors and alarms, and antitheft systems
- Updating compliance assessments (such as for Sarbanes-Oxley) whenever changes are made to the IT infrastructure
- Documenting all preventive measures in the disaster recovery plan
- Maintaining backup servers at various locations
- Conducting training sessions

Profiles

As part of disaster recovery planning, it is important to keep profiles of operations, applications, and inventory.

Operations Profile

The operations profile gives an overview of operations, governance and accountability, decision makers, and who is responsible for each part of the DRP. The profile contains the following parts:

- *System description*: This describes the system architecture and its key functionality. It provides details of the operating environment, physical location, user groups, and partnerships with external organizations and interfacing systems. It also describes the technical considerations that relate to the recovery point, such as backup and storage measures.
- *Governance and accountability*: Organizations should set a clear chain of command to avoid any disruptions in the plan. The disaster recovery officer is responsible for ensuring people's safety and implementing the procedures mentioned in the DRP. Figure 3-1 shows a sample diagram of governance and accountability.
- *Roles and responsibilities*: Organizations need to identify the roles needed to respond to a disaster. The DRP establishes several teams, each one assigned to participate in recovering separate operations. Members of the team are also in charge of daily operations system maintenance. Organizations can use a table like Table 3-2 to keep track of roles and responsibilities.

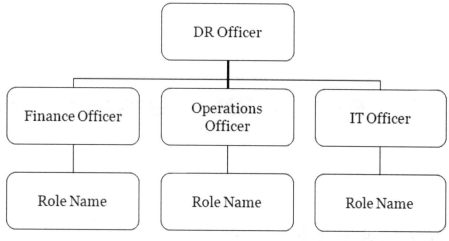

Figure 3-1 This is a sample chart of governance and accountability.

Role	Telephone Number	Organization	Area of Responsibility

Table 3-2 Organizations can use a table like this to keep track of roles and responsibilities

Application Profiles

It is important to keep profiles of all systems, including both priority systems and nonpriority systems. For priority systems, organizations should include both the RPO and RTO. Table 3-3 is a sample of a table that can be used to keep track of priority systems, and Table 3-4 is a sample of a table that can be used for other systems.

System	Critical Periods	RPO	RTO	Owner
Payroll	End of month	7 days	1 day	
Oracle	End of week	2 days	1 day	

Table 3-3 This is an example table for keeping track of priority systems

Name	Critical	Asset	Manufacturer	Job Run
Name of system	Yes/No	Yes/No	Manufacturer name	Daily/Weekly

Table 3-4 A table like this can be used to keep track of all other systems

Inventory Profile

Organizations should keep an inventory of all physical items that should be restored or replaced in the event of a disaster. Table 3-5 is an example of a table used to keep this inventory.

Manufacturer	Description	Model	Serial #	Own/Lease	Comments

Table 3-5   This is an example of an inventory of physical items

Notification and Activation Procedures

Organizations should activate the DRP if the system is unavailable for an extended period of time or if the facility is damaged and unavailable. When activating the plan, they should follow these steps:

1. The disaster recovery manager decides to invoke the DRP. If it is during normal business hours, deploy the emergency evacuation plan if necessary. If it is during off hours, notify the facilities manager about the situation. Contact emergency services if the situation warrants. The facilities manager and disaster recovery manager will evaluate the situation when it is safe to do so.

2. The disaster recovery manager contacts the disaster recovery site providers and gives the required level of information.

3. The disaster recovery manager contacts the necessary third-party recovery teams.

4. The disaster recovery manager contacts the operations managers.

5. The operations managers contact their individual teams, who are given their responsibilities.

6. The disaster recovery manager contacts the human resources manager.

7. The human resources manager contacts all personnel who are needed in the DRP to inform them of the invocation and instruct them to stand by for further instructions.

8. The disaster recovery manager contacts the public relations manager. The public relations manager is responsible for notifying clients, board members, stakeholders, and the media.

9. The disaster recovery manager provides directions and a map to the disaster recovery site to everyone who must be there.

10. The recovery team will familiarize itself with the disaster recovery site and begin the process of recovering the system.

Damage Assessment Procedure

The damage assessment procedure should include the following steps:

1. Determining the cause of the disruption
2. Estimating the affected physical space
3. Estimating the time required to repair services to normal operation
4. Evaluating the status of the equipment functionality and inventory
5. Reducing the additional disruption or damage

Response Checklist

Organizations should maintain a checklist of what must be done to effectively manage a disaster situation. This checklist ensures that all relevant activities have been performed within the required time frame. The checklist should include each activity, who is responsible for that activity, and when that activity should be carried out. Table 3-6 shows an example response checklist, and Table 3-7 shows a follow-up checklist for after the disaster has been handled.

Ref	Activity	Responsibility	Time Frame	Signoff
1	If there is a loss of site, coordinate with the business continuity plan team.		Immediate	
2	If there is loss of site, coordinate activities with the building officer to gain access to facilities.		Immediate	
3	Conduct the initial assessment of the incident, determine the severity, and formulate a salvage operation.		Within X minutes of the incident	
4	Conduct team leaders meeting.		Within X minutes of the incident	
5	Announce activation of the disaster recovery plan to the team leaders.		Within X minutes of the incident	
6	Determine availability of: backup data for the recovery of systems; access to the data delivered prior to the incident; receiving and processing data by alternate means; redirecting service to the alternate site.		Within X minutes of the incident	
7	Contact backup facilities as necessary.		Within X minutes of the incident	
8	Communicate activation of the disaster recovery plan to the alternate sites.		Within X minutes of the incident	
9	Monitor and review the recovery procedures.		Continuously	
10	Contact vendors.		Within X minutes of the incident	

Table 3-6   This is a sample response checklist

Action	Yes/No
Obtain emergency cash for immediate supplies.	
Arrange for transportation to backup site and vice versa.	
Arrange for living quarters, if required.	
Arrange for eating establishments.	
Identify all personnel and their telephone numbers.	
Arrange for sending and receipt of mail.	
Arrange for office supplies.	
Buy or lease equipment, as required.	
Decide the sequence to start up applications.	
Identify number of workstations needed.	
Check that all data are taken to the backup location.	
Arrange for transportation of supplementary items required at backup location.	
Take directions and connect to the backup location.	
Bring technical documentation and procedural manuals.	
Ensure staff members understand their tasks.	
Inform insurance companies.	

Table 3-7   This is an example follow-up checklist

Objectives				
1				
2				
3				
Preconditions				
1				
2				
3				
Documentation				
1				
2				
3				
Ref	**Task**	**Performed By:**	**Time Frame**	**Signoff By:**
1		Minutes/Hours/Days		
2				
Objectives				
1				

Table 3-8 Use a table like this to record recovery procedures

Recovery Procedures

Organizations need to maintain detailed instructions for recovering all systems at the backup site. These instructions should include the tasks the disaster recovery personnel should follow to recover systems, applications, or infrastructure in the required time frame. These tasks should include hardware acquisition, software installation, and retrieving and loading backup tapes. Table 3-8 shows an example recovery procedure table.

Testing and Maintenance Procedures

The disaster recovery plan should be tested and maintained properly, ensuring that the document remains relevant and reliable in case of a disaster. The document owner is responsible for updating the plan to reflect the recovery steps, contact details, and references that change over time.

Testing consists of a combination of these approaches:

- Scenario testing, in which recovery procedures are tested based on a scenario to ensure that they remain relevant
- Transferring systems to an alternate site to ensure that systems can be reproduced within a particular time frame
- Structured walk-through, designed to expose errors or omissions without the planning and expenses associated with performing a full operations test

Organizations can use a table like Table 3-9 to keep track of testing tasks.

Organizations should maintain a schedule, like the one in Table 3-10, indicating when each section of the DRP should be tested.

After performing a test, the team should fill out a report, like the one in Table 3-11.

Alternate Site Requirements

When searching for a suitable alternate site, organizations need to make sure they have the necessary resources to provide continuity of operations. These resources may include the following:

- Office space
  - Identify access to the office space.
  - Identify how much workspace each staff member requires.

Ref	Task	Responsibility	Time Frame	Signoff
1	Determine the testing approach to be adopted.			
2	Conduct testing meeting with participants.			
3	Test the developed plans.			
4	Identify gaps/needs in the current plan.			
5	Incorporate changes into DRP.			
6	Publish and distribute the final copies.			

Table 3-9   A table like this one can be used to keep track of testing tasks

Section of Disaster Recovery Plan	Scheduled Testing Date

Table 3-10   A schedule like this indicates when each section of the DRP should be tested

Disaster Recovery Test Report	
Site Name:	System Name:
Customer:	Contact:
Test Date:	Functional Area:
Test Type: Walkthrough Partial Simulation Full Simulation	
Description and Scope of Test:	
Proposed Changes to Disaster Recovery Plan:	
Approval: Reviewed By:_____ Disaster Recovery Manager Approved By:_____ Customer (optional)	Date: _____ Date: _____

Table 3-11   After performing a test, record its results in a form like this one

- Identify room or space that can be allocated for meetings.
- Identify the space for storing folders, papers, or equipment.
- Identify facilities for storing cash, checkbooks, and other valuable items.
- Office equipment
  - Ensure that there are services to enable normal business functions, such as phone lines, Internet access, and fax machines.
  - If possible, assign phones with a direct-dial facility.
  - Identify the fax facilities.
  - Identify requirements for standard office supplies, such as paper, pens, and copying facilities.

- Computer equipment
  - Identify the computer equipment required by the organization.
  - Specify the number of computers that can run the necessary applications. Confirm who will set up these applications.
  - Discuss access to the LAN and how the organization will assign logons and passwords.
  - Identify the number and types of printers that will be made available.

Returning to Normal Operations

Organizations should outline the activities needed to restore system operations at the original site or, if necessary, a new site. There should be as little a gap as possible between systems operating at the alternate site and at the new one, much like the changeover between the original site and the alternate site. Organizations can use a table like Table 3-12 to show these steps.

Ref	Task	Performed By:	Time Frame	Signoff By:
1	Describe the steps to restore the system.		Minutes/Hours/Days	
2				
3				
4				
5				

Table 3-12 Use a table like this one to show the steps needed to restore the original site or to move operations to a new site

Next, organizations should outline the procedures for maintaining the systems at the alternate site and the original or new site simultaneously, before the procedures are entirely changed over to the new site. Table 3-13 shows an example of this outline.

Ref	Task	Performed By:	Time Frame	Signoff By:
1			Minutes/Hours/Days	
2				
3				
4				
5				

Table 3-13 Create an outline like this to show how the systems at the alternate site and the original or new site can operate concurrently

Finally, organizations should outline the procedures for deactivating the alternate location. These procedures should:

- Ensure that sensitive information is managed properly
- Ensure that materials and equipment are labeled, packaged, and shipped to the original or new site
- Instruct the team to return to the original location or report to the new one

Organizations can use a table like Table 3-14 to create a deactivation plan.

Ref	Task	Performed By:	Time Frame	Signoff By:
1			Minutes/Hours/Days	
2				
3				
4				
5				

Table 3-14 Create a deactivation plan to shut down the alternate site

Communications Plan

Organizations must describe the communication process in the event of a disaster situation. External communication is required to keep key stakeholders informed of the project status, issues, and risks. When communicating with employees, organizations should do the following:

- Provide employees with a safe alternate working environment.
- Ensure employees' safety.
- Provide complete information about the current problem and regular updates on the situation.
- Provide appropriate contact information to all employees.

When communicating with clients, organizations should do the following:

- Ensure clients' safety.
- Continue to provide clients with their expected level of service.
- Meet all financial, legal, and contractual obligations.
- Provide a single point of contact.

Table 3-15 is a template for a communications plan.

What	Audience	Frequency	Prepared By	Purpose	Media

Table 3-15   Keep a communications plan to make sure employees and clients stay informed

Disaster Recovery Planning in a Virtualized Environment

Server virtualization is an effective tool for disaster recovery planning. It is easy to deploy and integrate, and offers several advantages, such as the following:

- Lower cost than physical servers
- Minimizes hardware downtime
- Recovers data quickly

When implementing server virtualization, organizations should consider the following:

- *Data protection (backups)*: Installing a conventional backup agent on every virtual machine provides data protection similar to the physical server environment.
- *Recovery granularity*: Granular (file-level) restoring facilities can be obtained by implementing image-level backups. This deployment provides rapid recovery with a lower software cost.
- *Restore performance*: I/O performance is the most significant feature when performing backups and restoring virtual servers.
- *RTOs/RPOs*: When there are applications with less tolerance for downtime (RTO = 0), a failover component is necessary to fulfill the recovery requirements. Similarly, for applications with stringent recovery point objectives and less tolerance for data loss, a replication solution is required for protecting data according to the backup schedule.

Chapter Summary

- Confidentiality is maintained through user authentication and access control.
- Application security can be achieved by implementing security techniques and following security guidelines.

- A distributed system is a collection of processors connected through a communication network.
- Firmware is programming written to the read-only memory (ROM) of a various electronic devices.
- Remanence is the residual representation of data that have been deleted.
- A disaster recovery plan assists and supports organizations in restoring the information technology functions after a disaster.
- Organizations perform BIA to identify the business's critical activities and the time frames within which systems must be restored when a disaster occurs.
- To make a disaster recovery plan effective, organizations must keep it up to date and applicable to current technology and business processes.
- The disaster recovery plan should be tested and maintained properly, ensuring that the document remains relevant and reliable.
- During the implementation of the recovery process, it is important for the DR teams to communicate and work together.
- Server virtualization is an effective tool for disaster recovery.

Review Questions

1. What are the aspects of information security?

   _____

   _____

   _____

   _____

2. What are the elements of application security?

   _____

   _____

   _____

   _____

3. What are the pros and cons of COTS software?

   _____

   _____

   _____

   _____

4. What are some database security issues?

   _____

   _____

   _____

   _____

5. What are the vulnerabilities of distributed systems?

6. What firmware security options are available?

7. What are the vulnerabilities in network security software?

8. What is remanence and how can it be overcome?

9. What makes an effective DRP?

10. What is a BIA?

11. What is an operations profile?

12. What are the requirements for an alternate site?

_____

_____

_____

_____

Hands-On Projects

1. Read about Internet security.

   ▪ Navigate to Chapter 3 of the Student Resource Center.

   ▪ Open Internet_Security.pdf and read the content.

2. Read about penetration testing.

   ▪ Navigate to Chapter 3 of the Student Resource Center.

   ▪ Open Netwk Vulnerability Test_wp.pdf and read the content.

3. Read about the evolution of security needs.

   ▪ Navigate to Chapter 3 of the Student Resource Center.

   ▪ Open Security.pdf and read the content.

4. Read about business continuity management.

   ▪ Navigate to Chapter 3 of the Student Resource Center.

   ▪ Open Business Continuity and Disaster Recovery Leaflet.pdf and read the content.

5. Read about disaster recovery planning.

   ▪ Navigate to Chapter 3 of the Student Resource Center.

   ▪ Open BCP.pdf and read the content.

6. Read about creating a backup plan.

   ▪ Navigate to Chapter 3 of the Student Resource Center.

   ▪ Open business_continuity.pdf and read the content.

7. Read about business continuity versus disaster recovery.

   ▪ Navigate to Chapter 3 of the Student Resource Center.

   ▪ Open Continuity.pdf and read the content.

Chapter 4

Business Continuity Management

Objectives

After completing this chapter, you should be able to:

- Build, manage, implement, and maintain a business continuity plan
- Understand the elements of business continuity management
- Develop business continuity strategies
- Develop a crisis communication plan
- Develop an emergency response plan
- Develop a contingency plan
- Utilize virtualization disaster recovery

Key Terms

Business impact analysis (BIA)   an essential function of a business continuity plan that includes analysis of vulnerabilities, risks, components critical to business functionality and/or survival, and a strategy for minimizing those discovered risks to keep the business operational during any critical disruption

Imaging   the process of creating a single file with the complete contents of a storage device

Load balancing   the process of sharing Web traffic across multiple servers

Recovery Point Objective (RPO)   the point in time to which an organization plans to recover its data after a disaster

Recovery Time Objective (RTO)   the maximum allowable time in which a business process must be restored after a disruption to avoid the negative consequences of a disaster or major disruption

Introduction to Business Continuity Management

Business continuity, or simply BC, is the ability of a business to continue operations with minimal disruption or downtime after a disaster. Business continuity management (BCM) is the process of managing risks and ensuring business continuity. This is an ongoing process with several different but complementary elements. This chapter introduces you to BCM and teaches you several forms of BCM, including business continuity plans, contingency plans, and virtualization data recovery.

Elements of Business Continuity Management

Business continuity management includes the following elements:

- *Risk mitigation plan*: By developing, implementing, and testing risk mitigation strategies, an organization is better protected from unexpected threats. There must be a detailed plan for risk identification, prioritization, monitoring, and mitigation. This allows the organization to systematically address potential risk events.

- *Business continuity plan*: Organizations should build comprehensive business continuity plans or BCPs. A BCP's main goal is to reduce losses to the organization, serve customers with minimal disruptions, and mitigate the negative effects of these disruptions on business operations.

- *Pandemic plan*: A pandemic can lead to human resource disruption, damaging the organization. It is necessary to prepare the company in case a health crisis causes organizational downtime.

- *Contingency plan*: BCM is, as a whole, preparing for unexpected events. Contingency planning includes preparing plans and strategies to effectively handle unexpected problems, emergencies, and catastrophic events.

- *Business recovery*: Business recovery involves restoring critical business functions within an acceptable time frame. Depending on the recovery strategies used, this can include temporary manual processing, recovery and operation on an alternate system, or relocation and recovery at an alternate site. This plan should consider aspects such as cost, acceptable outage time, and security.

- *Audits*: Organizations should perform regular audits on their business continuity processes. They should ensure they are well prepared and still appropriate to the changing business. Some aspects of the auditing process can be automated using audit management software.

Business Continuity Plan

Business continuity starts with a well-defined and well-documented business continuity plan that addresses all risks and secures systems vital to business operations. A BCP includes provisions for redundancies at all levels. That includes not just servers, storage, and networking equipment, but also other infrastructures such as air conditioning and power supplies.

The BCP should clearly lay out how to quickly recover from a disaster in order to reduce the disaster's impact. Figure 4-1 shows how the BCP is used to:

1. Understand the business
2. Build BCM strategies
3. Develop BCP response
4. Develop BCP culture
5. Exercise auditing and maintenance

A business continuity plan should address the following four components:

1. Readiness
2. Prevention
3. Response
4. Recovery/resumption

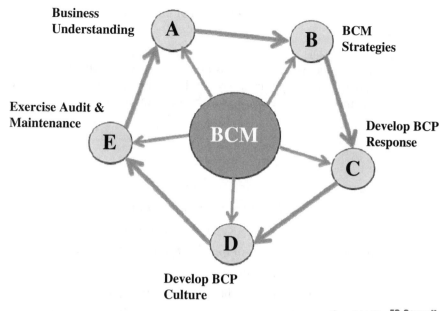

Figure 4-1   These are the five goals of a BCP.

Readiness

The readiness portion of the BCP covers preparatory steps and provides a strong foundation for the remainder of the BCP.

Assign Accountability

The senior leadership of the organization is responsible for creating, maintaining, testing, and implementing the BCP. All staff members must understand that the BCP is a high priority. It is also important that management at all levels understand their own level of accountability in the BCP.

- *Corporate policy*: The BCP should contain all steps to protect people, property, and business interests.
- *Ownership of systems, processes, and resources*: Organizations must clearly identify who is responsible for systems, resources, and key business processes.
- *Planning team*: A BCP team should be appointed to ensure widespread acceptance of the BCP.
- *Communicating the BCP*: The organization needs to communicate the BCP throughout all levels and departments of the organization. All employees should know the BCP structure and their roles within the plan.

Perform Risk Assessment

Risk assessment will identify and analyze the types of risk that can potentially impact the organization. Using existing information about known or anticipated risks, organizations should identify and review new risks that may impact the business and rate the likelihood of each risk. A risk assessment matrix mapping assets, vulnerabilities, probable threats, and risk mitigation methods can be used to identify risks and prioritize mitigation strategies.

Conduct a Business Impact Analysis (BIA)

After identifying the risks, the impact of an interruption in normal operations should be examined in a *business impact analysis (BIA)*. A BIA is an essential function of a business continuity plan that includes analysis of vulnerabilities, risks, components critical to business functionality and/or survival, and a strategy for minimizing those discovered risks to keep the business operational during any critical disruption. The following are the steps involved in a BIA:

1. *Identify critical processes*: Organizations must identify and document critical business processes. The document should include such processes as purchasing, manufacturing, supply chain, sales, distribution, accounts receivable, accounts payable, payroll, IT, and research and development. Organizations should assign the importance of these services as high, medium, or low.

2. *Assess crisis impact*:
   - Human cost
   - Financial cost
   - Reputation cost

3. *Determine maximum allowable outage and recovery time*:
   - Determine the period that a process can fail to function before the impact becomes unacceptable
   - Determine the acceptable amount of time for restoring the process
   - Identify and document backup processes
   - Evaluate the costs of alternate procedures versus waiting for the system to be restored

4. *Identify resources required for resumption and recovery*: These resources consist of personnel, technology, hardware and software, specialized equipment, and critical business records. Identifying, backing up, and storing critical business records in a secured location are important parts of an effective BCP.

Strategic Planning

Strategic planning addresses identification and implementation of:

- Methods to mitigate the risks and exposures identified in the BIA and risk assessment
- Plans and procedures to respond to any crisis

The BCP should contain multiple strategies to address different probable situations. It also addresses the duration of a business interruption and the extent of interruption. The strategies selected should be attainable, cost effective, likely to succeed, and relevant to the size and scope of the organization.

Crisis Management and Response Team Development

There must be a clear definition of the management structure. The team should contain representatives from human resources, information technology, security, legal, manufacturing, and other critical business support functions.

The crisis management team is supported by the required response teams, considering factors such as size and type, number of employees, and location. Response teams develop response plans to address the different aspects of a potential crisis, including site restoration, damage assessment, information technology, and administrative support. Response plans should be contained within the overall BCP.

Contact information for the personnel assigned to the crisis management and response teams should be included in the plan. Organizations should establish procedures to ensure that the information is kept up to date.

Prevention

Prevention includes limiting, preventing, or avoiding the impact of a crisis.

Compliance with Corporate Policy

Organizations should perform compliance audits on the BCP's policies and procedures. Any violations in the policy and procedures should be highlighted and corrected.

Mitigation Strategies

Cost-effective mitigation strategies should lessen the impact of a potential crisis. For example, a strong record management and technology disaster recovery program mitigates the loss of important data and documents.

Organizations must identify the different resources that contribute to the mitigation process. These resources, including the essential personnel and their roles and responsibilities, should be documented in the plan.

The resources that support the organization in mitigating the crisis should be monitored to ensure their availability and performance during the crisis. Some of these systems and resources include emergency equipment, local resources and vendors, system backups and off-site storage, and alternate worksites.

Avoidance, Deterrence, and Detection

The goal of avoidance is to prevent a crisis from happening in the first place by identifying, understanding, and addressing potential crises using risk assessment. Deterrence and detection can make a hostile action more difficult to carry out against the organization.

The facility security programs that support and enhance avoidance, deterrence, and detection are:

- *Architectural*: Natural or human-made barriers
- *Operational*: Security officers, employee security awareness programs, and protective security operations
- *Technological*: Intrusion detection, access control, recorded video surveillance, and package and baggage screening

Response

It is important to respond effectively, appropriately, and quickly during a crisis.

Recognize Potential Crises

- *Identify and recognize the danger signals*: A danger signal coupled with the likelihood of an event indicates an imminent crisis. Warning signs can include legislative changes, corporate policy changes, changes to the competitive environment, warnings of natural disasters, potential for civil or political instability, and changes to the supply-based environment.

- *Recognize and report potential crises*: Some departments or functions exist only to watch for the warning signs of an imminent crisis. The personnel employed in this department should be given proper training. A potential crisis should be communicated to all employees.

Notify the Teams

Once a potential crisis is recognized, the information should be given to the supervisor, a member of management, or whoever is responsible for crisis notification and management. Organizations must establish and document specific notification criteria, including who should be notified, when, and by whom.

Assess the Situation

Organizations must assess the problem and its severity at the beginning of the crisis. They should consider factors such as the size of the problem, its potential for escalation, and the impacts of the situation.

Declare a Crisis

Organizations must clearly define, document, and fit the specific parameters as to when a situation should be declared a crisis. The responsibilities for declaring a crisis should also be defined and assigned. Activities when declaring a crisis can include additional call notification, relocation, response-site and alternate-site activation, team deployment, emergency contract activation, and operational changes.

Execute the Plan

When developing the BCP, organizations should take into consideration the worst-case scenario and scale the response appropriately to match the actual crisis. When initiating a response, organizations should protect the following interests, with the most important listed first:

1. Secure personnel safety
2. Protect assets
3. Restore the critical business processes and systems
4. Reduce the length of business interruption
5. Prevent damage to the organization's reputation
6. Control media coverage
7. Maintain customer relations

Communications

- *Identifying the audiences*: The organization should identify the internal and external audiences to convey crisis and organizational response information to. It should divide the audiences into appropriate segments and communicate the required messages to each group.

- *Communicating with audiences*: These criteria should be taken into account in the crisis communications strategy:

  - Communications should be timely and honest.

  - Audiences should hear news directly from the organization before they hear it from any other source.

  - Communications should provide objective and subjective assessments.

  - All employees should be informed at approximately the same time.

  - Audiences should have the opportunity to ask questions, if possible.

  - The organization should provide regular updates and allow audiences to know when the next update will be issued.

- *Official spokesperson*: The organization should employ a single spokesperson to manage and disseminate crisis communications to the media and others. The personnel should be trained in media relations during a crisis.

Resource Management

The Human Element Organizations should devise a system by which all personnel can be accounted for after the onset of a crisis. They should arrange for crisis counseling as necessary and provide financial support to victims. The payroll system should remain functional throughout the crisis.

Logistics Logistical decisions made in advance impact the success and failure of a good BCP. Organizations must identify the primary crisis management center. This center is used for directing and overseeing crisis management activities. The organization should do the following:

- Set up alternate worksites during the recovery period.

- Examine the existing funding and insurance policies, and identify any additional funding and insurance.

- Establish critical vendor or service provider agreements, and maintain their contact information as part of the BCP.

- Make mutual aid agreements with other organizations to borrow required resources during a crisis.

Recovery and Resumption

Organizations should assess the damages once the crisis management team is activated. This damage assessment can be performed by the crisis management team or by a designated damage assessment team.

In the case of physical damage, the team is mobilized to the damaged site. The team makes an assessment of the extent of the damage and the time for which the facility will be nonfunctional. In case of less concrete damage to the business and information technology, the assessment is made as the crisis unfolds.

Resumption of Critical and Remaining Processes

When the extent of damage is known, organizations should determine and document the schedule for resumption. Prioritization should be based on the criticality of the process and other factors, including relationships to other processes, critical schedules, and regulatory requirements.

The resumption of the processes should be performed based on the prioritization schedule. The resumptions can take place at the alternate worksite. Organizations must make sure to document when the processes were resumed.

Once the critical processes have been resumed, the resumption of the remaining processes can be addressed. Where possible, the prioritization of these processes should be thoroughly documented in advance.

Return to Normal Operations

In this step, the organization is returned to normal, as well as possible. Each step of the process and all decisions should be carefully documented.

Implementing and Maintaining the Plan

The BCP is a living document that changes constantly to remain relevant and functional. It must be regularly tested, evaluated, and maintained. Employees must also be regularly trained to comply with the BCP.

Testing and Training

Organizations must train and educate the team members and the general employees to validate and enhance the BCP. Personnel should be trained regarding their individual responsibilities during a crisis. They should become familiar with the key components of the BCP and response plans. This training includes procedures for evacuation, check-in processes to account for employees, alternate worksite arrangements, and handling media inquiries.

Testing the BCP enables teams and employees to understand their roles and reveal any deficiencies in the BCP. Larger organizations may wish to establish a test team. Tests start relatively simple, with checklists and simple exercises. Eventually, tests become full-scale activations of the entire BCP, including the participation of public safety and emergency responders.

There are several different roles that test participants can fill, including the following:

- *Facilitators*: They posses all the knowledge about the test scenario and supervise the exercises. They introduce action messages simulating crisis situations and provide exercise oversight.

- *Controllers*: They introduce artificial stimuli at the direction of the facilitator. They make decisions during unanticipated actions or resource requirements. Controllers reduce damages by maintaining order.

- *Simulators*: They add realism to the scenario, portraying other companies, agencies, and organizations that interact with the participants.

- *Observers*: They are present to observe and document the performance. They should possess a strong knowledge about the subject matters and functions being evaluated. Observers evaluate the actions of the participants and the effectiveness of the BCP.

- *Participants*: They assume the crisis roles and perform actual or simulated activities appropriate to the type of exercise and scenario used.

Evaluation and Maintenance

Organizations should evaluate and review the BCP on a regular basis. In addition, they should conduct an evaluation after any of the following events:

- Risk assessment
- New regulatory requirements
- Occurrence of a crisis

After the review, organizations should modify any areas of the BCP that are shown to be insufficient. They should assign clear responsibility for BCP maintenance. Maintenance can be planned or unplanned and should reflect any changes in the operation of the organization that affect the BCP. The plan may need to be changed in the event of:

- Systems and application software changes
- Changes to the organization and its business processes
- Personnel changes (employees and contractors)
- Supplier changes
- Critical lessons learned from testing
- Issues discovered during the actual implementation of the plan in a crisis
- Changes to the external environment
- Other items noted during the review of the plan and identified during the risk assessment

Developing Business Continuity Strategies

Obtaining Management Approval

The easiest way to obtain management's approval is often to utilize an existing reporting process. That way, management is provided with regular status reports throughout the strategy development process. Senior management (particularly chief executive, financial, and operational officers) should review the developed strategies.

Preplanning

Organizations should review all the critical business processes and systems, *RTO* (*recovery time objective*: the maximum allowable time in which a business process must be restored after a disruption to avoid the negative consequences of a disaster or major disruption), *RPO* (*recovery point objective*: the point in time to which an organization plans to recover its data after a disaster), dependencies (such as vendors and suppliers), and the financial impact of prolonged outages. They should utilize the information in the business impact analysis (BIA) to ensure that new critical processes and systems are identified.

Continuity planners and business managers need to understand the potential impact of all relevant laws, industry regulations, and government codes, so it is necessary to determine who is responsible for maintaining current knowledge of these laws and regulations. Continuity planners and business managers must also be aware of the necessary types of audits and other reporting requirements.

Organizations must determine the worst-case scenario for which each strategy might apply and make sure there are strategies in place for new, emerging threats.

Planning and Development

Organizations must identify and incorporate risk mitigation strategies. They should identify vital records throughout the organization, including both electronic and paper, and make sure that a strategy exists for protecting these records. The BCP should include details of the backup and storage strategy for these vital records, such as location, method, and security.

Continuity planners should identify internal and external continuity resources. They should identify the available recovery alternatives available for each critical business function and assess the feasibility of using these alternatives.

Crisis Communication Plan

In addition to material damages, a crisis can harm an organization's reputation. Minimizing this damage requires a crisis communication plan. This plan offers several possible crisis scenarios and describes how to communicate with other persons and organizations during these scenarios. An efficient crisis communication plan should be flexible enough to adapt to specific situations as they unfold. The plan must be tested to ensure its effectiveness.

Preparing for a Crisis

The organization should first establish a crisis communication team. The team should meet regularly so that everyone is aware of his or her responsibilities. Next, the organization should show how to identify a crisis. It is important that any crisis be identified as early as possible.

Types of Crises

There are three types of crises:

- A sudden crisis is an immediate, unexpected crisis.
- A smoldering crisis begins small but grows larger. It is especially important to resolve these crises quickly.
- A bizarre crisis is unusual and unexpected.

Handling a Crisis

Once a crisis is indentified, organizations should take the following actions:

- Gather the facts.
- Convene the crisis communication team.

- Activate all relevant safety plans.
- Designate a command center and/or media center.
- Prepare a statement and background information.

Communication Guidelines

The following are some guidelines for communication concerning a crisis:

- Identify the stakeholders who should be informed about the situation.
- Have a single spokesperson to ensure a unified and consistent message to the public. The spokesperson should be informed of the latest developments.
- Provide guidance to the public in case of a health risk.
- Officials should develop simple messages for their stakeholders and the media. The messages should be delivered continuously and clearly.
- The crisis team should assess any possible tough questions that the media and public might ask.
- Communicate the facts of the crisis to the audience.
- Public affairs should control the flow of information by holding a series of press briefings.
- The spokesperson should keep records of all communications.
- Respond to the media quickly and fairly.

Emergency Response Plan

The emergency response plan describes the roles and operations of all units and personnel during an emergency. This plan should use a management system commonly known as the incident command system (ICS). ICS offers an organizational structure that assists in responding to all levels of emergencies, from simple to complex. It provides the flexibility to respond to an incident as its severity escalates.

The purpose of the ICS is to:

- Provide an organizational structure that grows quickly in response to the requirements of an emergency.
- Provide the incident commander (the designated person in charge of the emergency response) with the controls needed to direct and coordinate all operations and all agencies responding to the incident.
- Efficiently train employees on critical functions.
- Define staff positions who are responsible for managing a particular incident or incident level.

The emergency response plan should designate an emergency operations center (EOC). This is the centralized location for managing emergency operations.

There are three emergency severity levels:

1. *Level 1*: The emergency incident is managed without activating the EOC.
2. *Level 2*: This requires a multiunit response where the EOC is partially activated. Depending on the event, some EOC staff may be notified at the discretion of the incident commander.
3. *Level 3*: The emergency cannot be managed with normal resources. Additional personnel are requested to staff the EOC. In this level, a state of the disaster is declared.

Emergency Response Checklist

- Start a log of actions.
- Coordinate with emergency services.
- Identify any damage.
- Identify disrupted functions.
- Convene the response and recovery teams.
- Provide information to the staff.
- Decide on the course of action.

- Communicate decisions to staff and business partners.
- Provide public information to maintain reputation and business.
- Arrange a debriefing.
- Review the business continuity management plan.

Emergency Management Team (EMT)

In case of a major disaster, the emergency management team (EMT) will assemble and assess the situation. This team decides whether to implement the relevant business continuity plans. The BCP team leader will activate the plan once instructions are received from the operations manager of the emergency management team.

The BCP team leader will direct all ad hoc requests for decisions, assistance with facilities, acquiring outside services, etc., to the EMT through the operations manager. It will be the BCP team leader's responsibility to contact all the team members or their alternates and ensure that they convene at the emergency operations center.

Figure 4-2 shows the EMT's hierarchy.

Contingency Planning

A contingency plan, sometimes called a worst-case scenario plan or Plan B, helps sustain and recover vital corporate information after an emergency. IT contingency planning considers critical organizational assets, including business process continuity, organizational process continuity, and recovery planning. Recovery strategies and resources supporting the recovery must be in sync with one another.

Contingency planning includes the following plans:

- Business continuity plan (BCP), discussed earlier
- Business recovery plan (BRP), included in the BCP, outlining the restoration of business functions following an emergency
- Continuity of operations plan (COOP), helping to restore essential business functions at an alternate site temporarily
- Continuity of support plan/IT contingency plan, ensuring that services meet the needs of the IT system's users
- Crisis communication plan, outlining communication procedures

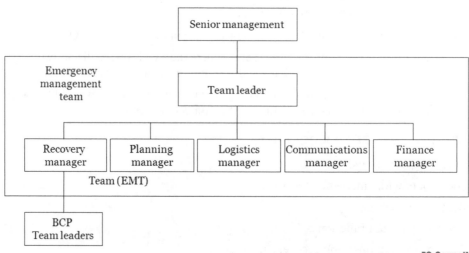

Figure 4-2 The EMT reports directly to senior management.

- Cyber-incident response plan, helping identify and mitigate malicious IT attacks
- Disaster recovery plan (DRP), part of the BCP explaining how to restore the operability of a system or facility
- Occupant emergency plan (OEP), addressing the procedures that should be carried out in situations that may jeopardize health and safety of personnel, the environment, or property

Contingency Planning and System Development

The system development life cycle (SDLC) is the process of developing an information system. This includes the following five phases, shown in Figure 4-3:

1. *Initiation*: The initiation phase includes determining the information system's goals and feasibility. The system's feasibility includes its system requirements and how well they match with operational processes. The requirements for a contingency plan should be analyzed based on the system's requirements and design.

2. *Development and acquisition*: Specific contingency plans can be incorporated as the concepts developed in the initiation phase are brought into the system design. The costs involved in modifying the system in the operation and maintenance phase can be minimized by robustness and redundancy in the system design.

3. *Implementation*: This phase involves testing the system as well as the contingency plan. The results must be documented after verifying the contingency plan.

4. *Operation and maintenance*: When the system is ready for operation, administrators should conduct a training and awareness program to familiarize users with the system and the contingency plan. Regular test runs should be conducted to verify the effectiveness of the contingency plan, and the plan should be updated based on the results of these tests.

5. *Disposal*: Legacy systems are replaced with newer systems in order to implement advanced applications. Until the new systems are tested, the older systems' contingency plans remain in effect. Some parts of the old systems can be used as spare parts for the new systems.

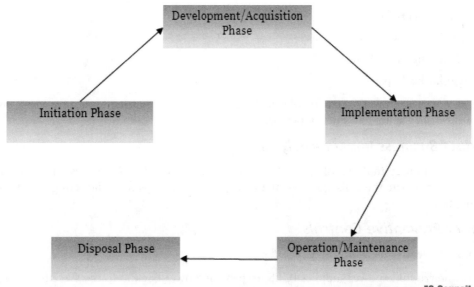

Figure 4-3   These are the five phases of the SDLC.

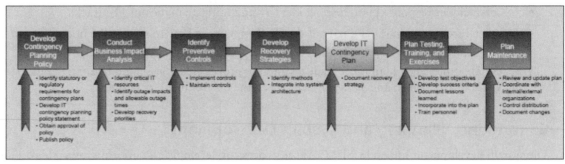

Source: http://www.nist.gov. Accessed 9/2009.

Figure 4-4   These are the steps of the IT contingency planning process.

IT Contingency Planning Process

Planning and maintaining an effective IT contingency plan includes the following steps, as shown in Figure 4-4:

1. Develop the contingency planning policy statement.
2. Conduct the business impact analysis (BIA).
3. Identify preventive controls.
4. Develop recovery strategies.
5. Develop an IT contingency plan.
6. Plan testing, training, and exercises.
7. Plan maintenance.

Develop the Contingency Planning Policy Statement

Developing a policy statement for the contingency plan ensures that it is both effective and easy to understand. The statement should clearly define the objectives of the contingency plan and everyone's responsibilities regarding the plan. Senior management should be involved in creating these definitions.

Key elements in the contingency planning policy statement include:

- Roles and responsibilities
- Scope
- Resource requirements
- Requirements for training
- Scheduling tests and exercises
- Scheduling maintenance
- Regular backups

Representatives from IT security, physical security, human resources, and IT operations should be consulted during the policy statement's development.

Conduct Business Impact Analysis

The business impact analysis (BIA) involves documenting the information system's requirements and processes in order to anticipate the consequences of a disruption. The steps for conducting a BIA can be found earlier in this chapter.

Identify Preventive Controls

Common preventive measures may include:

- Uninterruptible power supplies (UPS) to provide power backup to the system
- Gas- or diesel-powered generators for backup power
- Air-conditioning systems that continue to function after the failure of some components

- Fire suppression systems and fire/smoke detectors
- Water sensors in the computer room ceiling and floor
- Plastic tarps over IT equipment to protect them from water damage
- Heat-resistant and waterproof containers for backups and nonelectronic records
- Emergency master system shutdown switch
- Maintaining regular backups and storing backup media, nonelectronic records, and system documentation off-site
- Cryptographic key management and other access controls

Develop Recovery Strategies

Recovery strategies help in the quick restoration of IT operations after an emergency. These methods are covered in the following sections.

Backup Methods Critical data of the IT system should be backed up regularly, with more critical data backed up more frequently. Data can be backed up on a wide range of removable devices. Data storage facilities can also be located off-site, to protect them from threats facing the organization. Organizations should consider the following factors when choosing an off-site backup location:

- *Geographic area*: If the organization is affected by a local disaster, the storage facility should be far enough away that it will not be affected.
- *Accessibility*: Organizations should consider how long it would take to retrieve the backup from the remote site.
- *Security*: The storage facility should be secured from external and internal threats.
- *Environmental conditions*: The temperature of the storage facility, humidity controls, fire detection and prevention, and power management controls should be considered.
- *Cost*: Organizations should calculate the cost of operating the off-site backup facility and shipping the backups to the remote location.

Alternate Sites Contingency plans should consider an alternate site where the business functions of the organization can be carried out until the original facility returns to working order. It is important to prepare for long periods of time at the alternate site in the case of a major disaster.

There are three options available for an alternate site:

1. Site owned and operated by the organization
2. Site owned by an internal or external entity
3. Commercially leased facility

These alternate sites can be classified in terms of their operational readiness:

- *Cold*: Cold sites are cost-effective facilities with sufficient electrical power, air conditioning, and telecommunications to support a computer system. They do not actually house a computer system, so the computer and the necessary peripherals must be relocated to these sites after the disaster.
- *Warm*: These sites have the same conditions as cold sites, except they also contain part of the system's hardware and software. They are maintained in an operational condition to accommodate the disrupted system, so operations can resume quickly.
- *Hot*: Hot sites have similar computer systems already installed. Because of the computer systems, they are ready for operations as soon as the contingency plan is activated.
- *Mobile*: Mobile sites are facilities contained in a vehicle that can be driven to the alternate site. They house all the necessary equipment to meet the IT system requirements.
- *Mirrored*: Mirrored sites are built, maintained, and operated by the organization. They are identical to the primary sites that house the same equipment and facilities as the primary site. Data is stored simultaneously in the primary site and mirrored site.

Mirrored sites and hot sites are expensive but offer complete, fast recovery. Cold sites, though inexpensive, may take a longer time for recovery.

Equipment Replacement IT systems have to be quickly replaced if they are damaged in a disaster. Three basic strategies help in replacing the equipment:

1. *Vendor agreements*: Service-level agreements (SLAs) are made with hardware, software, and support vendors when the equipment is purchased and as the contingency plans are being developed. These agreements should specify how long it would take for the vendors to fix the affected systems or even replace them in the case of a disaster.

2. *Equipment inventory*: Required equipment should be purchased in advance and stored in an alternate site. The drawback of this plan is that the equipment could become obsolete, making it necessary to buy every new piece of equipment twice.

3. *Existing compatible equipment*: Equipment present at a hot site or compatible equipment from a different organization could be used.

Roles and Responsibilities Disaster recovery (DR) teams should be trained to implement the recovery strategies and contingency plans. These teams are responsible for bringing the IT system back to normal operations. Each team is led by a team leader, who directs the team members to their specific responsibilities and ensures that the team is coordinating with other teams while working on the contingency plan. The team leader is also responsible for decision making.

Cost Considerations The contingency planning coordinator ensures that the plan is implemented effectively, the personnel are trained, and a sufficient budget is allotted. The coordinator should ensure that the costs for equipment replacement, shipping, training programs, backup options, selection of alternate sites, and other resources are within the budget constraints.

Plan Testing, Training, and Exercises

The contingency plan (see IT Contingency Plan Development below) must be tested for its effectiveness. These tests will reveal any flaws in the plan and give the recovery teams valuable experience. The tests should address:

- Recoverability from backup media
- Synchronization of recovery teams
- Internal and external connectivity
- System performance with alternate equipment
- Restoration of normal operations
- Notifying relevant parties

Exercise formats include:

- *Classroom exercises*: This involves a walkthrough of the contingency plan procedures. None of the recovery operations are actually carried out, but it helps prepare teams for functional exercises.
- *Functional exercises*: Here, the disasters are simulated and the teams are expected to carry out the contingency plan as if it were, in fact, a real emergency.

Exercises should be planned in advance so that the team members are mentally ready and are available for the exercise.

Plan Maintenance

IT systems undergo numerous changes due to technology upgrades, changing business needs, and the policies of the organization. The contingency plan should be updated as these changes occur, in order for it to remain effective. The plan should be reviewed and modified regularly, at least once per year. Some elements may require more frequent changes, including:

- Operational and security requirements
- Redundancy of electronic data
- Technical procedures
- Hardware, software, and other equipment

- Contact information of the team members, vendors, and personnel at alternative sites and off-site
- Requirements of alternate and off-site facilities

Organizations should maintain a record of changes to the plan.

IT Contingency Plan Development

IT contingency plan development involves the following five phases:

1. Supporting information
2. Notification/activation phase
3. Recovery phase
4. Reconstitution phase
5. Plan appendices

Supporting Information

The supporting information consists of two components:

1. Introduction
2. Concept of operations

These components give key information to help in understanding, implementing, and maintaining the contingency plan. They also act as a guide and help the contingency plan coordinator in decision making.

The introduction component contains five sections:

1. *Purpose*: This defines why the IT contingency plan is being developed and its objectives.
2. *Applicability*: This subsection documents the business functions of the organization impacted by the contingency plan. Related plans that complement the IT contingency plan are identified and added to the appendix.
3. *Scope*: Specific issues that are addressed by the contingency plan are discussed here. This section also involves identifying the IT system for which the plan is being designed. The scope should also discuss any assumptions that were made in formulating the plan.
4. *References/requirements*: This subsection identifies laws and regulations that should be followed in preparing the contingency plan.
5. *Record of changes*: All changes made to the plan should be recorded and located at the beginning of the plan documentation.

The concept of operations component includes:

- *System description*: This gives a general description of the IT system for which the contingency plan is being formulated. The description should include system architecture, security devices installed in the system, and the location of the system. This information can be gathered from the system security plan.
- *Line of succession*: This section identifies the personnel member who will take over if someone is unable to perform his or her duties for the contingency plan.
- *Responsibilities*: This section includes the roles and responsibilities of the teams that are involved in implementing the IT contingency plan and the hierarchy of the teams. Responsibilities should be set to a team as a whole, not to individuals.

Notification/Activation Phase

This phase defines the primary actions that should be taken once an emergency is declared. It includes notifying the designated personnel (recovery staff), assessing the damage to the system, and implementing the contingency plan. After this stage, the designated personnel must be ready to implement the plan and recover the system functions.

- *Notification procedures*: System disruption can occur with or without warning. The recovery staff should be notified about the disruption as early as possible, so that they may be able to shut down the system and perform other preparatory actions. Procedures should be set as to how to notify the recovery staff during business and nonbusiness hours. The recovery personnel must be advised to regularly check their e-mails to avoid missing important security updates. The contingency plan should include the contact information of the recovery personnel and assessment teams.

- *Damage assessment*: To determine how the contingency plan will be implemented following an emergency, it is essential to assess the nature and extent of the damage to the system. The damage assessment team must be immediately notified about the disruption and then should assess the following as soon as possible:
    - Cause of the disruption/emergency and the areas affected
    - Chances of further disruptions and damages
    - Type of damage to the physical infrastructure and equipment
    - Inventory and functional status of IT equipment
    - Equipment to be replaced and the time required for returning to normal operations
- *Plan activation*: The IT contingency plan can be activated only when one or more activation criteria are met, as determined by the damage assessment team. The plan coordinator activates the plan after the damage assessment team gives its report. The criteria that should be identified in the contingency plan include:
    - Safety of personnel
    - Damage to the facility
    - Damage to the system
    - Importance of the system
    - Estimated time of the disruption

Recovery Phase

The activities in this phase involve repairing the damages and restoring the functions of the system to their normal operational conditions. If the damages cannot be repaired quickly, steps are taken to relocate the operations to an alternate site.

The system recovery sequence follows the priorities set in the BIA. Recovery procedures include:

1. Acquiring permission to visit the area of the disrupted system
2. Notifying internal and external business partners associated with the system
3. Acquiring supplies for recovery
4. Acquiring and installing hardware
5. Acquiring backup media and installing it
6. Restoring operating system and application software
7. Restoring system data
8. Testing system functionality and security controls
9. Connecting the system to the network
10. Operating alternate equipment

Reconstitution Phase

In this phase, business operations and systems are completely restored to their normal functional state. If normal operations cannot be restored to the original facility, the operations are transferred to a new facility. This phase also defines the teams that restore the system and the site.

The activities in this phase include:

- Ensuring basic infrastructure support and supplies
- Installing system hardware, software, and firmware
- Connecting the system to the network
- Testing the functionality of the restored system

- Backing up operational data on the contingency system and uploading to the restored system
- Shutting down the contingency system
- Terminating the contingency operations
- Securing sensitive materials at the contingency site
- Arranging for recovery personnel to return to the original facility

Plan Appendices

Additional relevant details that are not covered in the contingency plan documentation should be included in the appendices section. These details may include:

- Contact information of vendors and the contingency planning team
- Procedures and checklists for system recovery
- Detailed information about the equipment vital to support system operations
- Vendor SLAs and agreements with other organizations
- Details of the alternate site

Technical Contingency Planning Considerations

Contingency plans are necessary for several different IT platforms, and they may slightly differ for each platform, based on that platform's specific requirements.

Desktop Computers and Portable Systems

Computers and portable systems are the most common platforms used in organizations, so they are extremely important in contingency plans. Contingency considerations for computers and portable systems include:

- Storing backups off-site
- Encouraging individuals to back up data
- Providing guidance on saving data on personal computers
- Standardizing hardware, software, and peripherals
- Documenting system configurations and vendor information
- Using results from the BIA

Organizations need to consider the following when choosing backup media:

- Equipment interoperability
- Storage volume
- Storage life of the media

The following are a few types of backup media:

- Tape drives
- Removable storage devices
- Compact discs
- Network storage
- Replication or synchronization with portable devices
- Internet backup

One effective method of backing up data is *imaging*. Imaging involves creating a single file with the complete contents of a storage device. This creates a large file, but it makes it possible to restore the contents of the device with no changes whatsoever.

Servers

Any disruption in the server could bring a business to a standstill. The following contingency considerations address server vulnerabilities:

- Store backup media and software off-site.
- Standardize hardware, software, and peripherals.
- Document system configurations and vendors.
- Coordinate with security policies and system security controls.
- Use results from the BIA.

The BIA helps in selecting the right contingency solution for enhanced recovery capabilities. The security of critical data should be considered when selecting a contingency solution. Servers can have backup drives of their own, or a centralized backup system can be deployed by attaching a backup drive to one central server. Server data can be backed up in the following ways:

- *Full backup*: A full backup stores all data in a folder or a disk onto a single backup medium. This makes it easy to retrieve a particular file, but the backup process takes a long time.
- *Incremental backup*: Only the files that were created or modified after the last backup are captured here. It does not take long to make the backup, as less information is being backed up than the original full backup, but retrieving data to recover a system would require restoring the last full backup and then each sequential incremental backup from oldest to most recent in order to achieve a complete restoration.
- *Differential backup*: The files that were created or modified after the last full backup are stored. This takes less time than a full backup but more time than an incremental backup, as each time the differential backup is made, it will include all information that has been modified since the last full backup. It requires fewer media for system restoration because retrieving the data to recover the system involves only restoring the data from the last full backup and the latest differential backup.
- *Redundant Array of Independent Disks (RAID)*: A RAID is a type of virtual hard drive consisting of two or more hard disks. Because RAID uses multiple disks, reliability is increased.

Web Sites

These measures should be considered for Web site contingency planning:

- Document the Web site's hardware, software, and configuration.
- Document any programming changes.
- Coordinate contingency solutions with appropriate security policies and security controls.
- Coordinate contingency solutions with incident response procedures.
- Use results from the BIA.

When planning contingency solutions for a Web site, organizations should consider the sites' supporting infrastructures. This infrastructure includes the server hosting the Web sites and the local area network (LAN).
Load balancing is one solution, in which more than one server shares Web traffic. This provides redundancy, enabling at least one server to work when the other fails. Load balancing can be achieved by using DNS or reverse proxy.

- *DNS*: A URL request typed in a browser is directed to a DNS server. This maps the request to an IP address and then directs it to one of the servers.
- *Reverse proxy*: A proxy server is stationed between the client and the server. It receives requests from the clients, passes them to one of the servers, and then sends the response back to the client from the server. The reverse proxy server gathers all browser requests together, reducing the bandwidth.

Local Area Networks (LANs)

A LAN can be implemented using two architectures:

1. In a peer-to-peer network, users can transfer files from one computer to another.
2. In a client-server model, all computers in the network connect to a server and access data from that server.

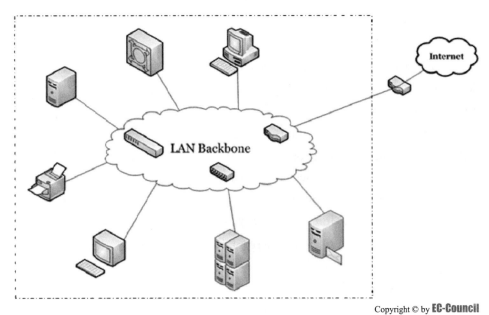

Figure 4-5   In most workplaces, computers are networked together.

Figure 4-5 shows a local area network.
Organizations should consider these measures for LAN contingency planning:

- Diagram the LAN.
- Document system configuration and vendor information.
- Coordinate with security policies and security controls.
- Use results from the BIA.

The BIA identifies key devices in the LAN, including:

- Cabling systems
- Network connecting devices (hubs, routers, and bridges)
- Remote access provided by servers on the LAN

Wireless networks may act as a contingency solution when wired LAN service is disrupted.

Wide Area Networks (WAN)

A WAN is a long-range communications network, which could use one or more of the following:

- Dial-up connections
- Integrated Services Digital Network (ISDN)
- T1
- T3
- Cable Internet
- DSL
- Fiber optic Internet
- Frame relay
- ATM
- Synchronous optical network (SONET)
- Wireless LAN bridge
- Virtual private network (VPN)

WAN contingency considerations include:

- Diagram the WAN.
- Document system configurations and vendors.
- Coordinate with security policies and security controls.
- Use results from the BIA.

WANs have these contingency solutions:

- Redundant communications links
- Redundant network service providers (NSPs)
- Redundant network connecting devices
- Redundancy from NSP or Internet service provider (ISP)

The NSP or ISP should be checked for the reliability of its core networks.

Distributed Systems

Distributed systems are used in situations in which the users and clients are dispersed over wide geographical areas. All these systems should be synchronized to avoid any processing errors. They have the following considerations:

- Standardize hardware, software, and peripherals.
- Document system configurations and vendors.
- Coordinate with security policies and security controls.
- Use results from the BIA.

Because the distributed systems are located over wide geographical locations, the BIA should address the risk of the system and its infrastructure. The contingency solutions for distributed systems are reflected in the solutions for LANs and WANs, because these systems are dependent on them. Any changes in the primary system should be reflected in the rest of the systems.

Mainframe Systems

Mainframes are large computers with the ability to perform critical and complex functions. These systems have centralized architecture in which the clients receive the output but are not involved in the processing.

The considerations for a mainframe are similar to the contingency considerations for other platforms discussed. A mainframe lacks the redundancy of a distributed system, making it very important to back up critical information. The following elements should be considered to determine the contingency requirements for a mainframe system:

- Store backup media off-site.
- Document system configurations and vendors.
- Coordinate with network security policy and system security controls.
- Utilize results from the BIA.

The contingency solutions should consider the fact that storage in a mainframe system exists at a single location, unlike distributed systems where the data is replicated at various locations. Organizations should use UPS and power monitoring systems to ensure that the system does not crash due to a power failure. They should also consider diesel- or gas-run generators to help ensure that power is always available.

Maintaining a warm or hot site is a good solution, although the size and expense of installing such a large system at an alternate site is not viable for most organizations. It may be possible to share a replacement mainframe system with other organizations.

Vendor support is a must for mainframe systems. Although vendors may not be able to fix the system within the outage time, they might help in replacing critical equipment. Service agreements with vendors should be updated regularly.

Preventive Controls

Preventive controls help mitigate risks. Some of these controls include:

- The organization should be designed to allow segregation of duties and roles.
- Standardize policies and procedures.
- Personnel should be trained to perform a particular job.
- Systems should follow standard design and architecture.

User Account Maintenance

Securing the user account information is a critical part of avoiding damage from intrusions. Login information in the wrong hands could lead to data theft or system crashes. User passwords can be secured using authentication methods such as Pluggable Authentication Module (PAM)–based authentication and database-based authentication. Installing filters and firewalls also helps protect the system from unauthorized access.

Processes for Timely Deletion of Accounts

Once accounts become inactive, system administrators should delete them in order to prevent attackers from using them. In the case of an employee leaving the organization, that user's account should be deleted after taking a backup of all the important data from that particular account profile. Users leaving the organization must assist the service/departmental managers in locating important files and e-mails required for further operations.

Virtualization Disaster Recovery

Virtualization makes use of a single physical server for running multiple virtual machines. That way, multiple users interact with the system as if they were each using their own individual system. Virtualization can be performed by a software layer called a virtual machine monitor (VMM). This increases efficiency, decreases costs, and increases the scalability and availability of enterprise storage environments.

Virtualization disaster recovery (VDR) technology allows organizations to quickly and effectively recover important business systems. VDR solutions reduce the downtime associated with traditional storage recovery solutions, allowing the organization to recover data immediately after the disaster recovery solution is installed, at a fraction of the cost.

Virtualization Benefits

Virtualization offers several benefits for organizations, including:

- Greater flexibility/agility in IT environments
- More balanced server workload
- Reduced physical size of the data center
- Reduced power consumption
- Reduced costs

Workload Portability

Workload portability means that workloads can be detached from their original hardware configuration, and entire software stacks can be moved to another physical or virtual host. This means that workloads can be circulated between similar virtual hosts in order to balance workloads.

Typical workload portability scenarios include:

- Physical-to-virtual host portability
- Virtual-to-physical host portability
- Physical-to-physical host portability
- In-and-out-of-imaging formats

Workload portability improves the flexibility, agility, and overall competency of data centers, allowing organizations to tackle challenges such as:

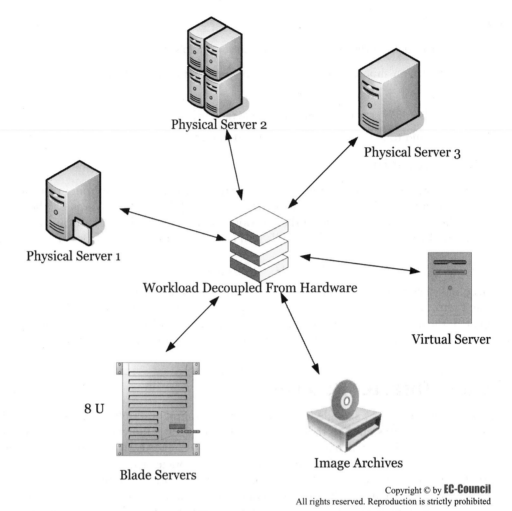

Figure 4-6   Virtualization allows for workload portability, where workloads can be circulated among similar hosts.

- End-of-lease hardware migration
- Server consolidation
- Disaster recovery

Figure 4-6 demonstrates workload portability.

Workload Protection

Workload protection involves copying the server's workload to a secondary location in case of a primary server outage or disaster. Keeping a bootable archive of the workload on the virtual recovery platform makes it much easier to quickly recover.

Using a virtualization process, multiple workloads are duplicated to a single virtual recovery environment over a WAN. This process gives complete protection to the physical or virtual workloads, providing an ability to replicate the entire workload, rather than just application data, to the virtual machine environment. It ensures that anything that is required to restore operations is present in a bootable virtual machine on the recovery server, at a significantly lower cost than one-to-one solutions.

Figure 4-7 shows workload protection with consolidated recovery.

Rapid Recovery

When a primary server outage or disaster strikes, the virtualized recovery server is activated to run the workload immediately. The workload executes in the virtual recovery environment until the primary server is restored. That way, recovery time and point objectives are achieved without requiring a high-cost and complex clustering environment.

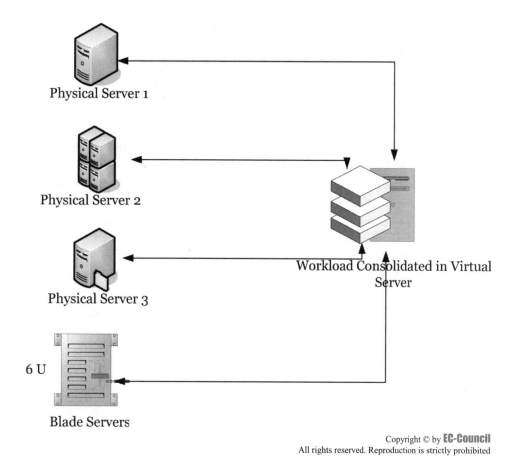

Figure 4-7 Protecting workloads in a virtual recovery environment has many of the benefits of one-to-one solutions at a significantly lower cost.

When planning a virtualized recovery environment, organizations should check for sufficient computer power and capacity to run the recovery workload for as long as it will take to restore the production server. If the physical host is insufficiently sized, the workloads may have to run in a degraded state, which may impact business operations.

At the recovery planning stage, a workload profiling and analysis solution is required. These solutions are used to monitor the workload and resource utilization trends for a certain period of time to estimate everything about resource utilization. These solutions guarantee that the recovery environment is perfectly balanced to take care of present and future workload requirements.

Ease of Testing

Organizations must thoroughly check their disaster recovery strategies, solutions, and methodologies. Conventional recovery solutions are complex in nature, so they cannot be tested regularly. Virtualization recovery solutions are easier to test, and these tests can be run without interrupting business operations.

Planning and Implementing an Virtualized Recovery Solution

The implementation of a successful virtualized recovery solution starts with creating a detailed plan. The steps in the planning phase are:

1. *Discover server inventory*: In this step, organizations discover and list all the assets in the IT environments, including the physical and virtual servers and data, applications, and operating systems. This information is included in the disaster recovery plan.

2. *Monitor server utilization*: Organizations monitor for workload information such as CPU, disk, memory, and network utilization rates in a particular period of time. This collected information provides invaluable workload profiling and capacity planning data.

3. *Build the disaster recovery plan*: Organizations develop the recovery plans to determine the exact virtual recovery site capacity. They must build sufficient headroom at the target virtualized recovery environment to ensure sufficient capacity to run consolidated workloads and resources in case of a disaster.

4. *Configure the virtual recovery environment*: Finally, organizations must match the physical production servers with the virtual recovery machines and configure the virtual recovery environment.

Implementing a virtualized recovery solution involves the following steps:

1. *Initial system backup*: Execute a complete system backup by transferring the entire server workloads to the target virtual recovery environment with the help of the workload portability solution.

2. *Ongoing incremental backups*: Automatically propagate all source changes to the target virtual recovery environment so that it always contains a current copy of the production environment.

3. *Run fire drills to test DR readiness*: Run disaster recovery fire drills to verify the application's integrity and recovery time. Run a test restore on the backup virtual machine to take an image of the virtual file associated with the virtual machine.

4. *Initiate one-click failover in case of system outage*: If the production server fails, initiate a system failover to rapidly start up the session.

5. *Rapidly restore systems*: When the production system is repaired, execute a virtual-to-physical workload transfer for restoring workloads to the original server.

Chapter Summary

- Business continuity management (BCM) involves managing risks and ensuring the availability of business functions.

- An emergency response plan describes the role and operation of all units and personnel during an emergency.

- An organization should have alternate worksites identified for business resumption and recovery.

- Organizations should implement evaluation and maintenance programs to keep the business continuity plan relevant.

- IT contingency planning represents a broad scope of activities designed to sustain and recover critical IT services following an emergency.

- Virtualization disaster recovery (VDR) technology allows organizations to quickly and effectively recover important business systems.

Review Questions

1. What are the elements of business continuity management?

   _____

   _____

   _____

   _____

2. What is a BCP?

   _____

   _____

   _____

   _____

3. What is an emergency response plan?

_____

_____

_____

_____

4. What is a crisis communication plan?

_____

_____

_____

_____

5. What are the five goals of a BCP?

_____

_____

_____

_____

6. What is a contingency plan?

_____

_____

_____

_____

7. How can a contingency plan be worked into the system development life cycle?

_____

_____

_____

_____

8. How do you conduct a BIA in the contingency planning process?

_____

_____

_____

_____

9. How is a contingency plan maintained?

_____

_____

_____

_____

10. What is virtualization?

_____

_____

_____

_____

11. What is workload protection?

_____

_____

_____

_____

12. What are the steps in planning and implementing a virtualized recovery solution?

_____

_____

_____

_____

Hands-On Projects

1. Read about IT risk management.

   ▪ Navigate to Chapter 4 of the Student Resource Center.

   ▪ Open Industry_BCM_Managing_Information_Technology_Risk.pdf and read the content.

2. Read about risk assessment.

   ▪ Navigate to Chapter 4 of the Student Resource Center.

   ▪ Open Risk Assessment Instructions.pdf and read the content.

3. Read about technology risk.

   ▪ Navigate to Chapter 4 of the Student Resource Center.

   ▪ Open Unpan.pdf and read the content.

4. Read about enterprise risk management.

   ▪ Navigate to Chapter 4 of the Student Resource Center.

   ▪ Open COSO_ERM_ExecutiveSummary.pdf and read the content.

5. Read about contingency planning for IT systems.

   ▪ Navigate to Chapter 4 of the Student Resource Center.

   ▪ Open Contingency Planning Guide for Information Technology Systems.pdf and read the content.

6. Read about the contingency planning process.

   ▪ Navigate to Chapter 4 of the Student Resource Center.

   ▪ Open contingency_planning_process.pdf and read the content.

7. Read about continuity of operation.

   ▪ Navigate to Chapter 4 of the Student Resource Center.

   ▪ Open coop.pdf and read the content.

8. Read about the benefits of virtualization.

   ▪ Navigate to Chapter 4 of the Student Resource Center.

   ▪ Open Benefits of Virtualization for BCDR.pdf and read the content.

9. Read about using virtualization for disaster recovery.

   ▪ Navigate to Chapter 4 of the Student Resource Center.

   ▪ Open Virtualization for Disaster Recovery.pdf and read the content.

10. Read more about virtualization for disaster recovery.

   ▪ Navigate to Chapter 4 of the Student Resource Center.

   ▪ Open Virtualization Technologies and Their Impact on Disaster Recovery Planning.pdf and read the content.

Managing, Assessing, and Evaluating Risks

Objectives

After completing this chapter, you should be able to:

- Conduct risk management
- Explain the importance of risk management
- Integrate risk management into SDLC
- Follow the risk management methodology
- Follow the risk assessment methodology
- Conduct system characterization
- Use security countermeasures
- Calculate residual risk
- List the responsibilities of an information systems security officer (ISSO)
- Evaluate information systems
- Conduct information system acquisition and disposition

Key Terms

Impact analysis a type of analysis that determines the impact that a threat could have on a system

Residual risk the risk that results from issues that were not covered by the assessment or that come up after the assessment

Risk assessment a quantitative or qualitative process that deals with the identification of possible risks and their impacts, and provides measures to be taken to reduce the risks

Risk mitigation a process that involves the implementation of risk control measures to minimize risk to an acceptable level

Risk variables the elements or factors in an environment that cause a corresponding degree of change in the exposure to a risk

Security countermeasures the actions or solutions used to prevent attacks

Security requirements checklist   a document that comprises essential and basic security standards that can be used to methodically evaluate and identify the vulnerabilities of information system assets in the management, operational, and technical security areas

Technical surveillance countermeasure (TSCM) techniques   techniques used to detect and neutralize the hostile penetration technologies used to gain unauthorized access to confidential and sensitive information

TEMPEST   a government project studying compromising electrical, mechanical, or acoustical energy emissions unintentionally emitted by electrical equipment/systems such as computers, monitors, or transmission lines, allowing the information therein to be captured

Threat   any event that could have a negative impact on the operations of the organization

Threat source   any incident or occurrence with the potential to cause harm to an information system

Vulnerability   any weakness in the operations or systems of an organization that could be exploited by a threat agent

Introduction to Managing, Assessing, and Evaluating Risks

Risk management is performed to identify threats and prevent them from severely affecting an organization. Risk management is an integral part of business continuity planning and all disaster recovery efforts. A *risk assessment* is a quantitative or qualitative process that deals with the identification of possible risks and their impacts, and provides measures to be taken to reduce those risks. When a risk assessment is complete, *risk mitigation* is performed to implement risk control measures to minimize the risk to an acceptable level. It involves all the risks identified in the risk assessment process. The efficiency of the risk management program and its implementation is then tested, and the results of this process are used to update the risk assessment and mitigation processes.

The DAA (designated approving authority) and the system-authorizing official are responsible for risk management and checking that risks remain within acceptable limits. If risks exceed the acceptable level, the authorities also provide additional security controls that need to be executed to remove the residual risks.

Importance of Risk Management

Risk management helps organizations avoid heavy losses. These losses can be financial or data-related losses. Risk management is important for the following reasons:

- It protects organizations' information assets.
- It protects business continuity and enables organizations to accomplish their business objectives.
- It minimizes the effect of risk on organizations' finances and earnings.
- It provides organizations with a sense of security.
- It helps organizations control IT systems-related mission risks.
- It enables organizations to maintain a balance between operational and financial costs.
- It helps organizations' management identify suitable controls for implementing required security measures.

Integration of Risk Management into the System Development Life Cycle (SDLC)

Integration of risk management into the system development life cycle (SDLC) enables an organization to minimize risks and helps management to select and implement appropriate risk control measures. Risk management should be integrated completely into SDLC to develop a more secure and robust system. The following phases comprise an IT system's SDLC:

1. Initiation
2. Development or acquisition
3. Implementation
4. Operation or maintenance
5. Disposal

SDLC Phases	Phase Characteristics	Support from Risk Management Activities
Phase 1—Initiation	Defines the requirements of an IT system and documents its scope	Recognized risks help in supporting the development of system requirements
Phase 2—Development or Acquisition	The IT system is designed and developed	Recognized risks help in supporting security analyses
Phase 3—Implementation	The security measures in a system are configured, activated, and tested for efficiency	The risk management process checks whether the system is implemented according to the modeled operations or checks against its requirements
Phase 4—Operation or Maintenance	The system is functioning and requires changes or modifications regularly based on the policies, processes, and procedures	Risk management activities aid in system reauthorization in case of changes made to the system
Phase 5—Disposal	This involves destroying, archiving, and moving information, hardware, or software	Performed on the system components to dispose of or change the hardware and software

Table 5-1   **The risk assessment process is performed in each phase of SDLC**

The risk management process is performed in each major phase of SDLC. Table 5-1 describes the characteristics of each phase.

Risk Management Methodology

It is important for organizations to maintain business continuity. Risk management is a part of the overall business continuity and disaster recovery processes. Successful risk management ensures that the risks facing an organization remain within acceptable levels and are mitigated before they cause harm. Organizations should also develop and maintain efficient risk management plans to overcome legal compliance issues.

Risk management plans are developed after a comprehensive risk assessment and require active management involvement. Management's involvement ensures that the effective risk controls can be identified and implemented successfully. Risk management involves the following steps:

1. *Risk identification*: This step involves the identification of all the risks facing an organization that may affect normal business operations.

2. *Risk assessment*: This step involves the determination of the potential impact of risks on business assets and operations.

3. *Risk prioritization*: Risk prioritization aids in the categorization of risk control methods. Risks are categorized according to the criticality of the systems and processes they may affect.

4. *Risk analysis*: Risk analysis is a systematic analysis of the causes of risks. It involves the analysis of threat sources and factors that give rise to risks.

5. *Development of strategies to manage the identified risks*: Different strategies are developed for the proper and effective management of the identified risks.

6. *Implementation of risk management plan*: After developing the strategies, the best suitable solution is established to counter the risks. Then the solution is implemented according to the plan.

Risk Assessment

Risk assessment may be defined as a set of guidelines and procedures used to identify and assess the risks that pose a threat to the business or project environment. It involves identifying and prioritizing security risks according to critical information assets and key business processes. It determines the probability and magnitude of the possible threats, vulnerabilities, and risks associated with an IT system. It also determines the level of risk and the resulting security requirements for each system.

Risk assessment for a new system is conducted at the beginning of the system development life cycle. Risk assessment for an existing system is conducted when major modifications are made to the system's environment.

Risk assessment also involves training the staff to understand the risks in business operations and make them aware of certain best practices that would prevent sensitive information from being exposed. The output of the risk assessment process enables the identification of security measures to minimize risk and aid in the risk mitigation process. The organization should plan, implement, and monitor a set of security measures for the identified risks.

Risk Variables

Risk variables are the elements or factors in an environment that cause a corresponding degree of change in the exposure to a risk. These variables determine the risks to an organization. The risk assessment process is a function of these elements. All the risk variables are interdependent and affect the probability of each other.

The risk identification phase of a risk assessment relies on the determination of risk variables. Accuracy in determination of risk variables influences the effectiveness of a risk assessment and risk mitigation controls. Risk variables are often determined by evaluations of certain assumptions or management's perception of risks in the operating environment, along with a statistical analysis of various business indicators. The determination is also influenced by management's previous disaster recovery efforts.

Threats

Information assets in an organization are vulnerable to threats. A *threat* is any event that could have a negative impact on the operations of the organization. Threats may be internal or external. Internal threats originate from within an organization, whereas external threats are created by outsiders who attempt to breach organizational security. For example, if an employee tries to breach the data access policies and tries to get control of information assets, it is an internal threat; if an outsider plants a Trojan in the organization's network and tries to steal information, it is an external threat.

The types of threats can be differentiated as follows:

- Intentional actions
- Unintentional actions
- Problems caused by system hardware or software
- Other events
  - Power failure
  - Telecommunication failure
  - Natural disaster

These threats can result in disclosure of assets, damage to assets, destruction of hardware or software, etc.

Risk Assessment Methodology

The following steps are involved in the risk assessment process:

1. System characterization
2. Threat identification
3. Vulnerability identification
4. Control analysis
5. Likelihood determination
6. Impact analysis
7. Risk determination
8. Recommendations to control the threats
9. Results documentation

Step 1: System Characterization

In this step, the limits of an IT system are determined in order to set the scope of the risk assessment, as shown in Figure 5-1. The IT system is characterized along with the circumstances under which it operates. To identify

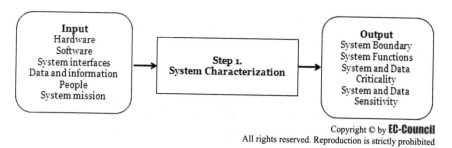

Figure 5-1 System characterization involves determining the scope of the risk assessment.

the risk to a system, a good knowledge of the system's processing environment is necessary. The organization needs to collect the following system-related information:

- Organization's hardware assets, including computer systems, networking devices, and other equipment
- Software assets
- System interfaces
- Data and information
- Users of the IT system
- Objective of the system
- System and data criticality
- System and data sensitivity

The following techniques can be used to gather information about an IT processing environment. The methods can be applied individually, or they can be combined to collect information.

- Preparing a checklist of questions that the technical and nontechnical management staff can use in on-site visits and interviews. This checklist should contain various management or operational controls planned or practiced by the IT system.
- Using automated tools to collect technical information such as vulnerability details.
- Collecting the following data on the planned IT system's security controls:
  - Policy documents
  - System documentation
  - System administration manual
  - System design documentation
  - Security-related documentation
  - Use of automated scanning tools

After gathering all the required information, the organization should design a system characterization template, such as the one in Figure 5-2.

Step 2: Threat Identification

In this step, different threats and threat sources are identified, as shown in Figure 5-3. A ***threat source*** is any incident or occurrence with the potential to cause harm to the information system. A threat source does not present a risk if there is no vulnerability that can be exercised for that particular threat source.

The following threat sources are common:

- *Human threats*: Human threats are more difficult to predict and identify due to their uncertain nature. The following human threats are common:
  - False data entry or deletion of data
  - Inadvertent acts

System Name:
Hardware
Software
System Interfaces
Data & Information
Persons who support the IT system
System mission (e.g. processes performed by the system)
System & data criticality (system's value or importance to the organization)
Functional requirements of the IT system
Users of the system
System Security policies (organizational policies, federal requirements, industry practices, laws)
System security architecture
Current network topology (e.g. network diagram)
Current information storage protection that safeguards system & data CIA
Flow of information relating to the IT system
Management controls used for the IT system (e.g. security planning, rules of behavior)
Operational controls (e.g. back-up, contingency, and resumption and recovery operations, personnel security...)
Physical security environment (e.g. facility security, data center policies)
Environmental security (temperature control, water, power)

Figure 5-2 A system characterization template is used to show the characteristics of a system.

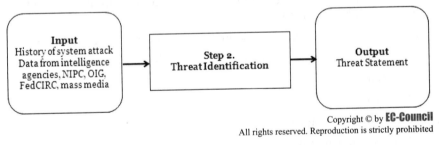

Figure 5-3 Threat sources must be identified in a risk assessment.

- Eavesdropping
- Impersonation
- Shoulder surfing
- User abuse or fraud
- Theft, sabotage, vandalism, or physical intrusions
- Espionage
- *Technical threats*: These threats arise due to system misconfigurations and errors in application development. Though there are procedural solutions for most technical threats, the complexity in current evolving technologies and weak interrelations between various stakeholders in the field make them difficult to avoid. The following technical threats are common:
  - Breaking passwords for unauthorized access to system resources
  - Sniffing and scanning of network traffic

- Data/system contamination
- Malicious code infection
- Spam and mail frauds
- Phishing that may result in loss of confidential private information
- DDoS attacks
- Application coding errors
- Unauthorized modification of a database
- Session hijacking
- System and application errors or failures

The threat identification process is performed in two steps:

1. *Threat-source identification*: The main objective of this step is to recognize the probable threat sources and develop a list of identified threat sources that are applicable to the information system being evaluated. While identifying threat sources, it is vital to consider all probable threat sources that may cause harm to the information system and its operations.

2. *Determination of motivation and threat actions*: The motivations for and resources used to perform an attack make humans potentially hazardous threat sources. A review of existing threat identification reports helps security personnel identify human threat sources that have a potential to harm an information system. The following reports are valuable sources of information on threat sources:

   - System break-in report
   - Security violation reports
   - Security incident reports

After identifying a potential threat source, security personnel must develop a report or estimation of motivation and resources to carry out a successful attack. The threat report, containing probable threat sources, should be tailored to the individual organization and its processing environment.

Step 3: Vulnerability Identification

A *vulnerability* is any weakness in the operations or systems of an organization that could be exploited by a threat agent. The main objective of this step is to prepare a list of information system vulnerabilities that could be exploited by the probable threat sources, as shown in Figure 5-4. Different types of vulnerabilities exist in information systems, and methods required to decide whether the vulnerabilities are present generally depend on the nature of the information system.

If the information system has not yet been developed, the identification of potential vulnerabilities should focus on security policies, intended security procedures, and system requirement definitions of the organization. If the information system is in the process of being implemented, the search for potential vulnerabilities should be expanded to include the intended security features described in the security design plan and the outcome of the system certification process and evaluation. If the information system is operational, the search for potential vulnerabilities should focus on analysis of security features and security controls.

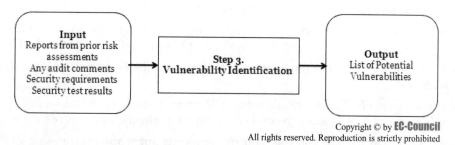

Figure 5-4 Vulnerability identification is performed through the use of security tests and prior reports.

The vulnerability identification process includes the following methods:

- *Vulnerability sources*: Potential vulnerabilities associated with an information system's processing environment can be recognized with the help of information-gathering techniques. A review of other organizational resources also helps in preparing useful questionnaires to recognize vulnerabilities that may be applicable to particular information systems. The Internet is also a good source for information gathering. Many vendors post known system vulnerabilities and their remedial measures to eliminate vulnerabilities. The following documented vulnerability sources should be considered in a vulnerability analysis:

  - Previous risk assessment reports on the information system.

  - Information system audit reports, security reports, and system test and evaluation reports.

  - Known vulnerability lists gathered from the Web.

  - Vendor advisories.

  - System software security analyses.

- *System security testing*: Many system security-testing methods are used to identify information system vulnerabilities depending on the criticality of the information system and available resources. This includes the following system security-testing methods:

  - *Automated vulnerability scanning tool*: This type of tool is used to scan system networks or a group of hosts for known vulnerable services.

  - *Security test and evaluation (ST&E)*: This method is used to identify system vulnerabilities during the risk assessment process. This method includes the development and implementation of a security test plan. The main objective of this method is to test the effectiveness of the information system security controls.

  - *Penetration testing*: This method is used to complement the review of system security controls and guarantee that different facets of the information system are secured. The main objective of this method is to test the information system from the perspective of a threat source and to spot potential failures in the information system security plans.

- *Development of security requirements checklist*: This step is performed by risk assessment personnel to verify whether the security requirements stipulated for the information system and gathered during system characterization are being met by present or intended security controls.

A *security requirements checklist* document comprises essential and basic security standards that can be used to methodically evaluate and identify the vulnerabilities of information system assets in management, operational, and technical security areas, as shown in Figure 5-5.

Step 4: Control Analysis

The organization analyzes the controls that are planned to be implemented or are already implemented in order to reduce the probability of a threat, as shown in Figure 5-6. The following aspects are included in a control analysis:

- *Control methods*: The following two methods must be incorporated to achieve security control:

  1. *Technical controls*: Technical controls are safeguards that are integrated into system hardware, software, or firmware, such as access control mechanisms, identification and authentication mechanisms, encryption methods, and intrusion detection software.

  2. *Nontechnical controls*: Nontechnical controls are management controls that include operational procedures, security policies and personnel, and physical and environmental security.

- *Control categories*: Technical and nontechnical control methods are classified into the following two categories:

  1. *Preventive controls*: These controls reduce the attempts made to violate security policies and thus include such controls as access control enforcement, authentication, and encryption.

  2. *Detective controls*: These controls alert the administrator when violations or attempts at violations of security policies occur. They include controls such as checksums, audit trails, and intrusion detection methods.

Introduction		
	Date carried out:	
	Testing Team details:	
	Network Details:	
	Scope of test:	
Executive Summary		
	OS Security issues discovered with appropriate criticality level specified:	
	Application Security issues discovered with appropriate criticality level specified:	
	Physical Security issues discovered with appropriate criticality level specified:	
	Personnel Security issues discovered with appropriate criticality level specified:	
	General Security issues discovered with appropriate criticality level specified:	
Technical Summary		
	OS Security issues discovered:	
	Web server security:	
	Database server security:	
	General Application Security:	
	Business Continuity Policy:	
Annexes	1:	
	2:	
	3:	

Figure 5-5   A security requirements checklist document comprises essential and basic security standards.

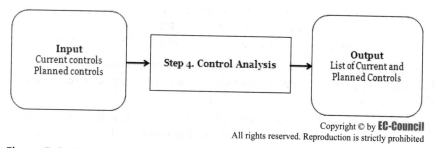

Figure 5-6   Control analysis evaluates current and planned controls.

It is essential to maintain and update the security requirements checklist, as the use of this checklist would be a benefit in analyzing controls efficiently. The security requirements checklist can be used to validate security compliance and noncompliance.

Step 5: Likelihood Determination

This step determines the likelihood of the occurrence of a threat, as shown in Figure 5-7. The following factors help in deriving the overall likelihood rating:

- Motivation and capability of the threat source
- Nature of the vulnerability
- Efficiency and existence of current controls

The likelihood level of a threat source can be described as high, medium, or low. These are described in Figure 5-8.

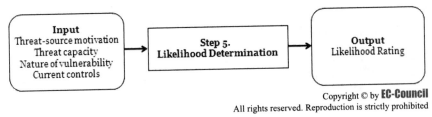

Figure 5-7   A number of factors determines the likelihood of a successful threat.

Likelihood Level	Likelihood Definition
High	The threat-source is highly motivated and sufficiently capable, and controls to prevent the vulnerability from being exercised are ineffective.
Medium	The threat-source is motivated and capable, but controls are in place that may impede successful exercise of the vulnerability.
Low	The threat-source lacks motivation or capability, or controls are in place to prevent, or at least significantly impede, the vulnerability from being exercised.

Figure 5-8   Threats must be assessed according to their likelihood.

Step 6: Impact Analysis

An *impact analysis* determines the impact that a threat could have on a system, as shown in Figure 5-9. To perform an impact analysis, it is necessary to know the system mission, system and data criticality, and system and data sensitivity. This information can be obtained from the following reports:

- *Mission impact analysis report*: Based on a qualitative or quantitative assessment of the sensitivity and criticality of assets, a mission impact analysis prioritizes the impact levels associated with the compromise of those assets.

- *Asset criticality assessment*: An asset criticality assessment identifies and prioritizes the sensitive and critical information assets that support the critical missions of the organization.

If these reports do not exist, the system and data sensitivity can be evaluated depending upon the confidentiality, integrity, and availability of the information. The three qualitative categories—high, medium, and low—are described in Figure 5-10.

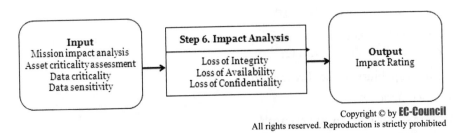

Figure 5-9   An impact analysis determines the effect that a threat could have on an organization.

Magnitude of Impact	Impact Definition
High	Exercise of the vulnerability (1) may result in the highly costly loss of major tangible assets or resources; (2) may significantly violate, harm, or impede an organization's mission, reputation, or interest; or (3) may result in human death or serious injury.
Medium	Exercise of the vulnerability (1) may result in the costly loss of tangible assets or resources; (2) may violate, harm, or impede an organization's mission, reputation, or interest; or (3) may result in human injury.
Low	Exercise of the vulnerability (1) may result in the loss of some tangible assets or resources or (2) may noticeably affect an organization's mission, reputation, or interest.

Figure 5-10   Impact ratings help organizations assess the value of addressing threats.

During an impact analysis, qualitative and quantitative assessments are also taken into account. A qualitative impact analysis prioritizes the risks involved and thus identifies the immediate improvement areas. A quantitative impact analysis provides the impact's magnitude measurement, which in turn is used for a cost-benefit analysis of the recommended controls.

Step 7: Risk Determination

Risk determination is a crucial task in a risk assessment effort, as shown in Figure 5-11. It is a complex process and depends upon various tangible and intangible factors. Though it is generally difficult to determine the exact level of risk to different organizational processes and assets, a careful consideration of various risk determinants gives an overall perception of risks faced by the organization. Risk determination involves a consideration of the following factors:

- *The probability of occurrence of an anticipated incident*: An incident is the result of a threat source exploiting system vulnerabilities.

- *The tangible and intangible impact of an incident on organizational resources*: Tangible impacts of an incident are easier to measure and can be represented by statistical analysis, whereas intangible impacts such as loss of reputation and customer trust are difficult to assess and can be determined only as a perception.

- *The control measures used to minimize impact*: Selection and implementation of control measures is based on risk determination and various management issues such as cost-benefit analysis and availability of resources.

Various standards bodies such as NIST have developed risk scales and risk matrices based on a categorization of risk levels as low, medium, and high, which help in determining the security posture of an organization.

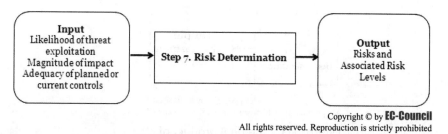

Figure 5-11   Risk determination takes all of the previous calculations and finds risks with associated risk levels.

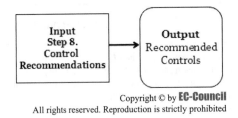

Figure 5-12 Recommended controls
are the results of the entire risk
assessment process.

Step 8: Recommendations to Control the Threats

Control recommendation and implementation is the main purpose of the whole risk assessment exercise, as shown in Figure 5-12. Risk assessment teams recommend the controls based on the likelihood, impact, and criticality of risk for a business operation.

Risk assessment teams need to consider these factors when recommending risk control measures:

- The control should meet the basic principle of a cost-benefit ratio.
- Controls should be implementable within the organization's ethics and security policy.
- The recommended solutions should be compatible with the organization's existing system.
- Controls must be within legislative and regulatory boundaries.
- The reliability of controls should be verified by using previous case studies and preimplementation tests.
- The controls should not go against the safety requirements of personnel and resources.

The implementation of controls depends on many business and management issues. Senior management in the organization has to determine the effectiveness of controls based on technical feedback and available case studies.

Step 9: Results Documentation

Each step of a risk assessment and the results should be properly documented, as shown in Figure 5-13. Documentation is critical to a risk assessment. An official, detailed, and clear risk assessment report helps senior management make decisions on policies, procedures, and system, operational, and management changes.

The documentation should be well structured and include supporting information. It should provide miscellaneous information that could help senior management implement mitigation strategies and allocate resources to mitigate risks in order to reduce potential losses. Figure 5-14 is a general risk assessment report.

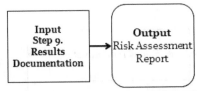

Figure 5-13 The final product of
the risk assessment process is a risk
assessment report.

Risk No.	Vulnerability	Threat	Risk	Risk Summary	Risk Likelihood Rating	Risk Impact Rating	Overall Risk Rating	Analysis of Relevant Controls and Other Factors	Recommendations

Figure 5-14 A risk assessment report is the final result of a risk assessment.

Attack Methods

Attacks against information systems have a number of potential targets. These attacks are differentiated in the following ways

- Attacks aimed at disclosing information; the following attacks are common examples:
  - Manipulation of a user's client
  - Eavesdropping on the network
  - Stealing a user's session
  - Manipulating the program files on the application server
  - Stealing backup copies with a known password
  - Exploiting vulnerabilities in the server operating system
- Attacks against information integrity; the following attacks are common examples:
  - Stealing an existing user ID
  - Circumventing the system's security controls
  - Manipulating data when they are transferred over the network
- Attacks aimed at causing unavailability; the following attacks are common examples:
  - Physical destruction
  - Crashing network interface software or the operating system
  - Manipulation of the network's components
  - Flooding
  - Attacking an operating system
  - Attacking an application file server

Attack Phases

By assessing the different phases of an attack, security personnel can understand the security measures necessary for each phase, as shown in Figure 5-15. The following three phases constitute an attack:

1. *Probing stage*: This is the stage in which the attacker finds loopholes in the security system. If the attack is detected at this stage, it will be easy to mitigate the risk before damage is done to the system.

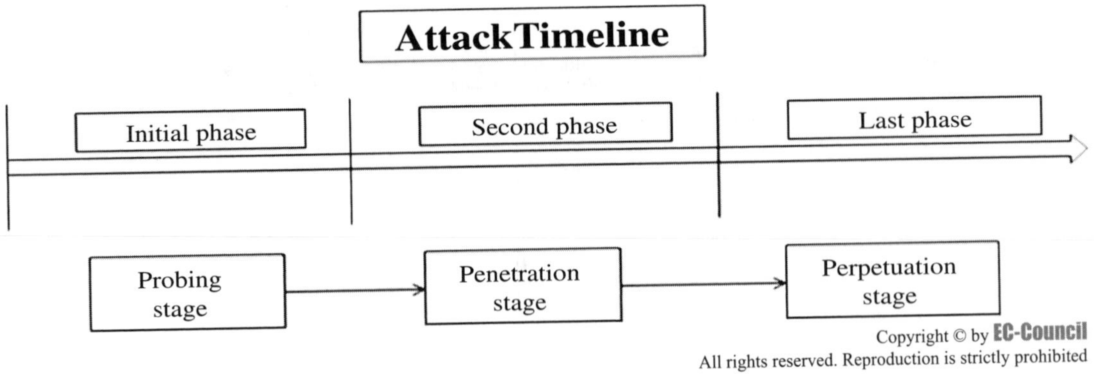

Figure 5-15 Attacks occur in three phases.

2. *Penetration stage*: In this stage, an attacker attempts to surpass the security controls so as to harm the information security system. This phase can cause harm to a system, but it is not targeted specifically at information, so the damage is usually repairable. It is similar to a thief damaging a fence or an alarm system. Attacks such as unauthorized access and denial of service (DoS) are examples of this type of attack.

3. *Perpetuation stage*: In this stage, the attacker successfully penetrates into the network or system to perform malicious activities. These attacks can result in disclosure of information, manipulation of data, and destruction of information.

Countermeasures

Security Countermeasures

Security countermeasures are the actions or solutions used to prevent attacks. The following types of controls are implemented to prevent attacks:

- Technical security controls
- Operational security controls
- Management security controls

Technical Security Controls

Technical security controls involve the use of technological measures to control risks. The following are some examples of technical controls:

- Supporting technical controls; this includes the following controls:
  - Identification
  - Cryptographic key management
  - System protections
- Preventive technical controls; this includes the following controls:
  - Authentication and authorization
  - Access control enforcement
  - Protected communications and transaction privacy
- Detection and recovery technical controls; this includes the following controls:
  - Auditing and restoration of the secure state
  - Intrusion detection and containment
  - Virus detection and eradication

Operational Security Controls

These controls are implemented by the organization considering the present set of requirements and good organizational practices. Operational security controls include the following examples:

- Preventive operational controls:
  - Control the media access to data
  - Restrict the data distribution to external sources
  - Safeguard the computing facility
  - Provide backup capability
  - Secure IT assets from damage due to fire
  - Provide an emergency power source
- Detection operational controls:
  - Maintain physical security
  - Ensure environmental security

Management Security Controls

These controls, in combination with technical and operational controls, are implemented to handle, control, and minimize the risk of loss and to secure the mission of an organization. These include the following controls:

- Preventive management security controls; the following controls are common examples:
  - Allocate security responsibility so that sufficient security is maintained
  - Develop and maintain system security plans
  - Implement personnel security controls
  - Organize security awareness programs and technical training
- Detection management security controls; the following controls are common examples:
  - Execute personnel security controls
  - Perform reviews of security controls
  - Perform periodic system audits
  - Conduct ongoing risk management
- Recovery management security controls; the following controls are common examples:
  - Provide continuity of support
  - Establish an incident response capability

Technical Surveillance Countermeasures

Technical surveillance countermeasure (TSCM) techniques are used to detect and neutralize the hostile penetration technologies used to gain unauthorized access to confidential and sensitive information.

TSCM programs recognize and allow the user to correct utilizable technical and physical security vulnerabilities. TSCM techniques involve the following procedures:

- *Detection*: Detecting devices that contain threats
- *Nullification*: Using passive and active measures to neutralize the threat devices
- *Isolation*: Restricting the use of secure areas and ensuring the proper construction for those areas
- *Education*: Providing education to people regarding threats, installation of new equipment, and renovation

Weighing the Costs and Benefits of Risk Management

The cost of a potential attack can be calculated according to the data loss and the business affected by the data loss. The execution of the attack handling and response plans also incurs costs for resources and materials.

The cost of an attack is calculated depending on estimates of the following necessities:

- Loss of business because the information resources are not available
- Compromising productivity from non-IT staff
- Labor and materials cost of the IT staff related to detection and repair of the breached resources
- Labor cost of obtaining forensic evidence and prosecuting the attacker
- Public relations consulting costs

Risk Countermeasure Analysis

A risk countermeasure analysis is conducted to weigh the effectiveness and economic benefits of countermeasures. Countermeasure analysis is conducted through the following steps:

1. *Prioritize actions*: After the risk assessment is finished, the first step is to give priority to the task with the highest risk.
2. *Evaluate the recommended control options*: The suggested controls are analyzed to judge their effectiveness.
3. *Conduct the cost-benefit analysis*: The worthiness of the countermeasures is taken into consideration before they are implemented.
4. *Select the cost-effective control*: The most cost-effective solution is chosen from the various solutions suggested.
5. *Assign responsibility*: The appropriate person must be given the responsibility to implement the controls.
6. *Develop a safeguard implementation plan*: The countermeasures should be implemented as per the plan, and all the safety precautions should be taken while doing this.
7. *Implement selected control*: Finally, the countermeasures should actually be implemented.

Cost-Benefit Analysis

A cost-benefit analysis is performed on the solutions suggested for countering the risk. The cost of the risk mitigation controls is compared with the probable economic impacts of the threat. Organizations look for other options if the cost of the data loss due to the risk is less than the cost of the proposed controls.

Cost-benefit analysis also helps organizations decide the most effective solution to implement. If there is more than one option to counter the risk, then the cost-benefit analysis will help the organization choose the most economically viable solution. Figure 5-16 illustrates the cost-benefit analysis process.

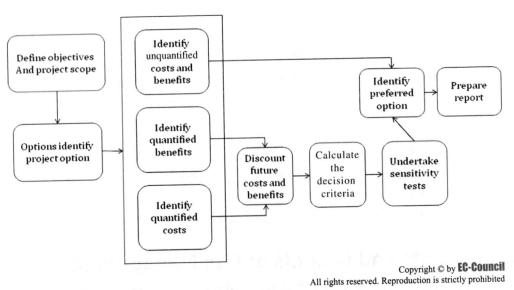

Figure 5-16 The cost-benefit analysis process allows organizations to gauge the economic viability of countering risks.

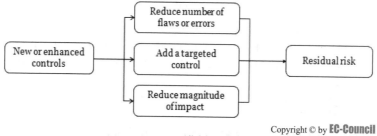

Figure 5-17   Residual risk takes unforeseen issues into account.

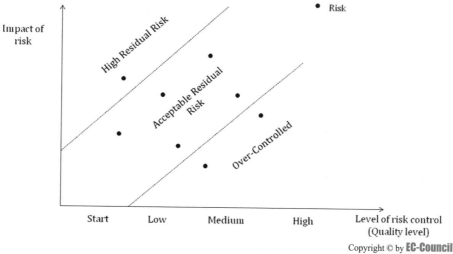

Figure 5-18   Residual risk can be graphed to determine its severity.

Residual Risk

After the implementation of countermeasures to counter the risk factors, there may still be issues that were not covered or that come up after the assessment. This possibility is called *residual risk* (Figure 5-17). It is impossible to be sure that all risks have been taken into account. Thus, the residual risk is always there, even after the implementation of the best suitable countermeasures.

Residual risk should always be taken into account by organizations performing a risk assessment. Sometimes, there are issues that cannot be mitigated by the implementation of any possible solution; those kinds of issues are also categorized as residual risk. The graph in Figure 5-18 can be used to determine the severity of residual risk.

Risk Assessment Responsibilities

Information Assurance

Information assurance refers to policies, procedures, and solutions that help minimize the risks in an information system. There are five common security principles that system developers and risk acceptors should consider when deciding on an appropriate level of information assurance:

1. *Confidentiality*: Confidential information should not be disclosed to unauthorized individuals, processes, or devices.

2. *Integrity*: Protecting the information against unauthorized modification or destruction.

3. *Availability*: Providing reliable information access to authorized users.

4. *Authentication*: Verifying the authorization of individuals to receive specific categories of information.

5. *Nonrepudiation*: The sender of the information should be given a delivery proof, and the recipient of the information should be given the identity of the information sender, so neither can deny having processed the data.

Maintenance Responsibilities

System Activities for Chronological, Analytical Reconstruction and Maintenance of System Components

Information systems acquire, process, and store information. These systems are accessed by users and organizations for normal operations and decision making. Maintenance of information assurance depends on access controls implemented in systems. Organizations should keep chronological records of all system processes and accesses to ensure security and responsibility for any incident involving the information system. System activity records should include the following activities:

- File access
- Buffer activity
- System call statistics
- Disk activity
- Page-out and memory operations
- Kernel memory allocation
- Interprocess communication
- Page-in activity
- Queue activity
- Unused memory
- CPU utilization
- System table status
- Swap activity
- Terminal activity

Security Product Integration

With the evolution of technology, integrating different security products such as firewall, antivirus, and anti-spam systems becomes increasingly complex. Providing the functionality of these products is an essential aspect of establishing a consistent security profile. Finally, the association of these technologies is also essential for the delivery of technology solutions to support compliance programs that are more critical to organizations in today's business environment.

Security product integration provides the following benefits:

- Provides increased efficiency by creating a unified system
- Provides complementary technologies designed to help the organization's IT security
- Reduces network outages caused by worms and viruses
- Contains association of the features and functions across different product types
- Offers functionalities such as installation, implementation, tuning, and training

Maintenance of User Accounts

The process of user account maintenance begins with the creation of a new user account. For example, when a new employee joins the company, his or her new account should be created and assigned to the correct organizational unit (OU) in the Active Directory structure. The organization should assign the correct group policies to the OU. When an employee changes positions at the company, that employee should also be moved within the OU structure. When an employee quits, the account should be disabled and moved out of the ordinary OU structure. Short-term or temporary employees should be given accounts with a particular expiration date.

Processes for Timely Deletion of Accounts The timely deletion of user and group accounts is important for information assurance. Attackers can exploit unused accounts to gain unauthorized access to system resources and compromise system security. Account deletion policies should consider these factors:

- *Expiration period*: An expiration time is set on an employee's account to provide a grace period before the employee's account is actually inaccessible to the user.

- *Suspension period*: After the user's expiration period has elapsed, the user's account is suspended for a set number of days, during which the user cannot access the account.

- *Account deletion*: After the end of the suspension period, all the data associated with the account are deleted.

- *Backup cycle time*: After the account is deleted, the data associated with the account will still be stored on the backup media for a set period of time.

Change Control

Change control is a method used to ensure that the changes to a system are made in a controlled and coordinated manner. It minimizes the possibility of making unnecessary modifications to the system. A change control method should be implemented for the following reasons:

- Minimal disruption to services

- Reduction in back-out activities

- Cost-effective utilization of resources

Change control is commonly used in different products and systems. For IT systems, it is the main feature of the broader discipline of change management. Change controls for computer and network environments include the following examples:

- Patches to software products

- Installation of new operating systems

- Upgrades to network routing tables

- Changes to the electrical power systems

Maintenance Procedures Concerning Life Cycle Operations and Analysis Issues

The maintenance of an application system starts when the system is put into operation, as shown in Figure 5-19. In the maintenance phase of the system life cycle, ongoing system maintenance should be performed to ensure the performance and functionality of the system match the business requirements of the users.

System maintenance includes the following steps:

1. *Maintenance planning*: The maintenance plan should be prepared well before the system is put into operation. The following information should be included in the maintenance plan:
   - Role assignments
   - Maintenance activities
   - Maintenance resources and facilities

2. *System nursing*: This period should start before the development team delivers the system to the maintenance team. Monitoring and tuning is conducted during this period to ensure a smooth transition of the system.

3. *System monitoring and tuning*: This step involves continued monitoring and tuning of the application system operations and should be performed to ensure smooth operation and to increase efficiency and effectiveness.

4. *System maintenance cycle stage*: System maintenance goes through these stages:
   - Initiation
   - Impact analysis

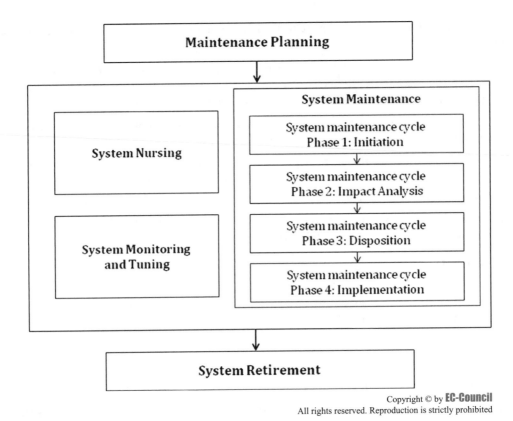

Figure 5-19   System maintenance is an essential aspect of risk management.

- Disposition
- Implementation

5. *System retirement*: This is the process of removing an existing system from active use by replacing its operations with a new system. This process should be designed with detailed procedures.

Responsibilities of Security Personnel

Responsibilities of Information Systems Security Officer (ISSO)

Information systems security officers (ISSOs) have the following responsibilities:

- Ensure that information systems are operated in accordance with security policies
- Implement the security policies and safeguards on all personnel having access to information systems
- Report the security status of information systems to the information systems security manager (ISSM)
- Maintain the system security plan
- Ensure that TEMPEST measures have not been altered; *TEMPEST* is a government project studying compromising electrical, mechanical, or acoustical energy emissions unintentionally emitted by electrical equipment/systems such as computers, monitors, or transmission lines, allowing the information therein to be captured
- Ensure that all computers display access warning banners
- Provide training and awareness activities to users
- Work with the physical security personnel to provide physical security for information system assets
- Provide protective or corrective measures when a security problem is identified
- Support the accreditation of the information systems

- Ensure that security audits are reviewed periodically and that audit records are archived for future reference
- Report incidents to an ISSM by creating a security incident reporting mechanism
- Develop proactive and corrective measures to prevent security problems

Responsibilities of System Administrator

The system administrator is a member of the IT department who maintains the computer system and network. The administrator's responsibilities may vary from one organization to another.

Generally, administrators are responsible for installing systems, supporting and maintaining servers, and planning the IT infrastructure to support the organization's business objectives. The administrator is also responsible for responding to service outages and other system-related problems.

The system administrator should make decisions in the following areas:

- *Audit mechanism*: Ascertain the validity and reliability of information.
- *Software options*: Decide which software is to be installed and allowed on a system.
- *Access permissions*: The access to important information should be given only to authorized personnel.
- *Maintenance of user authentication data*: Maintain data for user authentication purposes.
- *Detecting and preventing unauthorized system access*: Use tools and software to restrict unauthorized access to the system.

Responsibilities of Information System Owner

The information system owner is a member of senior management who defines objectives and priorities, oversees and approves the development of all deliverables documents, manages resource allocations, and decides on the acquisition of new services for an information system.

The responsibilities of the system owner and data owner may be different, depending on the size of the system. The system owner is accountable for all modifications and improvements made to a system, including making decisions for the overall replacement of a system. The system owner plays the role of steering committee chairperson and allocates portions of the budget and high-level resources for system maintenance. The system owner also manages the accreditation process that determines when a system change is ready for implementation. The system owner must also be aware of new technologies, risks, threats, regulations, and market trends.

Responsibilities of System Developers

The system developer is the expert who has the technical knowledge necessary for providing solutions related to an information system's services and requirements. The system developer controls the process of system development. System developers obtain information about the customer's requirements and develop the system according to those requirements.

System developers have the following responsibilities:

- Defining the process for selecting and purchasing new information technology
- Verifying the functionality of an application
- Providing risk methodologies to evaluate measures taken to protect the system
- Analyzing maintenance practices, procedures, and measures to ensure an acceptable level of risk

Responsibilities of Agency Vendors as Members of the Risk Management Team

Members of the risk management team are responsible for the following tasks:

- Identifying the organization's exposures to accidental loss
- Implementing the required financial protection measures with the help of the risk transfer, risk avoidance, and risk retention programs
- Developing and updating a system to communicate the components of the risk management program throughout the organization
- Designing master insurance and self-insurance programs
- Maintaining sufficient insurance coverage at a reasonable cost

- Determining cost-effective ways to build a protection system for loss prevention
- Implementing loss prevention or loss retention programs
- Providing guidelines to handle all property and liability claims involving the organization
- Managing claims for both insured and uninsured losses
- Complying with local insurance laws
- Establishing deductible levels
- Distributing insurance premiums
- Issuing certificates as necessary
- Developing risk management policies and procedures

Automated Testing

Automated tests contain consistent and repeatable test methods. They provide a high degree of efficiency by allowing testers to rapidly test predefined controls. In addition, the automated tools help to test the system's security. Creating automated tests requires a thorough understanding of a system's architecture in order to make sure the tests cover as much of the system as possible.

There are two major issues regarding the use of automated tools:

1. They are limited to testing the parameters for which they were designed.

2. It may be difficult to map the use of an automated tool to all necessary requirements.

Information System Auditing

Information system auditing involves the evaluation of a system's processes and security to verify the validity and reliability of information. It involves recording events such as modifications, access, deletions, and additions of data in an information system.

Auditing procedures must include the following tasks:

- Creating an annual audit program
- Selection of the auditor and team leader
- Planning specific types of audits
- Conducting audits
- Recording observations
- Determining corrective actions
- Implementing corrective actions
- Confirming the effectiveness of the corrective actions

Verification of Tools and Techniques

Verification of Techniques

Verification of information assurance tools and techniques is a complex process and requires a thorough analysis of various functional and structural components. Verification techniques can be broadly categorized in the following ways:

- *Dynamic testing*: Dynamic testing refers to the verification of tools and techniques in their operational state. It involves the execution of the system components. In this testing, the system is made to run on different test input cases, and the results are analyzed to determine the efficiency of tools and techniques. Dynamic testing is categorized into the following three types:

  - *Functional testing*: This refers to testing the functional efficiency of the system.

  - *Structural testing*: This testing makes use of knowledge of the internal structures of an information system to assess the performance of the system and its various components.

- *Random testing*: Random testing involves selecting test cases from all possible test cases. It uses randomly determined inputs to detect the faults that cannot be easily detected by other testing techniques.
- *Static testing*: Static testing does not involve the implementation of a system or component. Some static testing techniques are performed manually, while others are automated. Static testing is categorized into the following two types:
  - *Consistency techniques*: This testing checks for the consistency of various system variables and program properties.
  - *Measurement techniques*: Measurement testing is a quantitative testing that aims to determine the probability of vulnerabilities in a system, considering various determinants such as understandability and the structure of the system.
- *Validation techniques*:
  - *Formal methods*: Formal methods involve the use of mathematical and logical techniques to determine the characteristics of the hardware and software components of a system.
  - *Fault injection*: This method involves the intentional creation of faults to test how the system operates under different fault conditions.
  - *Dependability analysis*: Dependability analysis is a method that involves identifying hazards and providing methods to reduce the risk of hazards.
  - *Hazard analysis*: Hazard analysis is a method that involves identifying hazards, their root causes, and potential countermeasures.
  - *Risk analysis*: Risk analysis is a process identifying the possible consequences of each hazard and the possibility of it occurring.

Acquisitions

System Acquisition

System acquisition is a process that starts from the time the decision is made to select a new system until the time a contract has been negotiated and signed. The process of selecting or acquiring a system can take anywhere from a few days to a couple of years depending on the size, structure, and needs of an organization.

The system acquisition process includes the following steps:

1. Define the project's objectives.
2. Determine the system's goals.
3. Determine the system's requirements.
4. Find a potential supplier or vendor.
5. Develop and distribute the Request for Information (RFI) and Request for Proposal (RFP).
6. Identify other options for acquiring the system.
7. Evaluate the vendor's proposal.
8. Conduct a cost-benefit analysis.
9. Prepare a summary report.
10. Conduct a contract negotiation.

Selecting and Purchasing New IT Solutions

The following points should be kept in mind when selecting an IT solution:

- *Understand and prioritize business objectives*: Understanding business objectives allows management to identify what a business really needs. It is essential to review all available solutions in an organization before selecting a new system.
- *Vendor demonstration*: When purchasing a new solution, management should make sure the vendor demonstrates how the solution will meet the business and operational needs. In the demonstration, vendors will explain all the features of their solution. This is a good time to ask questions about the solution.

- *Compare prices accurately*: To compare prices accurately, management should ask vendors if their figures contain real-time agent adherence, Web access for agents and supervisors, maintenance and support, and training. Comparing prices will give a clear idea about the price of the solution compared to other solutions.

- *Seek solutions that can be remotely installed*: Management should find a vendor who provides solutions that can be installed remotely. On-site installation will increase the ownership cost and also require more time compared to a remote installation.

- *Make ROI calculations*: Many vendors provide an ROI (return on investment). Some vendors make statistical adjustments. Creating an ROI tailored to the organization will aid the decision-making process.

Software Acquisitions

The software acquisition process includes the following steps:

1. *Requesting software*: This step involves identifying the software needs and obtaining approval from the IT department to purchase that software.

2. *Purchasing licenses for software*: In this step, the complete purchase order request is sent to the IT department for verification and approval. If any changes are required in the request order, the IT department contacts the requesting department.

3. *Receiving software*: After receiving the software, the IT department follows the company's check-in procedure to ensure that the new software is added to the software inventory.

4. *Distributing software*: The IT department provides the software to the requesting department. The IT department also contacts the requesting department to schedule the installation of the software.

5. *Ensuring software documentation is available to end users*: Copies of the end-user license agreement should be made available to the end users in the receiving department.

System Disposition/Reutilization

The system disposition plan is a major consideration in the disposition of an information system. The purpose of this plan is to provide an approach for ending the operating life of the system. It ensures that all data are properly archived or transferred to another system.

System disposition/reutilization includes the following procedures:

- *Notifications*: The plan for identifying the users of a system before it is shut down and notifying those users

- *Data disposition*: The plan for archiving, deleting, or transferring the data files from one system to another system, before the system is shut down

- *System documentation disposition*: The plan for archiving, deleting, or transferring documentation from one system to another system, before the system is shut down

- *Equipment disposition*: The plan for archiving, removing, or transferring hardware and other devices from one system to another system, before the system is shut down

Tools

Xacta IA Manager

Xacta IA Manager (Figure 5-20) combines security compliance and risk assessment functionality with business process automation to establish a centralized governance, risk, and compliance management platform that facilitates compliance assessment, continuous risk assessment, sustained compliance management, and security process automation.

Xacta IA Manager includes the following functions:

- Enforces processes for compliance with FISMA, FDCC/SCAP, DIACAP, DCID, GLBA, HIPAA, ISO 17799, SOX, and more

- Collects extensive IT asset inventory data

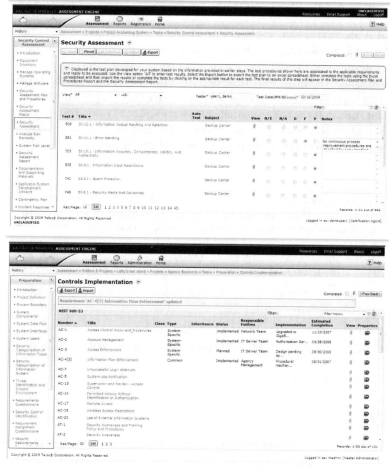

Source: http://images.telos.com/files/external/XIAM-SP8d-Brochure.pdf. Accessed 9/2009.

Figure 5-20   Xacta IA Manager handles many aspects of risk management.

- Detects, identifies, and remediates threats to system security
- Continuously assesses security posture
- Automates security policies and enforces procedures
- Generates the reports and documentation needed for regulatory compliance

SecureInfo RMS

SecureInfo RMS supports all phases of the DoD Information Assurance Certification and Accreditation Process (DIACAP) and National Institute of Standards and Technology (NIST) certification and accreditation process, and guides users through the steps necessary to create consistent documentation. It includes a content library that links and maps all federal, Department of Defense (DoD), service branch (Air Force, Army, Navy, Marines), and intelligence community security requirements to applicable information assurance (IA) controls. It includes the following features:

- Complete set of standards documents and templates
- Flexible workflow, including e-mail alerting, document management, privilege-based access/control, and expired certification and accreditation package alerts
- Extensible reporting framework supports Federal Information Security Management Act (FISMA) reporting, plans of action and milestones (POA&Ms), DIACAP reporting, and user-defined configurable reports
- Common enterprise directory support enables a centralized database for system users (supports Lightweight Directory Access Protocol [LDAP] and Microsoft Active Directory)

Trusted Agent FISMA (TAF)

Trusted Agent FISMA is an enterprise compliance and oversight tool that manages the collection and reporting of a component's information associated with key information security practices and controls. It comes with a digital dashboard that aggregates the data collected in Trusted Agent FISMA and is used as a visual tool using a traffic light display to gauge the progress of the department-wide information security program.

The digital dashboard serves as a management tool to ensure the components take a risk-based, cost-effective approach to secure their information and information systems, identify and resolve current information security weaknesses and risks, and protect against future vulnerabilities and threats. It allows management to monitor the components' remediation efforts to identify progress and problems.

eMASS

The Enterprise Mission Assurance Support System, or eMASS, is a government-owned, commercial off-the-shelf (COTS) software-based certification and accreditation solution. It is purposefully designed to be flexible for future upgrades and changes. eMASS includes the following features:

- eMASS Web certification and accreditation is a government-developed package that facilitates and automates the security certification and accreditation process.

- The product leads the user through a step-by-step process that identifies risks and assesses network and system configuration compliance with DITSCAP and other applicable regulations.

- eMASS's functionality includes the ability to explain and distribute security directives, handbooks, and detailed technical security configuration guidelines and security best practices to system administrators.

Chapter Summary

- The maintenance of an application system starts when the system is put into operation.
- Risk analysis is a process identifying the possible consequences of each hazard and the possibility of [it] occurring.
- Residual risk is the risk or danger that remains after the implementation of new or enhanced controls.
- Risk assessment is the process of identifying and assessing the resources that pose a threat to the business or project environment.
- Risk management is the process of identifying risk, addressing risk, and taking steps to eliminate or reduce risk to an acceptable level.
- Risk management should be implemented in all phases of SDLC.
- IT system administrators should have a thorough knowledge of the system processing environment.

Review Questions

1. Discuss the roles and responsibilities of the system administrator in the risk evaluation process.

_____

_____

_____

_____

2. Explain the different steps of the system acquisition process.

_____

_____

_____

_____

3. What are the responsibilities of system developers?

_____

_____

_____

_____

4. Explain the risk analysis process.

_____

_____

_____

_____

5. Discuss the importance of cost-benefit analysis for the implementation of risk control measures.

_____

_____

_____

_____

6. What are residual risks? Suggest appropriate controls to contain residual risks within an acceptable limit.

_____

_____

_____

_____

7. Discuss the various steps of the risk assessment methodology.

_____

_____

_____

_____

8. Describe the process of threat identification.

_____

_____

_____

_____

9. Explain how risk management can be integrated with an IT system's SDLC.

_____

_____

_____

_____

10. Explain the characteristics of the development and acquisition phase from a risk management perspective.

_____

_____

_____

_____

Hands-On Projects

1. Navigate to Chapter 5 of the Student Resource Center. Open IMAToolsTechniques.pdf and read the following topics:
   - Executive Summary
   - Risk Identification Techniques
   - Analysis of Risk by Drivers

2. Navigate to Chapter 5 of the Student Resource Center. Open ai00033.pdf and read the following topics:
   - Introduction
   - Risk Management Cycle

3. Navigate to Chapter 5 of the Student Resource Center. Open FRMWRK_ERA.pdf and read the following topics:
   - Introduction
   - PROBLEM FORMULATION

4. Navigate to Chapter 5 of the Student Resource Center. Open 4014.pdf and read the following topics:
   - Scope Applicability
   - Infosec Performance Standard for the ISSO (Entry, Intermediate & Advanced Levels)

Chapter 6

Risk Control Policies and Countermeasures

Objectives

After completing this chapter, you should be able to:

- Determine countermeasures
- Develop policies for risk analysis
- Conduct a cost-benefit analysis
- Categorize information
- Conduct configuration management
- Identify system security policies
- Implement change control policies
- Develop access control policies
- Manage electronic records
- Develop policies for capturing audit logs

Key Terms

Countermeasure   any action, device, procedure, or technique used to reduce vulnerabilities or risks

Introduction to Risk Control Policies and Countermeasures

Because there are inherent risks in running any business or organization, they must be dealt with in a number of different ways. Some risks can be totally eliminated if doing so will not harm the organization; however, other risks are necessary factors in running particular types of organizations. For example, running a publicly accessible Web site increases the risk of hacking attacks, but Web sites are necessary for most organizations.

After risks to an organization have been identified, organizations must respond to them through the use of countermeasures. *Countermeasures* are any actions, devices, procedures, or techniques used to reduce vulnerabilities or risks. Specific devices, such as firewalls, can eliminate certain risks, but there are other risks that must be dealt with through the use of policies. For example, mistakes by staff and personnel often pose a threat to information that can equal or surpass the threat of malicious hackers. This problem cannot be solved by a device, so a policy must be enacted to deal with it. Risk control policies take into account the degree of risk that an organization is willing to accept in a number of different areas and mitigate risks accordingly.

Countermeasures

Determining Security Countermeasures

Because there are different vulnerabilities possible, it is necessary to determine the specific countermeasures for each type of threat. Countermeasure determination is an important factor in the success of any risk management and business continuity effort.

Countermeasures should be selected based on the following criteria:

- Threat statement and assets to be protected
- Incident and events type
- The relevant resources that are available
- Effectiveness to handle the threats

Determine Countermeasures Based on Threat Capabilities and Motivations

Organizations can determine the proper countermeasures using the following steps:

1. Identify potential countermeasures to reduce the threats.
2. Identify the level of risk reduction with the use of countermeasures.
3. Determine the cost required for the chosen countermeasures.
4. Conduct the cost-benefit analysis and the trade-off analysis of countermeasures.
5. Analyze the options to be prioritized and recommend those options to the decision-maker.

Risk Control Policy Development Factors

Development of IA Principles and Practices

Development of information assurance principles and practices takes the factors discussed in the following sections into account.

Organizational Security Policy

Organizational security policies are the basis of any information assurance effort. Organizations should develop and implement appropriate security policies in order to achieve IA. The security policies should be developed after the risk assessment process and should be based on commonly accepted policy standards defined by various organizations such as NIST (National Institute of Standards and Technology) and the ISO (International Organization for Standardization).

Implementation of organizational security policies in accordance with organizational business objectives ensures long-term information security for the organization. These security policies must be well documented and made available to all concerned stakeholders. Management should develop a comprehensive program to make employees aware of these security policies.

Defined and Documented Security Infrastructure

The security infrastructure includes all the control measures implemented in an organization to protect information systems, such as intrusion detection systems, firewalls, and antivirus systems. The security infrastructure varies according to the operating environment and risk perception of an organization.

Organizations should clearly define and document the entire available security infrastructure in order to provide an immediate response to the security requirements of the system. Documents related to security infrastructure should be readily available to all the users and user groups that are responsible for information assurance.

Education

Training and awareness are major components of an information assurance program. Policy and control implementation will be useless if employees and other stakeholders are not aware of these policies. Information assurance principles encourage organizations to develop comprehensive training and awareness programs. These training programs should cover anyone who has access to the information system. Employees of the organization should be aware of security issues related to their field of work and duties.

Asset Management

Information asset management in an organization refers to the acquisition, maintenance, and security of all the assets that store or process information. Organizations should develop and implement asset management policies to ensure the accountability of information systems. Asset management provides a baseline for information assurance and helps the organization develop appropriate security controls for the system.

Business Continuity

Business continuity and information assurance are interdependent concepts in an information system. Any compromise related to information assurance may lead to business discontinuity and vice versa. Organizations should develop and implement comprehensive business continuity plans that help protect information in case of a disaster or security incident. These plans should include technical and procedural controls to back up and restore data in case of a disaster.

Regulatory Compliance

Regulatory compliance ensures that an information system meets a certain base security level. Compliance issues are often interlinked with information assurance in an organization. Organizations should develop and implement required policies, controls, and infrastructures to achieve compliance with established standards and laws. This ensures information security and also saves organizations from legal liabilities arising due to any compromise in information assurance.

Laws and Procedures in Information Assurance (IA) Policy Implementation

The following domestic and international laws address IA policy implementation:

- *Official Secrets Act*: The Official Secrets Act is used for the protection of official information related to national security. This act requires employees to avoid unauthorized disclosure of information. It requires employees who are working with confidential information to sign a statement that they agree to follow the restrictions of the Official Secrets Act.

- *Data Protection Act*: The Data Protection Act is mainly used for the protection of sensitive and confidential data. This act requires that personal data be protected safely and accessed only by authorized users. This act is part of a piece of legislation that manages the protection of personal data.

- *Computer Misuse Act*: The Computer Misuse Act is a law that makes activities such as hacking computer systems, helping a person access the information of another person, and the unauthorized modification of computer materials illegal.

- *Freedom of Information Act*: The Freedom of Information Act provides the right to access information held by public authorities unless there are good reasons to keep it confidential. This act defines the agency's records that can be disclosed, provides a list of mandatory disclosure procedures, and provides nine exceptions to disclosure.

Security Test and Evaluation

Security test and evaluation (ST&E) is performed to review the security controls of information systems. Testing helps to ensure a secured operating environment by fulfilling the security requirements.

The objective of ST&E is to uncover flaws present in the design, implementation, and operations performed by information systems. The ST&E team has the following responsibilities:

- Developing the test plan
- Executing the plan
- Documenting the test results

Security Test and Evaluation Methodology

The main objective of ST&E is to verify whether the system configuration and operational environment covers the basic security requirements of the information system, which is a prerequisite for the certification and accreditation process. The security test and evaluation methodology uses the following steps:

1. *Establish test objectives*: This helps to ensure the protection of the information systems by deciding how to test whether the appropriate security controls and the best practices and procedures for risk mitigation have been implemented.

2. *Develop the initial ST&E plan*: In this phase, the team creates a draft of the ST&E plan, which should include all the basic test objectives, procedures, and execution processes that are to be initiated while testing; the separate test procedures for each and every component of the information system; and the complete test procedures for management, operational, and technical security controls. In this phase, the involvement of the system owner can identify the components of the system and thus help the team in finalizing the plan.

3. *Develop ST&E procedures*: In this step, the test objectives are validated using test procedures that were developed initially. The team then verifies whether the system has met the stated test objectives. The team develops the initial security test and evaluation procedures depending upon the validated objectives, which include all the steps in detail so as to verify the effectiveness of all security controls. Once the effectiveness of all security controls is verified, the team has to perform a dry-run execution in order to check if all the objectives, procedures, and scripts are compatible with the system being tested.

4. *Conduct ST&E and document results*: Documentation should be clear and concise and should cover all the aspects of the ST&E procedure.

Roles and Responsibilities of the ST&E Team

The ST&E team has the following responsibilities:

- *Executing test procedures*: The ST&E team executes the test using the test procedures that are provided in the plan. It is essential for other technical personnel, such as system administrators, to be present during testing so they can witness and aid in the execution of the test procedures.

- *Interpreting the results*: The ST&E team must record the results such as whether the objectives being tested were met, not met, or not tested.

- *Conducting out-brief*: Once the results of the testing are documented, an informal out-brief is conducted between the ST&E team and the system owner in order to discuss and fix the critical findings (failure comments).

- *Developing the ST&E report*: The ST&E team develops an ST&E report, which includes the results documentation of each and every component of the information system tested, comments related to test objectives and procedures, and the findings of all the objectives. Each finding should include the following information:
  - *Test objective*: A test objective verified by the ST&E team
  - *Test objective number*: Identifier for the test objective
  - *Finding description*: A detailed description of how and why the test objective was not met while testing
  - *Control tested*: Document whether the management, operational, or technical controls were tested
  - *Recommendation*: Recommended steps to correct the findings

Automated Security Tools

Automated security tools enable security personnel to automate various incident management processes in an information system. These security tools may be used for traffic filtering and pattern analysis, log monitoring and management, security alerts, and operating system security. Automated tools acquire information from various system and traffic indicators, analyze the information, and alert administrators about any suspicious behavior in the system and network. The features and functionalities of automated security tools depend on the factors discussed in the following sections.

Event Logs

Event logs are important sources of system information on Windows systems. Automated security tools can analyze event logs for any suspicious system event. They can query large log databases for a historical analysis of patterns in system events and detect specified anomalies.

Processes

Automated tools monitor system processes for any suspicious processes and alert the system owners. Automated tools may detect the processes associated with malware in the system. System administrators should be aware of essential system processes and be able to recognize suspicious processes, because automated tools may also give false positives and terminate essential services.

Automated security tools can also alert in case a critical process is not available or turned off unexpectedly. They can be programmed to restart these processes and prevent essential services from being turned off.

Automated tools should be carefully configured to avoid false positives and negatives. Before reacting to any security alerts from these tools, administrators should manually verify the results. Though human intervention is required, automated tools can simplify the complex monitoring and analysis process.

System Counters

System counters are system performance indicators. Automated tools can use these indicators to alert system owners about suspicious system activity. System counters include cache memory usage, CPU utilization and usage history, paging file usage, and others. Any sudden changes in these counters indicate suspicious activity. For example, automated tools can alert administrators if virtual memory usage suddenly or unexpectedly increases or if the activity of the Winlogon process suddenly increases.

Services

Services offered by systems and their availability provide an indication of a system's health and security. Any loss in availability of these services may be an indication of system compromise. Automated tools can monitor the availability of these services and alert system administrators if there is any variation in expected service characteristics. These automated tools can also be configured to alert for the presence of any unnecessary or suspicious services. Automated tools can ensure the availability of critical system services.

Files

Files are the main repositories of information in any system. The creation, deletion, and manipulation of important files should be recorded and reported to system owners so that they can verify the file operations. Creating fake large files and deleting and manipulating important system and user files are the main characteristics of malware programs. Automated tools can alert system owners about any suspicious file operations.

There are a large number of commercial off-the-self security tools available that offer easy and affordable security capabilities to organizations, but the procurement of these automated security tools should follow a stringent process; otherwise, there are chances that the organization may end up with certain tools that are either not able to meet security requirements or may even create vulnerabilities in the system.

Cost-Benefit Analysis

A cost-benefit analysis (CBA) determines how well, or how poorly, a planned action will turn out. It shows whether the costs related to a planned action are worth the benefit the planned action will provide. Various CBA opportunities include staff addition, purchasing assets/equipment, developing a new workflow or modifying the workflow, and remodeling facilities.

CBA justification is organized into the following categories:

- *Hard dollar savings*: These are quantitative and easily calculated savings that represent real savings. They deal with the reduction and elimination of expenses through staff or supplies. Hard dollar savings provide the strongest case of justification.

- *Soft dollar savings*: These savings are qualitative and less directly calculated. They represent savings that cannot be recovered. They include saving management time or freeing up record space.

- *Cost avoidance*: Cost avoidance addresses the future cost reduction of the organization. Some of the items that are considered cost avoidance are temporary staff, additional file equipment/assets, and overtime.

Developing a Risk Assessment Methodology

The following are the steps in developing a risk assessment methodology:

1. *Build the risk assessment team*: Creating a risk assessment team is an important task for an organization because this team is responsible for reporting assessment results to management.

2. *Set the scope of the project*: A risk assessment team should identify the following parameters:
   - The objective of the assessment project
   - Department that needs to be assessed
   - Responsibilities of the team members
   - Persons to be interviewed
   - Standards to be used by the team
   - Documentation that has to be reviewed
   - Operations to be observed

3. *Identify assets covered by the assessment*: It is important to identify the assets that are involved in the assessment project. An assessment project may cover assets such as software, hardware, data, facilities, and current controls that protect those assets.

4. *Classify potential losses*: The team must classify the potential losses that could result from damages to an asset. Potential losses to assets may result from the following:
   - Physical damage to an asset
   - Denial of service
   - Modifications to an asset
   - Unauthorized access
   - Disclosure of information

5. *Identify threats and vulnerabilities*: In this step, the team identifies threats that exploit vulnerabilities to attack an asset. The following are some of the types of threats to an asset:
   - Natural threats
   - Accidental threats
   - Human accidental threats
   - Human malicious threats

6. *Identify existing controls*: Controls are protection measures that minimize the possibility of threats. The team should identify the controls that are presently implemented and determine their effect in the context of the current analysis.

7. *Analyze the data*: Data will be analyzed by collecting the required information to determine the risks. The following techniques are used to analyze data:
   - Preparing a list of assets
   - Corresponding threats to an asset
   - Determining the type of loss to an asset
   - Determining the vulnerabilities of an asset

8. *Determine cost-effective safeguards*: The following factors are necessary to determine a cost-effective safeguard:
   - Cost required to implement the safeguard
   - Total annual cost required to operate the safeguard
   - Duration or validity of safeguard

9. *Generate the report*: The team generates a risk assessment report that contains the following:
   - List of assets covered by the assessment project
   - Threats and vulnerabilities to an asset
   - Determination of risk
   - Safeguards to minimize the effect of threats
   - Cost-benefit analysis to evaluate the cost of the assessment project

Security Requirements

Security requirements are defined to ensure a reasonable level of security for computer systems and networks. They refer to the level of security necessary to ensure that computers and networks are not compromised in any manner. Security requirements are defined for the following reasons:

- Controlling user access
- Detecting intrusions by unauthorized users
- Preventing unauthorized malicious programs
- Preventing intentional data corruption
- Keeping confidential data and communication private
- Enabling security personal to audit the status and usage of security mechanisms

Security requirements for information assurance adhere to the following principles:

- *Integrity and consistency*: Integrity and consistency refer to the assurance that information can be accessed and modified only by authorized users. The main function of this security requirement is to protect the information from being modified by unauthorized users and to ensure a logical consistency of information.
- *Identification, authentication, and auditing*: Identification and authentication are the basic security requirements for information assurance. They refer to the process of verifying a user before granting access to information. The main purpose of performing the process of identification and authentication is to provide security to the information so that unauthorized users do not have access to it. Auditing is also a security requirement for information assurance because it helps to monitor all events related to security.
- *Authorization*: Authorization is the process of controlling access to resources such as services and files. It determines if a user should be granted access to a particular resource or information.

Physical Security Requirements

Physical security describes the measures taken to protect personnel, critical assets, and systems against deliberate attacks and accidents. Physical security is intended to prevent attackers from accessing the resources of an organization.

Physical security is necessary for every organization to secure its assets. Physical security measures are usually taken according to needs and circumstances. To guard property and prevent unauthorized entry, security guards and/or intruder detection systems should be used at access points.

The need for and location of security barriers depends on the cost of what is being protected. For systems and other information facilities, it is important to define a highly secure area (a sealed place in the building), such as a locked room, office, or utility cabinet.

The following physical security measures should be implemented by all organizations:

- Lock up the server room, so that no one can physically damage the server.
- Set up surveillance cameras to monitor and record when someone is in a high-security area.
- Place network devices in locked rooms.
- Use rack-mount servers.
- Protect portable devices such as laptop and handheld computers.
- Back up all data so that they can be recovered later in the event of a disaster.
- Disable unnecessary drives and ports so that employees cannot copy company information.
- Secure printers.

Information Categorization

The information of an organization is categorized according to its sensitivity to loss or disclosure. This categorization is used to define necessary access control requirements. Whoever is responsible for the information should assess its sensitivity level based on its value to the organization and the impact its loss would have. After the categorization, an overall management review must be performed. An overall data assessment method should be used to make any adjustments. All personnel who are responsible for information categorization must agree to use the same definitions.

Information Categorization Levels

The following categorization levels are commonly used:

- *Sensitive*: This type of information requires special protection measures to ensure its integrity by protecting it from unauthorized modification or deletion. This type of information requires higher assurance of accuracy and completeness. Financial transactions and regulatory actions are the best examples of this type of information.

- *Confidential*: This type of information is the most sensitive and can only be used within the organization. It is free from disclosure under the provisions of the Freedom of Information Act or other applicable federal laws and regulations. Its unauthorized disclosure may seriously impact the organization.

- *Private*: This is personal information that can only be used by an employee. Disclosure of this information can seriously impact the employee. Examples of private information include the following:
  - Contact details
  - Work product information
  - Credit card details

- *Public*: This is information that does not belong to any of the above-mentioned categories. Disclosure of this information does not have any serious impact on the organization.

Risk Acceptance

Risk acceptance is the process of accepting the possibility and consequences of a particular risk. It is the final stage in the risk management process. Business risk presents an opportunity to gain profit and the potential to take losses. Organizations should manage their risks to maintain balance between the opportunities for gain and the potential for loss.

The amount of risk that an organization can accept is also known as its *risk appetite* or *risk tolerance*. Risk appetite or risk tolerance is different for every organization, depending on the culture, the industry, the line of business, and the potential gain.

Risk acceptance depends on the following factors:

- Financial capacity of organization to absorb the consequences of risk
- Level of conservatism of the decision maker
- Amount of risk inherent in the business activity normally carried out by the organization
- Diversity of the business
- Extent to which risk can be transferred or reduced

Risk Acceptance Process

The risk acceptance process is a top-level approach for integrating the concept of risk acceptance into a system safety program. It provides the framework for satisfying the requirements of the Discretionary Function Exclusion under the U.S. Federal Tort Claim Act. The Discretionary Function Exclusion protects both the government and contractors, if they follow an intelligent discretionary decision process.

The risk acceptance process involves the following steps:

1. *Develop a risk acceptance statement for remaining exposures*: This statement includes detailed information on residual risks, probability of occurrence of a security incident due to such risks, possible impacts of such risks, and methodologies used to assess such risks. Senior management, who can decide on the

risk acceptance level for the organization, must endorse this statement. Risk acceptance statements are required to achieve compliance with established standards and overcome legal issues that may arise due to residual risks.

2. *Approve the risk acceptance statement*: After the development of the risk acceptance statement, it is sent to the risk management team for assessment. This statement is also forwarded to other stakeholders that may be affected by the risk acceptance.

3. *Document results*: The outcomes of the risk acceptance process should be thoroughly documented and made available to all stakeholders. This document acts as a guide for the chief information officer to maintain risk control measures implemented in the organization.

Accuracy and Reliability of an Information System's Data

Information systems depend on data to fulfill their purpose. The accuracy and reliability of the data are critical for the system's normal operation. Organizations should implement preventive controls to detect and prevent undesirable data from entering the information system. Inappropriate or malicious data may give rise to several system vulnerabilities or may even lead to a system crash.

The preventive controls for maintaining the accuracy and reliability of an information system's data include the following:

- Maintenance of access privileges to appropriate personnel
- Verification of sensitive transactions
- Authentication before allowing users to enter and manipulate data

Configuration Management

Configuration management is a field of management that focuses on establishing and maintaining the integrity of an information system throughout its life. It is responsible for making changes to hardware, software, firmware, and test documentation throughout the life cycle of an information system. It ensures that project documentation correctly describes and controls the functional and physical characteristics of the end product being developed.

Configuration management policies cover the following activities:

- Configuration management planning
- Configuration identification
- Configuration change management process implementation
- Configuration status accounting documentation
- Configuration verification and audit process
- Configuration interface management

Configuration management helps the organization manage information and track changes that take place during the life cycle of the information. Noting the changes helps in finding the origin of problems and solving them as quickly as possible.

System Configuration and Management Board (SCMB)

The system configuration and management board (SCMB), also known as the configuration control board (CCB), is a group that plays a vital role in an organization's information systems. This board is managed by the chief information officer (CIO) and is made up of voting representatives from every department of the organization.

The main goal of the SCMB is to make decisions that increase network efficiency and utility. Security is an important part of this decision-making process, so members of this board must provide for security concerns during every phase.

There are two main responsibilities of the SCMB:

1. Controlling the baseline
2. Evaluating and approving the planned changes

System Certifiers and Accreditors

- *System certifiers*: Activities of system certifiers are as follows:
  - Performing complete multidiscipline assessment of technical and nontechnical security features
  - Supporting accreditation process
  - Identifying assurance levels to meet all applicable security policies
- *System accreditors*: System accreditors are responsible for the following tasks:
  - Approving the system for operation
  - Ensuring that the system is adequately tested prior to accreditation
  - Developing certification, security, and security evaluation plans
  - Implementing the certification process
  - Evaluating the risk assessment and developing a residual risk statement

Risk Management Methodologies to Develop Life-Cycle Management Policies and Procedures

Risk management methodologies to develop policies and procedures for information system life-cycle management must include the following steps:

1. Assess the life-cycle management policies and procedures.
2. Define roles and responsibilities.
3. Perform a system characterization.
4. Analyze vulnerabilities and controls.
5. Identify the threat sources.
6. Calculate the probability of each threat's occurrence.
7. Perform an impact analysis.
8. Determine the level of risk.
9. Develop a risk mitigation policy.
10. Estimate the level of residual risk.
11. Prepare the risk assessment report for business decisions.

Role of Security Awareness as Part of a Risk Management Plan

A security awareness program allows organizations to improve their security posture by providing required training to their employees to protect information assets. To protect the organization's information assets, employees must understand the organization's security policies and their responsibility in protecting the assets.

The security of an organization must be an ongoing process and should include continuous training, communication, and support. A one-time security action is not sufficient to identify the ever-growing threats to the organization.

Security awareness programs enable organizations to accomplish the following goals:

- Comply with laws and regulations
- Reduce unpredictable costs
- Improve security posture
- Protect information assets
- Reduce information security risk

Education, Training, and Awareness

Education, training, and awareness are important from the perspective of the organization because a trained employee increases productivity and also saves time. Educated staff will always help protect organizational data from leakage. Many times, data breaches are caused by the mistakes of employees who make uninformed mistakes. Educating employees reduces the chances of these types of mistakes.

Security Laws and Applicability to Risk Management Plan

- *Federal Information Security Management Act of 2002 (FISMA)*: The Federal Information Security Management Act provides a legal framework for protecting federally owned and operated computer systems. It covers non–national security systems. It assigns data protection responsibility in the federal government to various agencies. This act requires the head of an agency to conduct annual reviews of information security programs in order to reduce risk.

- *Gramm-Leach-Bliley Act (GLBA)*: The Gramm-Leach-Bliley Act requires financial institutions to protect the security and confidentiality of a customer's financial information. This act contains three sections:

  1. *Financial privacy rule*: This controls the disclosure of financial information.

  2. *Safeguards rule*: This rule states that financial institutions must use security measures to protect financial information.

  3. *Pretexting provisions*: This prohibits pretexting activities such as obtaining private information using false pretenses.

- *Health Insurance Portability and Accountability Act of 1996 (HIPAA)*: This law ensures the integrity and confidentiality of individually discovered information. It requires health care units to implement new security policies for disclosure of health information. It protects against reasonably anticipated threats and unauthorized disclosure. The health care units covered by HIPAA include:

  - Health care plans
  - Health care clearinghouses
  - Health care providers

- *Sarbanes-Oxley Act*: This law provides protection to investors against corporate accounting fraud. It sets guidelines to improve the accuracy and reliability of corporate disclosures. This act includes the following provisions:

  - CEOs and CFOs are responsible for the financial reports of their organizations.
  - CEOs and directors may accept loans from their organizations.
  - Insider trades are immediately reported.
  - Insider trades are prohibited during fund blackouts.

- *Counterfeit Access Device and Computer Fraud and Abuse Act of 1984 (CFAA)*: This law governs an array of computer-related crimes. The main purpose of this act is to focus directly on computer abuses. It helps federal prosecutors prosecute criminal computer activities.

- *Electronic Communications Privacy Act (ECPA)*: This act makes provisions for the access, use, disclosure, interception, and privacy protections of electronic communications. This act prohibits illegal access and certain disclosures of communication contents.

Policy Development

The process of developing policy commonly involves research, analysis, discussion, and synthesis of the information to produce proposals. Policy development contains the following steps:

1. *Define the issue or problem*: Policy development begins with defining the issues or problems for which the policy is being developed.

2. *Collect the required information on the issue*: This step of policy development deals with collecting the information required for developing a successful policy. The following information is collected in this step:

   - Sample policy language
   - Experience from other policies

- Local inputs
- Education research
- State association seminars
- State laws and regulations

3. *Secure recommendations from the supervisor*: After collecting the information, the board listens to recommendations for developing the policy.

4. *Discuss the issue with the management board*: In this step, the superintendent, who is responsible for managing the policy development, discusses the issues that were defined in previous steps.

5. *Outline the policy*: After discussing the issues with management, the superintendent obtains solutions from management to develop a policy. The superintendent develops and submits a sample policy to verify that this policy will cover all the issues of the organization.

6. *Adopt the policy*: In this step, management verifies a sample policy and approves the policy to be implemented in the organization. Before approving the policy, management goes through the various steps to verify the policy.

7. *Distribute the policy document to the organization's employees*: Once management has approved the policy, the policy document is distributed to all the employees of the organization. Every employee must follow this policy before performing any activity or operation on a computer.

8. *Oversee the policy's implementation*: This step deals with managing the policy's implementation after distributing it to all the employees.

9. *Review and evaluate the policy*: In this step, the policy is evaluated and reviewed to identify any necessary modifications.

Information Security Policy

Information security policies define a set of standard procedures and methodologies to protect information and information systems from various attacks. The policy statements clearly define the objectives of information security efforts in conjunction with an organization's business objectives and outline the control measures to safeguard the information.

Information security policies are developed after a thorough analysis of perceived business risks and criticality of information systems in achieving business objectives. In general, information security policies provide guidelines for the following tasks:

- Preparing an information security plan and implementing security control measures
- Performing an information security risk assessment and estimating the acceptable level of risk
- Periodically testing the security control measures to find out the efficiency of the information system
- Performing an audit of the information infrastructure

System security administrators should identify the existing policies implemented in the organization before creating new policies and updating the existing policies. Implemented policies can be identified by testing organizational procedures for standard policy guidelines.

Standard Information System Security Policies

The following information system security policies are standard:

- *Protect passwords*: Information systems rely on passwords for authentication and authorization of system users. Any compromise of passwords may enable unauthorized people to access sensitive and confidential information. Password security is a key for the information security in an information system. Passwords can be protected by taking the following protection measures:
  - Do not share passwords with others.
  - Do not use dictionary words, keyboard sequences, words spelled backward, or foreign words.
  - Use as many characters as allowed.
  - Use punctuation marks or symbols.

- Use a mix of uppercase and lowercase characters.
- Do not write passwords where someone else can see them.
- Change passwords every 90 days.

- *Protect confidential information*: Users should never place confidential data such as Social Security and credit card numbers in an unlocked area on the computer. They should not post Social Security numbers or user IDs in a public location or on the Internet.

- *Update systems with patches and security fixes, and update antivirus software*: Administrators should ensure that all systems contain the latest patches, security fixes, and antivirus software. Unprotected computer systems are vulnerable to outside attacks and data loss, and leave the organization's network vulnerable to damage and failure.

- *Use secure applications*: Users should not use unsecured applications. Unsecured applications collect and transmit personal data and leave organizations open to network attacks.

- *Back up data*: Administrators should protect important information and data on systems by backing up computer data.

- *Use a password-protected screensaver*: All users should utilize password-protected screensavers to lock the computers when they are not in use. This helps protect information systems from insider threats and helps ensure information privacy.

- *Use discretion when dealing with e-mail*: E-mail attacks are common. The following steps should be taken to secure e-mail accounts:

  - Evaluate the source of the received mail before opening and responding.
  - Disable the preview feature of the e-mail client.
  - Treat each received attachment as a possible virus attack.
  - Avoid submitting e-mail addresses on Web sites.
  - Implement spam filters.
  - Quarantine suspicious e-mail.
  - Conduct vulnerability tests on e-mail systems.

Change Control Policies

Change control is the process used to request, review, plan, approve, and implement changes to a system. It helps an organization maintain the changes taking place. Information changes and system changes can be documented using change control policies. These policies are decided on by management and are implemented to assess changes within an organization.

The following steps should be followed for the change control process:

1. Change request submitted
2. Change evaluated
3. Validation assessed
4. Implementation planned
5. Approval to implement given
6. Implementation and qualification
7. Approval to close change
8. Special treatment of "emergency changes"
9. Special treatment of "routine changes"

Change control policies provide the following guidelines:

- The possible impact of any change should be evaluated prior to accepting a change request.
- Changes in an information system should be carried out in a way that will not affect the existing system in a harmful way.

- A change log/directory should be maintained.
- Changes should be premeditated and access to make changes should be given only to qualified personnel.
- All changes should be controlled through the change management process.
- Reviews should be done prior to implementation of any change.
- Changes should be planned only for those systems that are capable of carrying out the work.

System Acquisition Policies and Procedures

System acquisition policies should adhere to the following guidelines:

- Examine the sufficiency of the planned system as a solution for the data processing problems under consideration.
- Assess the impact of the acquisition on the organization's personnel.
- Assess the impact of the acquisition on the organization's information systems.
- A cost-effective substitute should be considered.
- Recognize the possible growth of expenses and ensure that the financial needs associated with the acquisition are understood.
- Satisfy the organization's reporting and authorization requirements.

Acquisition and Upgrade of Software Components

The software acquisition policy should contain the following steps:

1. *Requesting software*: The requesting personnel should work with the IT department to identify the software needs. He or she should then obtain approval from the IT department manager to purchase the software.

2. *Purchasing licenses for software*: The requesting personnel then sends the completed purchase order request to the IT department for verification and approval. The IT department then sends the approved purchase order request to the purchasing department, where it is processed.

3. *Receiving software*: After receiving the software, the IT department follows the organization's check-in procedure to ensure that the software is added to the software inventory.

4. *Distributing software*: The IT department provides the software to the requesting department.

5. *Ensure that software documentation is available to the end users*: A copy of the end-user license agreement and manuals related to the software must be provided to the receiving department.

Risk Analysis Policies

Risk analysis policy should include the following steps:

1. Identify the frequency of a particular type of disaster.
2. Determine the effect of the disaster.
3. Analyze the speed of occurrence of the disaster.
4. Approximate the duration of the disaster.
5. Determine the impact of the disaster based on whether or not vital records are destroyed.
6. Identify the effects of the disaster such as:
   - Employee availability
   - Employee injuries
   - Loss of operating resources
   - Loss of organizational assets
   - Damages to facilities

7. Identify the required redundancy levels in the organization to accommodate critical systems and functions, including:

   - Hardware
   - Information
   - Communications
   - Personnel
   - Services

8. Estimate the potential dollar loss, including the following losses:

   - Loss of business opportunities
   - Loss of financial management capabilities
   - Loss of organizational assets
   - Negative media coverage
   - Loss of stockholder confidence
   - Loss of goodwill
   - Loss of income
   - Loss of competitive edge
   - Legal actions

9. Determine the cost of contingency planning.

General Risk Control Policies

General risk control policies should abide by these guidelines:

- Create clear objectives, and identify and estimate the major risks involved in achieving those objectives.
- Incorporate risk responses into a system of internal controls to protect the company's assets.
- Check the effectiveness of the risk and internal control management system.
- Follow the company's group guidelines and standards.
- Provide accountability to manage risks within approved boundaries.

Access Control Policies

An access control policy defines access to information systems for different categories of users. Access control standards are applied by the organization to control access to its information assets. These standards ensure suitable access controls for an organization's operation and security needs.

A security policy for access control depends upon the following points:

- *Managing access control standards*: Management must establish access control standards for information systems and must provide restrictions to prevent unauthorized access to increase the operational efficiency of the organization.

- *Managing user access*: The owner of a system must authorize access to the system. The following information security issues should be considered when implementing the security policy:

  - Unavailability of managed access controls may result in unauthorized access to information systems.
  - Logon screens and banners must be removed because they help unauthorized users gain access.
  - Assigning inappropriate privileges to inexperienced staff may result in processing problems and accidental errors.

- *Protecting unattended equipment*: Equipment must be protected appropriately, especially when left unattended. Unauthorized access to unattended equipment may result in harmful and fraudulent activities.

- *Managing network access control*: Access to network resources must be maintained strictly to prevent unauthorized access. Computing and information systems and peripherals must be accessed only after explicit authorization.

- *Securing access to operating system software*: Organizations must restrict access to operating system commands to only those persons who are authorized to perform system administration activities. All systems, from small PCs to large servers, must be hardened to remove needless development tools and utilities prior to delivery to end users.

- *Monitoring user system access and utilization*: Access to user systems must be logged and observed to recognize potential misuse of the systems. Sometimes, users may perform unofficial activities that are against the company's policy, which may cause damage or information loss. System access must be monitored regularly to prevent unauthorized access and to confirm that access control standards are effective.

- *Controlling access to files and documents*: Access to shared files must be carefully controlled to ensure that only authorized individuals have access to them. Uncontrolled access may result in unauthorized copying and modifying of information.

- *Controlling remote user access*: Remote-access control processes must provide proper safeguards through strong detection, verification, and encryption techniques. Remote users may need to communicate directly with their organization's systems to send and receive data. These types of users are physically remote and also connect through public networks, which may increase the threat of unauthorized access.

Personnel Security Policies

Personnel security policies provide the following guidelines:

- The roles and responsibilities as mentioned in the information security policy should be documented in the job descriptions as applicable.

- Verification of permanent employees should be performed at the time of job application through the following processes:
  - Character references
  - Confirmation of qualifications
  - Identity checks through documents such as passports
  - Proof of submission of passport application

- Managers should be aware of the activities of their employees.

- All employees should sign confidentiality and nondisclosure agreements at the start of employment.

- Employment terms and conditions should be precisely stated in the confidentiality agreement.

- Appropriate actions should be taken to separate duties in order to reduce the chance of unauthorized modification of information.

- Resources of information processing should not be used for other purposes.

Communications Security Policies

Communications security policies provide the following guidelines:

- Data paths related to online processing must be error free and secure.
- Telecommunication devices such as routers and hubs must be protected.
- Valuable information must be encrypted before being sent over a communications network.
- Virtual private networks (VPN) must use encryption according to the organization's cryptography policy.
- Internal/external desktop modems in the organization must be handled only by authorized personnel.
- Contractor sites must comply with an organization's security policies to obtain access to the organization's network.
- Communication cables that carry data must be protected from interception or damage.
- The data owner must ensure that communication protection measures are established for each data system.

Security Policies for Types of Permitted and Prohibited Actions on a System

The following actions on a system are prohibited:

- Sharing, transferring, and distributing information or data in violation of any applicable laws
- Performing an action that violates system or network security
- Performing an illegal action that may result in a criminal or civil liability
- Using a computer to irritate, harm, abuse, or harass others
- Sharing passwords with other people
- Installing or running unauthorized software on the computer
- Downloading and storing pornographic material on the computer

Declassification and Destruction Policies

Media Declassification Information that the organization no longer uses should be destroyed. Declassification of media is done by the following methods:

- *Declassifying tapes*:
  - A tape containing confidential and important information should be degaussed before being released for destruction.
  - All markings and labels indicating the previous use of the tape should be removed.
  - The tape should be destroyed by incineration or disintegration.
- *Declassifying disks*:
  - Disks containing information that is no longer useful should be disposed of after removing the labels.
  - Disks can be destroyed using metal destruction, incineration, or a chemical destroyer.
- *Declassifying memory*:
  - Magnetic core memory should be declassified and destroyed by pulverizing, smelting, and incinerating methods.

Policies for Destruction of Sensitive Information Information stored at a location other than the office may be at risk, as theft and hacking of the information is possible. Physical media that are used for data storage should be kept at a secured location.

It is advisable to destroy sensitive information storage devices as soon as the information is no longer needed. The information storage media destruction should be done in a thorough manner, as it is important to destroy the information completely.

Some media and data destruction methods are as follows:

- *Nonvolatile magnetic media, such as hard disk drives*: Pattern wiping, incineration, and physical destruction
- *Write-once optical media, such as CD-ROMs and DVD-Rs*: Abrasion, incineration, and physical destruction
- *Write-many optical media, such as CD-RWs and DVD-RWs*: Abrasion, incineration, and physical destruction
- *Solid-state media*: Pattern wiping and physical destruction
- *Paper-based media*: Shredding and incineration

Emergency Destruction Planning and Procedures (EDPP) Emergency destruction planning must address the following issues:

- Reporting fire incidents and initial firefighting by assigned personnel
- Assigning on-scene responsibility for protecting the organization's resources
- Securing or removing classified material and evacuating the area

- Protecting resources when admission of outside firefighters is necessary
- Reporting possible exposures to the organization's resources from unauthorized personnel during the emergency
- Posting emergency inventory of classified resources and reporting losses

Emergency destruction procedures must address the following issues:

- Adequate number of destruction devices
- Availability of electrical power
- Secure storage facilities
- Sufficient protected destruction areas
- Personnel assignments

Organizations must ensure the following to develop a successful destruction plan:

- All duties under the plan must be clearly described.
- All authorized persons must be aware of the plan.
- All assigned personnel under the plan must know their responsibilities.
- Training exercises must be conducted periodically.

Policies for Capturing Audit Trails

Audit trails maintain a record of information system activity. With the help of appropriate tools and procedures, they also detect security violations, performance problems, and errors in applications.

An audit trail contains a list of computer events about an operating system, an application, or activities of a user. Computer systems may contain many audit trails, each of which is related to a particular user activity. Auditing is the process of analyzing management, operational, and technical controls.

An audit trail is used to help system administrators make sure that the information system has not been adversely affected by hackers, insiders, or technical problems. Audit trails also help to achieve the following security-related objectives:

- Individual accountability
- Reconstruction of events
- Intrusion detection
- Problem analysis

The following policies should be implemented for capturing audit logs:

- Logs must be protected from unauthorized users and integrity problems.
- To protect the integrity of logs, there should be proper segregation of duties among those who administer system/network accounts.
- Consideration should be given to the location of logs and moving logs to a central spot.

Policies Regarding Audit Data Usage, Management, and Maintenance

- Proper controls and audit logs should be designed into the application of information systems.
- Control and audit logs should include the justification of input data, internal processing, and output data.
- Log records must be categorized into the following types:
  - Accounting records
  - Database records
  - Audit logs

Audit Record Policies

Auditable Events Audits help to maintain the security and integrity of critical information and processes. Information security audits check the level of information security in an organization. The audit process identifies risks in the operating environment. The auditor identifies the events that are needed to control and operate efficiently and effectively in order to minimize risk.

Auditable events are categorized into three categories:

1. Technical
2. Physical
3. Administrative

The following practices should be included when auditing events:

- Create a policy statement, develop an audit plan, and educate employees before implementing the audit policy.
- Clearly define the auditable events.
- Determine the tools, databases, and procedures to collect, organize, and analyze the audit data before starting the auditing process.
- Test the audit configuration settings before implementing them.
- Collect account logon and management event logs.
- Collect policy change events.
- Audit application and service success or failure events.
- Audit directory service access.
- Audit access and privilege assignments.

Personal Access Policies A policy for auditing personal access to computer systems provides the following guidelines:

- Systems are required to log users' system logins and logoffs with dates and times.
- Systems must be able to read, create, update, delete, and print user access for systems containing confidential data.
- All audit records must be identified by record keys or numbers.
- Systems must log unsuccessful login attempts and access violations.
- Functions of security administrators must be logged.
- Functions of system administrators must be logged.
- Unauthorized access, modifications, and deletions of audit records must be restricted.
- Audit records must be available for 90 days and must be backed up for a minimum of two years.

Risk Associated with Agency-Specific Policies and Procedures

Organizations should avoid agency-specific policies and procedures due to these risks:

- Agency-specific configuration management policies and procedures leave organizations unable to adopt new technologies.
- Agency-specific policies and procedures may render an organization noncompliant to some of the established standards.
- Configuration change management becomes difficult if a loophole is discovered in the products and services of the agency.
- Switching to different solutions from another vendor requires a significant financial and human resource investment.

Chapter Summary

- Understanding the system's processing environment is necessary while identifying the risks in a system.
- A cost-benefit analysis determines whether the cost to implement an action is worth the benefit the action will have.
- The system configuration management board (SCMB), also known as the configuration control board (CCB), is a group that plays a vital role in an organization's information systems.
- The process of developing policy commonly involves research, analysis, discussion, and synthesis of information to produce proposals.
- System certifiers perform comprehensive multidiscipline assessments of technical and nontechnical security features.
- System accreditors ensure that a system is adequately tested prior to accreditation.
- Risk management is the process of identifying risk, addressing risk, and taking steps to eliminate or reduce risk to an acceptable level.

Review Questions

1. Explain the change control procedure.

   _____

   _____

   _____

   _____

2. Explain configuration management. How do access controls and other administrative measures help in configuration management?

   _____

   _____

   _____

   _____

3. How are media declassified?

   _____

   _____

   _____

   _____

4. What are different media and data destruction methods?

   _____

   _____

   _____

   _____

5. What are the considerations in developing ST&E plans and procedures?

_____

_____

_____

_____

6. Discuss the laws that influence IA policy implementation.

_____

_____

_____

_____

7. Describe the policies and procedures for capturing audit logs.

_____

_____

_____

_____

8. Discuss the role of emergency destruction planning and procedures in information assurance.

_____

_____

_____

_____

9. What are the physical security requirements that organizations should implement in order to achieve IA?

_____

_____

_____

_____

Hands-On Projects

1. Navigate to Chapter 6 of the Student Resource Center. Open MBT_Automated_Security_Testing.pdf and read the following topics:

   ▪ Introduction

   ▪ Modeling Variables and Data Types

2. Navigate to Chapter 6 of the Student Resource Center. Open NAVSO P5239-07 ISSO Guide.pdf and read the following topics:

   ▪ INFORMATION SYSTEMS SECURITY OFFICER ROLE

   ▪ INFORMATION SYSTEMS SECURITY OFFICER RESPONSIBILITIES

3. Navigate to Chapter 6 of the Student Resource Center. Open RMPoliciesandProcedures.pdf and read the following topics:

   - Objectives
   - Authority and Responsibilities

4. Navigate to Chapter 6 of the Student Resource Center. Open costbenefit.pdf and read the following topics:

   - Identification of the Assets and Values
   - Management and Control

Chapter 7

Data Storage Technologies

Objectives

After completing this chapter, you should be able to:

- Use network attached storage (NAS)
- Use direct attached storage (DAS)
- Understand the difference between NAS and DAS
- Use storage area networks (SAN)
- Understand the difference between SAN and NAS
- Secure storage area networks with iSCSI
- Implement SAN security

Key Terms

Data phase   the phase in which data are transmitted between the SCSI initiator and the SCSI target

Introduction to Data Storage Technologies

Home users are usually able to store as much data as they need on their desktop's hard drives, but many organizations require much more space. In addition, they need to be able to share data with others in the organization quickly and reliably. This chapter familiarizes you with three different data storage technologies: network attached storage (NAS), direct attached storage (DAS), and storage area networks (SANs).

Network Attached Storage (NAS)

Network attached storage (NAS) is a dedicated, hard disk–based storage technology. It is attached directly to a computer network, providing data access to network clients using a client-server design.

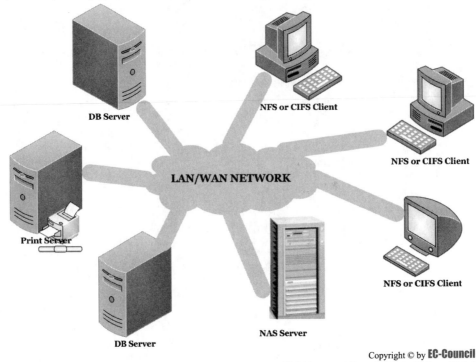

Figure 7-1   All of these clients can access the NAS server.

The hardware device, called a NAS box or NAS head, functions as the interface between NAS and network clients. It runs on an embedded operating system.

Clients usually access NAS through an Ethernet connection. NAS appears as a single node on the network with the IP address of the head device. NAS can store any type of file and includes built-in features such as secure authentication and disk space quotas.

Figure 7-1 shows the topology of a network including NAS.

NAS Architecture

A basic NAS may contain only one head, or it may share internal storage space across multiple heads to increase bandwidth. The storage capacity of NAS systems is determined by drive support, the number of drives present, and the capacity of the drives. NAS systems commonly use low-cost, high-density SATA drives, as well as some other drives including ATA, SCSI, and SAS drives. Higher-end NAS models use Fibre Channel drives.

Workgroup-type NAS systems contain at least a terabyte (1 TB) of capacity, spread across two or more hard disks. Enterprise-class NAS systems can use many disks to provide substantially more storage. Several NAS systems include RAID support to protect data, implementing common RAID levels such as RAID 0, RAID 1, RAID 5, RAID 6/DP and RAID 10. NAS systems also contain onboard RAM to cache data from all the disks. Small NAS devices contain a 128-MB to 256-MB cache, while enterprise-class NAS systems contain can contain 8 GB or more.

Some NAS products provide multiple Ethernet connections for network interface aggregation, redundancy, or failover. NAS boxes operate independently and can be aggregated into clusters. Similar to clustered computing, NAS clusters are used as a single device in the LAN. Each clustered element can share the data load, and each box in the cluster can provide failover if another box fails, which improves storage performance.

Figure 7-2 shows an example NAS architecture.

NAS Protocols

NAS uses the following protocols to communicate with clients in the LAN:

- *Networking protocols*:
  - *IPX (Internetwork Packet Exchange)*: This protocol connects clients and servers using Novell's NetWare. It functions at the network layer of the communication protocols, so it does not require a direct connection to exchange packets.

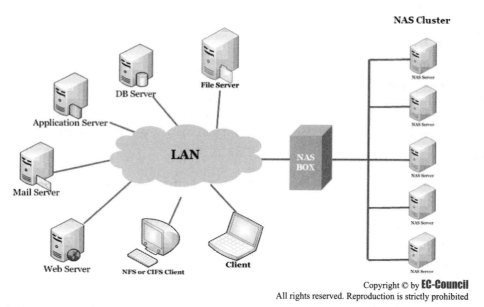

Figure 7-2   Note that a cluster of NAS servers can be behind a single NAS box.

- *NetBEUI*: This is an advanced version of NetBIOS. It is mainly used to communicate between computers within a local area network running Windows NT, LAN Manager, and Windows for Workgroups products.
- *File exchange protocols*:
  - *Network File System (NFS)*: This protocol was developed by Sun Microsystems and uses the Remote Procedure Call (RPC) method to communicate.
  - *Server Message Block (SMB)*: This protocol is used by the client application to read and write files on the server. It is used on the Internet on top of the TCP/IP protocol or other protocols such as Internet Packet Exchange (IPX) and NetBEUI.
- *Internet application protocols*:
  - *File Transfer Protocol (FTP)*: This is a standard Internet protocol that enables file exchange between computers on the network using the TCP/IP protocol.
  - *Hypertext Transfer Protocol (HTTP)*: This is an application protocol that runs on top of the TCP/IP protocol on the Internet.

The Need for NAS

NAS is useful for the following reasons:

- *Security*: A properly implemented NAS system offers a level of data security. Most NAS implementations are based on the Linux OS, making them less vulnerable to viruses and other malware when compared to Windows-based systems.
- *Power consumption*: NAS systems are energy efficient. In the case of a power failure, NAS can shut down the hard disk drives and remain idle. The power utilization of NAS, depending on how many hard disk drives are included, is about 5 W to 20 W.
- *Network access*: Network storage restricts unwanted or unauthorized network communications to the Internet. It is possible to set up a home page using NAS, providing a Web server with DDNS (Dynamic DNS). In addition to regular Web content, it can be used to access cameras as a remote surveillance server.
- *Larger storage capacity*: NAS was originally designed to offer larger storage capacity than existing storage media. However, with increasing growth in the storage market, NAS capacity looks smaller than it used to.
- *NAS hardware platform*: The present NAS model consists of SATA-II slots, USB 2.0 high-speed host ports, and Gigabit Ethernet. NAS looks similar to a regular PC, without display and input devices. NAS typically uses a RISC-based embedded application computer or x86 PC.

NAS Types

NAS Disk-As-Disk

A NAS disk-as-disk target is a disk array that stores the disk behind a NAS head, creating a single shared volume. This type of system is easier to maintain than traditional disk arrays.

A disk-as-disk target provides an inexpensive method for backing up the disk and provides additional benefits when used with traditional backup systems. Disk-as-disk systems require a SAN or NAS unit. SAN units are more powerful but are also more difficult to maintain and share; they will be discussed later in this chapter.

Scalable NAS

Scalable NAS is a storage system that accommodates file-based content that is always growing and must always be available. Advantages of scalable NAS include:

- *Scalability*: Scalable systems provide more computing power and storage capacity when necessary.
- *Manageability*: Newly added content and devices can be managed efficiently.
- *Affordability*: Scalable systems have reduced cost of ownership and reduced administrative expenses due to their ease of management.

NAS solutions are commonly used by IT managers because they can be more easily managed than DAS and SAN systems. The NAS market is divided into two separate segments: low priced and low performance. Non-scalable NAS are well suited for homes and offices. More expensive devices that provide high performance and scalability require special management skills. Scalable NAS is perfectly suited for sites that require a high degree of data growth.

Scalable NAS is commonly used by providers and distributors of high-definition material. This can include any form of rich media such as video pre- and postproduction, prepress, 3-D modeling, satellite imagery, and many aspects of high-performance computing.

Scalable NAS is useful for companies involved in the following:

- Delivering streaming video to users
- Providing Web 2.0 file servers
- Digital archiving
- Storing any other massive amounts of data

Open-Source NAS Implementations

FreeNAS

FreeNAS has the following features:

- Occupies less than 32 MB memory once installed on the hard disk
- Can be run directly from a storage device
- Supports protocols such as CIFS (via Samba), FTP, NFS, SSH, rsync, AFP, UPnP, iTunes/DAAP Server and BitTorrent
- Provides FreeBSD IPFW packet-filter and traffic-accounting facility
- Provides extensions for SlimServer via SlimNAS and XBMSP via ccXstream
- Contains iSCSI targets to create virtual disks
- Supports all network cards (wired and wireless) supported by FreeBSD
- Supports all hardware RAID cards supported by FreeBSD
- Has a Web-based configuration interface, shown in Figure 7-3

Installing FreeNAS To install FreeNAS, follow these steps:

1. Download the latest FreeNAS ISO image and burn it onto a CD.
2. Boot the system from that CD.
3. Select option **7** to install FreeNAS on the hard disk.

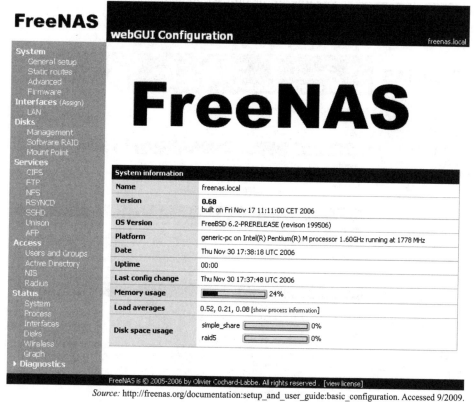

Source: http://freenas.org/documentation:setup_and_user_guide:basic_configuration. Accessed 9/2009.

Figure 7-3   This is the FreeNAS Web configuration interface.

4. Select option **2** to create two UFS partitions on the hard disk. One partition will be for FreeNAS, and the other will be for storage space.

5. The installer will show the names of the detected CD-ROM drives. Enter the name of the CD-ROM drive with the FreeNAS disc.

6. The installer will show the names of the detected hard drives. Enter the name of the hard drive to which FreeNAS should be installed.

7. Once installation is complete, press Enter to continue.

8. Select option **2** to return to the main menu, and then select option **5** and press Y to reboot the system.

9. Once the system reboots, it is necessary to configure the network. First, select option **1** to assign the network interface.

10. FreeNAS provides the list of interfaces. Type the name of the interface to use, or enter **A** to autodetect.

11. To add another LAN interface, enter its name, or just press Enter to move on.

12. Press Y to reboot FreeNAS.

13. Once FreeNAS reboots, select option **2** to set the LAN IP address that FreeNAS will use.

14. FreeNAS will ask if it should use DHCP. Press N.

15. Enter a static IP address for the system.

16. Enter the subnet mask.

17. FreeNAS will confirm that the IP has been set and will give instructions for entering the Web GUI. Press Enter.

18. Select option **6** to test the network connection.

19. Enter a known internal IP address. FreeNAS will attempt to ping it. If the ping is successful, FreeNAS is installed correctly. Press Enter.

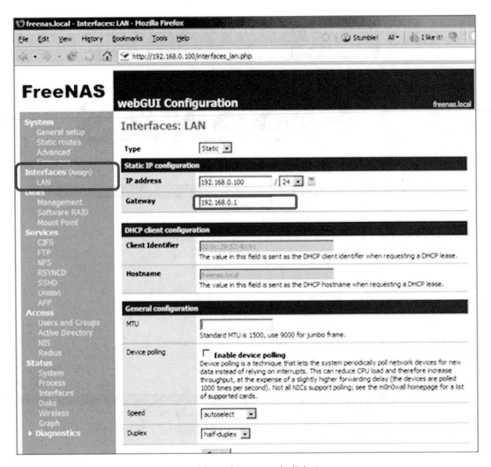

Figure 7-4   Enter a gateway IP address here, and click **Save**.

Configuring FreeNAS   To configure FreeNAS after it has been installed, follow these steps:

1. Log into the FreeNAS Web interface by entering its IP address, assigned during setup, into a Web browser on any system on the network.

2. Enter the login information. The default username is **admin**, and the default password is **freenas**.

3. The welcome page will be displayed.

4. In the left navigation pane, click **LAN** under **Interfaces**.

5. Enter a gateway IP address, as shown in Figure 7-4, and click **Save**.

6. On the FreeNAS machine, return to the FreeNAS terminal.

7. Select option 5 to reboot the system, and press Y to confirm.

8. Return to the Web interface.

9. On the left navigation pane, click **General setup** under **System**.

10. Fill in the two DNS servers and change the administrator password, as shown in Figure 7-5, and click **Save**.

Configuring a Hard Drive for Use with FreeNAS   To configure a hard drive for use with NAS, follow these steps:

1. Enter the FreeNAS Web interface.

2. In the left navigation pane, click **Management** under **Disks**.

3. Click on the + sign.

4. Select the disk from the drop-down list.

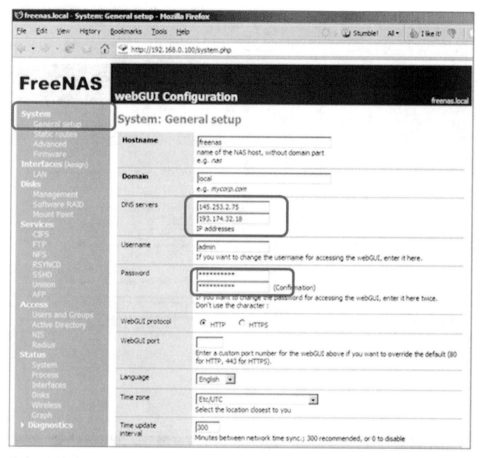

Figure 7-5 Fill in the two DNS servers and change the administrator password, and then click **Save**.

5. Select **UFS** under **Preformatted FS**, as shown in Figure 7-6, and click the **Add** button.

6. On the next page, click the **Apply changes** button.

7. Next, the partition must be mounted before it can be used. In the left navigation pane, click **Mount Point** under **Disks**.

8. Click on the + sign.

9. Select the information that matches the disk that was just added, and create a share name and description for this disk. Then click the **Add** button.

Enabling Services on the FreeNAS Server To enable a service, click on that service under **Services** in the left navigation pane. Click the check box on the top right of the page that loads, and then click **Save**. It may be beneficial to enable the following services:

- CIFS
- FTP
- SSHD

Openfiler

Openfiler, from Xinit Systems, converts an industry-standard x86/64 system into a full-fledged NAS/SAN appliance or IP storage gateway. It is based on Linux and has the following features:

- Supports protocols including NFS, SMB/CIFS, HTTP, FTP, and iSCSI
- Supports network directories including NIS, LDAP, Active Directory, Windows NT4 domain controller, and Hesiod

Figure 7-6   Select **UFS** under **Preformatted FS**, and click the **Add** button.

- Supports the Kerberos authentication protocol
- Supports volume-based partitioning such as ext3, JFS, and XFS
- Supports both hardware and software RAID with monitoring and alert facilities, volume snapshot, and recovery
- Supports active/passive high-availability clustering, MPIO, and block-level replication
- Scales to over 60 TB

NASLite

NASLite turns a basic computer into a dedicated SMB/CIFS, NFS, AFP, FTP, HTTP, and rsync file server. It boots from a variety of IDE, SATA SCSI, USB, Firewire, or hardware RAID devices. Content can be accessed simultaneously using any of the supported protocols. Its features include:

- Fully automated monitoring and intelligent resource management
- Daily mirror backups between local or remote drives to ensure data safety
- Easy to operate and to administer
- Remote administration through telnet
- Boots directly into RAM
- Large partition and file support
- S.M.A.R.T. support
- Wide range of PCI hardware support

Network Attached Storage (NAS)   **7-9**

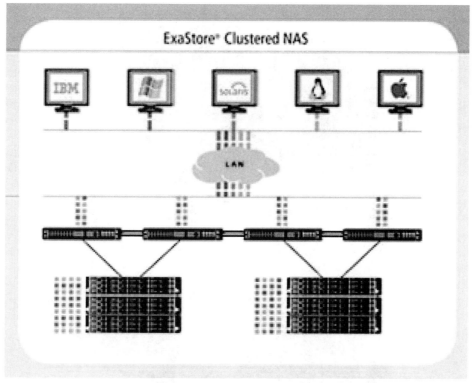

Figure 7-7   ExaStore Clustered NAS is both high performance and scalable.

ExaStore Clustered NAS System

ExaStore Clustered NAS is a high-performance, scalable solution, allowing administrators to expand capacity and performance as needed without affecting applications or users. It is an enterprise-class storage system offering the following features:

- Data protection
- Data vaulting
- Digital media
- Broadcasting
- Postproduction
- Disaster recovery
- Global content delivery
- High-performance computing
- Hosted storage services
- Web services

A diagram of ExaStore Clustered NAS is shown in Figure 7-7.

NAS Appliances

ioSafe R4 NAS

ioSafe R4 NAS is designed for businesses, enterprises, remote/branch offices, and government agencies. It is both fireproof and waterproof, and it is powered by ReadyNAS. R4 NAS is shown in Figure 7-8.

Figure 7-8   R4 NAS is both fireproof and waterproof.

Figure 7-9   The ioSafe 3.5 Pilot hard drive is an internal
fireproof and waterproof hard drive.

ioSafe 3.5 Pilot Hard Drive

The ioSafe 3.5 Pilot hard drive is an internal fireproof and waterproof hard drive for digital data storage. The Pilot series of disk drives are compatible with home media servers, desktops, storage arrays, and external storage devices. They work with Windows, Linux, and Mac systems over the SATA I interface. These fire-safe disks have a 5,400-rpm rotational speed, 8-MB buffer size, 5.5-ms average latency, 12.0-ms read seek time, and 2.0-ms average track-to-track seek time. One of these disks is shown in Figure 7-9.

ioSafe 3.5 Squadron Hard Drive

The ioSafe 3.5 Squadron Hard Drive is another internal fireproof and waterproof hard drive for digital asset storage. The Squadron series of internal disk drives are compatible with desktops, storage arrays, home media servers, and external hard drive enclosures, and work with Windows, Linux, and Mac systems over the SATA II interface. The Squadron hard drive is shown in Figure 7-10.

ioSafe Solo Hard Drive

The ioSafe Solo is an external hard drive that uses a standard USB connection and usually requires no setup. The Solo is available in 500-GB, 1-TB, and 1.5-TB models. The Solo is able to withstand fires and is rated up to 1,550°F per the ASTM E119 industry standard. The Solo can also be submersed in freshwater or salt water for three days at a depth of up to 10 feet. The Solo is shown in Figure 7-11.

Figure 7-10   The ioSafe 3.5 Squadron hard drive supports SATA II.

Figure 7-11   The ioSafe Solo is a simple but sturdy USB hard drive.

Figure 7-12   Disk2Disk can be either fixed capacity or scalable.

Disk2Disk

TCG America's Disk2Disk NAS solutions can be either fixed capacity or scalable. The Disk2Disk system is shown in Figure 7-12.

LaCie 5big Network

The 5big Network is a five-bay RAID solution for small and medium workgroups or offices with capacities of up to 7.5 TB. It supports seven RAID modes, including RAID 5 and RAID 6, and is housed in a sleek and durable aluminum tower with five lockable, removable drive trays.

Its stackable design helps to save space, and its browser-based access and management system allows administrators to quickly set up the 5big Network and allow multiple users to share, store, and access data without using the bandwidth of a central server. This solution additionally features Active Directory support for easy integration into Windows-based networks and a wake-on-LAN function. Compared to traditional four-disk RAID towers, it uses 25% less energy and makes 37% less noise.

The LaCie 5big Network is shown in Figure 7-13.

Figure 7-13 The LaCie 5big Network is an aluminum tower with five drive trays.

Figure 7-14 The RELDATA 9240i uses virtualization to perform multiple replication functions.

RELDATA 9240i Unified NAS Storage System

RELDATA's 9240i Unified Storage System delivers integrated iSCSI SAN, NAS, and WAN replication functions on a single virtualized platform. It is shown in Figure 7-14, and its features include the following:

- Reliable, high duty-cycle SAS storage
  - High-performance and high-capacity drives
- Storage system investment protection
  - Redeploy and add legacy third-party disks with RELDATA heterogeneous virtualization
  - No vendor storage lock-in
- Software licensing per 9240i instead of onerous licensing based on capacity
- High-performance networking
  - Six Gigabit Ethernet ports (expandable up to 16 ports)
  - Up to eight 10-Gigabit Ethernet ports for even higher performance
- Integrated local and WAN data replication
- Optional integrated iSCSI
- Clustered storage systems
  - Linearly scalable capacity from gigabytes to petabytes
  - Linearly scalable performance in IOPS and throughput

Synology RS407

The Synology RS407 is a four-bay NAS shown in Figure 7-15 with the following features:

- Hot-swappable hard disks
- RAID 0/1/5/5 + spare/6 support
- Uses 21 W to 68 W of power
- Windows Active Directory support
- IP camera video recording
- Encrypted network backup
- Encrypted FTP with hack prevention
- Multiple Web site hosting with PHP + MySQL

Figure 7-15   The Synology RS407 is a four-bay NAS.

NAS Vendors

The following companies manufacture NAS products:

- Addonics
- BlueArc
- Freecom
- Hitachi
- Broadberry

Direct Attached Storage (DAS)

A direct attached storage (DAS) system is directly attached to a single host computer or server. When it is attached to a server, network workstations must access that server to connect to the storage device. DAS can use one of many types of drives, including ATA, SATA, SCSI, SAS, and Fibre Channel. The main alternative for direct attached storage is storage area network (SAN), discussed later in this chapter.

DAS is an inexpensive storage system for small- and medium-sized businesses. Small organizations use DAS for file transfer and e-mail, while larger organizations are more likely to use DAS in mixed storage environments such as those that also use NAS and SAN. Organizations that begin with DAS but later switch to networked solutions can use DAS to store less critical data.

Table 7-1 and Figure 7-16 show the differences between NAS and DAS.

Storage Area Network (SAN)

A storage area network (SAN) is a high-speed subnetwork used to transfer large amounts of data. Typically, a SAN is connected to several data storage devices containing disks for data storage. SAN supports data storage, data recovery, and data duplication for enterprise networks via high-end servers, multiple disk arrays, and Fibre Channel interconnection technology. It provides an interface between storage devices that enables systems to access data backups as if they were available locally.

SAN architecture, shown in Figure 7-17, consists of links from the storage system to the user, servers, and network equipment.

DAS	NAS
Directly attached to a computer or server	Attached to the network and provides centralized data access to multiple clients
Used for localized file sharing in environments with a single server or a few servers	Used by organizations to achieve fast data access in a simple, cost-effective manner
Provides block-level I/O	Provides file-level I/O via CIFS and NFS
Provides disk-level high availability with the help of RAID solutions	Provides disk-level high availability with the help of RAID solutions

Table 7-1   These are the differences between NAS and DAS

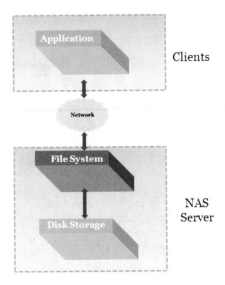

Figure 7-16   The fundamental difference between NAS and DAS is that NAS includes the network.

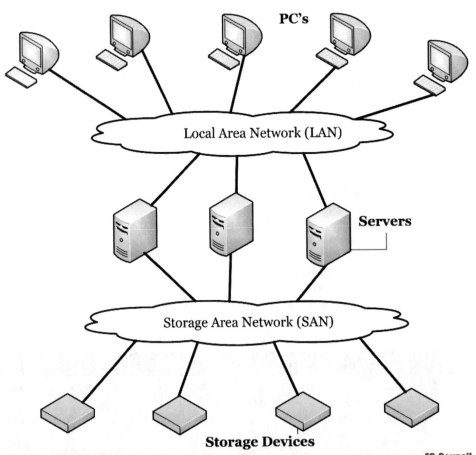

Figure 7-17   A storage area network (SAN) links storage devices to other parts of the network.

SAN Protocols

The protocols used in storage area networks include:

- *Fibre Channel Over Ethernet (FCoE)*: This protocol is used for mapping Fibre Channel frames over full-duplex IEEE 802.3 networks. It makes it possible to move Fibre Channel traffic across existing Ethernet infrastructures and extend the capacity of a SAN. This is mainly useful in data centers.

- *Small Computer System Interface (SCSI)*: SCSI is a bus that connects devices like printers, hard disks, and scanners to a computer. It provides higher data communication rates compared to standard ports, allowing more than one device to be connected to a single port. There are many variations of this interface, including SCSI-1, SCSI-2, SCSI-3, and SAS.

- *Serial Attached SCSI (SAS)*: This standard is a substitution for the parallel SCSI physical storage interface, providing faster data transmission and easier configuration. The SAS controller can be connected to several ports using a SATA cable for communication between devices. This cable is a thin point-to-point connection using a simple cable mechanism that does not require the interconnecting of devices. Using SAS can enhance the performance of every drive in an array by 1.5 Gbps.

- *Network Data Management Protocol (NDMP)*: This protocol is used to manage network databases throughout an organization. It controls data backup, restoration, and transfer between the main storage devices and the secondary storage devices via network-based mechanisms. The architecture of NDMP is based on the client-server model.

- *Internet Storage Name Service and iSNS Protocol (iSNS and iSNSP)*: Fibre Channel devices and iSCSI are discovered automatically and configured using this standard. iSNS allows for the configurate of each storage device with its respective initiators and targets using a management model.

- *Internet Small Computer System Interface (iSCSI)*: iSCSI is based on the TCP/IP protocol used to establish connections between IP-based storage devices, hosts, and clients. It aids in quick data transfers between the elements of a data storage network.

- *Internet Fibre Channel Protocol (iFCP)*: This standard provides Fibre Channel fabric services to Fibre Channel devices over a TCP/IP network.

- *Fibre Channel over IP (FCIP)*: This protocol is used to interconnect clusters of Fibre Channel SANs over IP-based networks and thus form a single SAN in one Fibre Channel fabric. The connectivity between SAN clusters through LANs or WANs depends on IP-based networks.

Working of SAN

While SAN is used for storage, it is significantly different from a server or any other storage device. SAN is highly scalable and can provide added security by only offering files to users on the same network. SAN is also capable of transferring data rapidly between two separate servers—for instance, transfers between an FTP server directory and a user's file server. It also connects networks that are separated by large distances. Since the devices on a SAN are connected together, backing up data requires only one backup server, reducing backup requirements.

Differences Between SAN and NAS

SAN and NAS have the following key differences:

- SAN is a devoted network that is connected via multiple gigabit Fibre Channel switches and host bus adapters, while NAS is directly connected to a network via TCP/IP using Ethernet CAT 5 cables.

- Because NAS runs on a TCP/IP network, it is subject to latency and broadcast storms. It is in contention with other users and network devices for bandwidth. SAN does not have this issue.

- SAN is highly secure thanks to its zoning and logical unit numbers, while NAS is not very secure, typically using access control lists for security.

- While NAS does support RAID levels, two different levels cannot be mixed in the same device.

iSCSI

Internet Small Computer System Interface (iSCSI) is an IP-based storage networking standard for linking data storage facilities. iSCSI is used to handle data storage over large expanses. Because it is IP-based, data can be transmitted over the Internet, LANs, or WANs.

The protocol architecture is based on the client-server model when the devices are present in close proximity and connected using SCSI buses. The main function of iSCSI is encapsulation and reliable delivery of data. This protocol provides a method for encapsulating SCSI commands over an IP network and operates on top of TCP/IP.

Working of iSCSI

iSCSI is the transmission of SCSI (Small Computer System Interface) commands over an IP network. It contains two types of devices: initiators and targets. A SCSI initiator is a server that starts the communication by sending the command to be executed, while a SCSI target is a storage device that responds to the initiator and carries out the commands.

Figure 7-18 shows the layers of iSCSI.

The target responds to and executes the commands that it receives from the initiator. These commands are exchanged using command descriptor blocks (CDBs), shown in Figure 7-19.

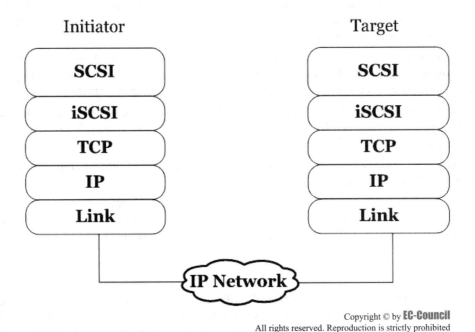

Figure 7-18   This shows the layers of iSCSI.

Bit	7	6	5	4	3	2	1	0
Byte								
0	Operation Code							
1		Command Specific Parameters						
n-1								
n	Control							

Figure 7-19   This is the structure of a SCSI command descriptor block (CDB).

SCSI commands are performed using data phases. In each *data phase*, data are transmitted between the initiator and the target. The SCSI command is terminated by the target once the operation is completed. Authentication between initiators and the user occurs using names provided by the vendors. iSCSI initiators establish a session to send a SCSI command to the target. In this session, the initiator forms numerous multiple TCP connections using a TCP port. The target connects via a TCP port to listen for incoming requests. The initiator then uses the login method to validate the initiator and target, and establishes the session as an iSCSI session.

The initiator transfers the data using SCSI commands via an iSCSI message. SCSI assigns the numbers to the commands, which are transferred from the initiator to the target, carried by the iSCSI protocol data unit (PDU) as Command Sequence Numbers (CmdSN). These numbers are unique for every session. It also assigns these numbers to the responses carried by the iSCSI PDU as the Status Sequence Numbers (StatSN). The initiator contains an Expected Status Sequence Number (ExpStatSN) to determine the status of a transfer request. If the StatSN and ExpStatSN are different, the connection may be indicated as a failed connection. The Domain Name Service (DNS) is used to resolve the iSCSI URL to an IP address. Basically, this just means that the initiator of the communication sends numbered pieces of data to the target, and the target responds with these numbers so that each system knows when to start and terminate the data communication.

Figure 7-20 shows the basic header statement (BHS) for a SCSI initiator command, while Figure 7-21 shows the BHS for a SCSI target response.

Securing Storage Area Networks with iSCSI

iSCSI provides a number of security features, including the following:

- An iSCSI SAN supports Gigabit Ethernet and a point-to-point architecture for the switched network, making packet sniffing difficult. It limits access to only particular users or administrators.

- A virtual private network (VPN) helps in protecting data transfers over a public network. This is done by encrypting the data transmitted between an iSCSI initiator and the client using the IPSec protocol.

- When packets are protected by IPSec and a firewall at the IP level, iSCSI uses authentication methods so that only authorized users can access the storage.

- iSCSI protects the data by physically regulating access to iSCSI SAN devices and separating SANs from other networks.

Fibre Channel SAN

Fibre Channel SAN is a multigigabit technology used for data storage running over a fiber-optic cable. The main purpose of Fibre Channel is to increase cable length and simplify connections rather than increasing the speed.

Byte	0	1	2	3
	Opcode	Opcode-specific fields Reserved		
4	Logical Unit Number (LUNs)			
8				
12	Initiator Task Tag			
16	Expected Data Transfer Length			
20	CmdSN			
24	ExpStatSN or EndDataSN			
28				
+	SCSI Command Descriptor Block (CDB)			
4				

Figure 7-20   This is the basic header statement for a SCSI initiator command.

Byte	0	1	2	3
0	Opcode	Opcode—specific fields	Reserved (o)	
4	Reserved (o)			
8				
12	Initiator Task Tag			
16	Basic Residual Count			
20	StatSN			
24	ExpCmdSN			
28	MaxCmdSN			
32	EndDataSN or Reserved (o)			
36	R2TEndDataSN or Reserved (o)			
40	Bidi-Read Residual Count			
44	Digests if any			
48	Response Data or Sense Data (optional)			

Figure 7-21   This is the basic header statement for a SCSI target response.

Fibre Channel SAN is a network technology in which servers are directly connected to storage devices using the SCSI bus protocol. Fibre Channel SAN offers a performance-enhanced network in which multiple servers communicate with multiple storage devices. It allows for any-to-any connectivity of the server to storage using components such as routers, hubs, gateways, and servers. It also allows for multiple servers to access multiple storage systems using redundant paths, resulting in high data availability and speed.

The following topologies are supported by Fibre Channel:

- Point to point
- Arbitrated loop
- Switched fabric

Fibre Channel SAN provides these benefits:

- Reduces the IT management costs associated with storage
- Allows for quick access to a storage device
- Allows organizations to create, store, share, and coordinate data
- Allows addition of a new device or removal of a failed device without interruption

Comparison of Fibre Channel SAN and iSCSI SAN

Both technologies have advantages and disadvantages. The iSCSI protocol is based on TCP/IP, which ensures data reliability using TCP acknowledgement and cyclic redundancy check (CRC). CRC must be enabled in the iSCSI SAN to ensure the integrity of the data.

Data on a Fibre Channel SAN are considered reliable because it runs over trusted connections such as Class 3, which provides error recovery at the upper-layer protocols. A Class 3 acknowledged connection also helps prevent long-term outages in the SAN.

Features	Fibre Channel SAN	iSCSI SAN
Industry specifications	Specified by Fibre Channel FC-0	Specified by IEEE, IETF, and Storage Networking Industry Association (SNIA)
Data rates	100 Mbps to 800 Mbps	10 Mbps to 10 Gbps
Communication media	Optical fiber, coaxial cable, and twisted pair	Optical fiber, coaxial cable, and twisted pair
Maximum distances for point-to-point links	50 m to 10 km	100 m to 120 km
Hunt groups	Group of associated N_Ports at a single node	Not available
Multicast	Transmits to all N_Ports on a fabric	Transmits to all N_Ports on a switched network
	Transmits to a subset of the N_Ports on a fabric	Transmits to a subset of the N_Ports on a fabric
Topology	Fabric or switched, point to point, and arbitrated loop	Switched, point to point, star, ring

Table 7-2   These are some of the differences between Fibre Channel SAN and iSCSI SAN

Fibre Channel SAN provides higher security than iSCSI because it provides isolation in the data center in order to prevent unauthorized access to the data. An improperly configured iSCSI SAN can be compromised by joining together unauthorized devices on the network. These risks can be prevented by an IT manager's implementing standard network security practices.

Table 7-2 shows some of the differences between Fibre Channel SAN and iSCSI SAN.

Benefits of SAN

SAN provides the following benefits:

- Storage consolidation reduces cost
- Storage or server can be easily added without interruption
- Data are backed up and restored quickly
- High-performance interface, over 100 Mbps
- Supports server clusters of eight or more servers acting as a single reliable system
- Disaster tolerance
- Reduced cost of ownership

SAN Security

A storage area network should protect data from internal and external threats and attacks, and must allow only authorized users to access the data. Consolidating servers on the network increases the risk of a single security breach having a widespread impact on the organization. The connectivity between the SAN and IP network may increase the risk of IP network threats including man-in-the-middle and denial-of-service attacks. A SAN must encrypt sensitive data during data transfer.

Data can be secured from unauthorized access by securing logical unit numbers (LUNs). A LUN is a secondary level of device recognition. There are pros and cons for both hardware-based LUN security and software-based LUN security. The security of a SAN is completely dependent upon the user's authorization or authentication.

SAN security includes these concepts:

- *Host adapter–based security*: Security measures for the Fibre Channel host bus adapter can be implemented at the driver level.
- *Switch zoning*: In a switch-based Fibre Channel SAN, switch zoning refers to the masking of all the nodes connected to the switch.
- *Storage-controller mapping*: Some storage subsystems accomplish their LUN masking in their storage by mapping all host adapters against LUNs in the storage system.

- *Software measures*: SAN security can be implemented using software tools to control access to data and maintain its reliability.

Though expensive, tools used to manage access to volumes also help prevent data corruption. These tools provide different access privileges to each user for accessing the different data volumes. Only one user can access a particular volume at a time.

Threats to a SAN

The storage area network may be vulnerable to risk because it stores and transfers critical data. There are different levels of threats faced by the SAN:

- *Level one*: These types of threats are unintentional and common in workplaces. They may result in downtime and loss of revenue. These threats can be prevented by administrators.

- *Level two*: These types of threats are simple malicious attacks using existing equipment and easily obtained information. Preventive measures used for level-one threats are also used for these types of threats.

- *Level three*: These types of threats are large-scale attacks, coming from skilled attackers using uncommon equipment. Level-three attacks are difficult to prevent.

Pros and Cons of Using a SAN

- *Reasons to use a SAN*:
  - Better disk utilization
  - Fast and extensive disaster recovery
  - Better availability for applications
  - Faster backup of large amounts of data
- *Limitations of a SAN*:
  - Installing an effective SAN is expensive
  - Increased administration cost
  - Impractical for use with a single application
  - Requires a fast WAN connection, which may be costly

SAN Considerations for SQL Server Environment

SAN provides these features for SQL servers:

- Increased database size
- Clustered environment
- Performance advantages
- Storage efficiencies
- Faster disaster recovery

Various considerations when using SAN with an SQL server are as follows:

- *Caching*: SAN provides a significant cache, but the availability decreases when multiple servers share this cache.
- *LUNs*: A SAN administrator divides the SAN storage into LUNs and considers these units as a partition or drive.
- *RAID*: Before purchasing, organizations should test the SAN using a representative load to ensure that RAID 5 performs well for tempdb, log files, and intensive filegroups.

SAN Network Management Systems

Apple's Xsan

Xsan is an enterprise-class SAN file system introduced by Apple. It is a 64-bit cluster file system specifically designed for small and large computing environments that demand the highest level of data availability.

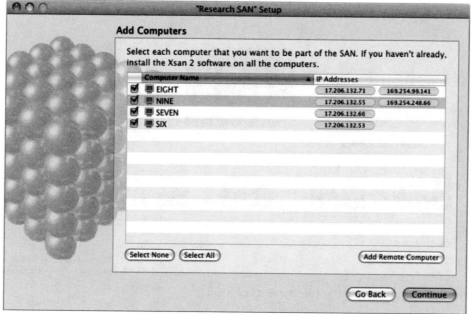

Source: http://www.apple.com/xsan/. Accessed 9/2009.

Figure 7-22   Xsan is an enterprise-class SAN system from Apple.

It enables multiple Mac desktop and Xserve systems to share RAID storage volumes over a high-speed Fibre Channel network. Each client can read and write directly to the centralized file system.

Xsan is shown in Figure 7-22, and its features include the following:

- Easily manage user access to data on SAN volumes
- Share terabytes of data simultaneously over a high-speed Fibre Channel network
- Use optimized workflow configuration settings for maximum performance
- Access volumes from multiple servers concurrently and copy data between them directly over high-speed Fibre Channel
- With Spotlight, Cover Flow, and Quick Look, scan through thousands of files on the SAN volume to find content
- Eliminate potential single points of failure with mission-critical redundancy

Xsan Components Xsan consists of the following components, shown in Figure 7-23:

- *SAN volume*: Xsan consolidates data into a single storage volume accessible to all systems on the storage area network (SAN). Adding capacity is as easy as attaching more RAID storage systems to the Fibre Channel network.
- *Fibre Channel network*: The SAN volume connects to the Xsan metadata controller and all Xsan clients through a high-speed Fibre Channel switch. Apple has qualified many popular third-party switches for use with Xsan.
- *Xsan metadata controller*: The metadata controller acts as the "traffic cop" for the SAN. When an Xsan client attempts to read or write to a file, it gets permission from the metadata controller, and then accesses the data directly on the SAN over high-speed Fibre Channel. Any Xserve or Mac Pro running Mac OS X Server can be an Xsan metadata controller.
- *Xsan clients*: Mac desktop or Xserve systems running Xsan have direct block-level access to files stored on the SAN volume and full read/write capability. As performance needs grow, Xsan allows the addition of servers and computers to the SAN. With Xsan, one SAN can handle hundreds of clients.
- *Ethernet network*: File system metadata is handled over a private Ethernet network shared by all systems connected directly to the SAN. This frees up Fibre Channel bandwidth for high-performance storage throughput.

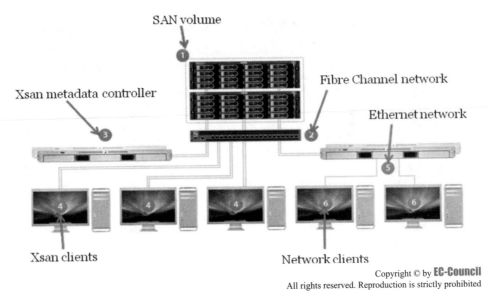

Figure 7-23 These are the components of Xsan.

- *Network clients*: An Xserve with Mac OS X Server and Xsan can share data from the SAN volume with an unlimited number of networked computers over the Ethernet network using file-sharing protocols, such as AFP, SMB/CIFS, and NFS.

Brocade Fabric Manager

Brocade Fabric Manager manages multiple Brocade switches and fabrics in real time. In particular, it provides essential functions for efficiently configuring, monitoring, dynamically provisioning, and managing Brocade data center fabrics on a daily basis.

As a single-point management platform, Brocade Fabric Manager facilitates the global integration of management tasks across multiple fabrics, thereby lowering overall storage costs. It is shown in Figure 7-24, and its features include the following:

- Monitors and administers large numbers of Brocade Fabric OS switches, directors, and the Brocade DCX Backbone—including multiple Brocade data center fabrics
- Performs end-to-end management tasks across multiple devices and fabrics in a single operation
- Optimizes fabric utilization and capacity planning through real-time and historical analysis and performance monitoring
- Visualizes and tracks changes to fabric configuration and state information through multiple views at multiple levels of detail
- Allows users to launch Brocade Fabric Manager from other enterprise management applications or to launch other applications from Brocade Fabric Manager
- Enhances asset management and analysis through detailed device tracking, including exporting to a spreadsheet
- Displays the fabric layout through a topology map that specifies Interchassis Link (ICL), Interswitch Link (ISL), switch, and device details
- Identifies, isolates, and manages data center events across large numbers of switches and fabrics

Cisco Fabric Manager

Cisco Fabric Manager is a Web-based application that simplifies the management of Cisco switches in SANs through an integrated approach to switch and fabric administration. The program offers storage administrators fabricwide management capabilities, including discovery, multiple-switch configuration, and continuous network monitoring and troubleshooting. This approach greatly reduces switch setup times, increases overall fabric reliability, and provides robust diagnostics for resolving network problems and configuration inconsistencies.

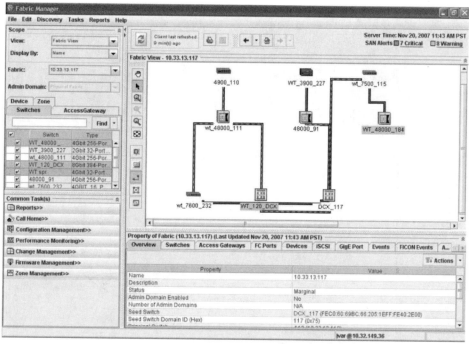

Source: http://www.brocade.com. Accessed 9/2009.

Figure 7-24 Brocade Fabric Manager manages multiple Brocade switches and fabrics in real time.

With the Cisco Fabric Manager GUI, storage administrators can compare switch configurations side by side, perform configuration policy checks across switches, set alarm thresholds to report to third-party fault-management applications, view individual device and aggregate statistics in real time, and analyze historical performance statistics. All these capabilities are available through a secure interface that facilitates remote management from almost any location.

Cisco Fabric Manager is shown in Figure 7-25, and its features include the following:

- *Switch-embedded Java application*: This application integrates switch and fabric management in a single performance-optimized tool that ships with every Cisco MDS 9000 Family and Nexus 5000 Family switch.

- *Fabric visualization*: Cisco Fabric Manager performs centralized automated discovery and displays storage network topology, connectivity, and zone and virtual SAN (VSAN) highlighting, allowing for the identification of network health and configuration concerns at a glance.

- *Multiple views*: Cisco Fabric Manager simplifies the configuration and monitoring of multiple switches and facilitates configuration replication with fabric, device, summary, and operation views.

- *Comprehensive configuration across multiple switches*: Cisco Fabric Manager provides integrated fabric-, switch-, and port-level configuration. It also simplifies zone, VSAN, Fibre Channel over IP (FCIP), Internet Small Computer System Interface (iSCSI), IBM Fiber Connection (FICON), and intelligent services configuration.

- *Flexible monitoring and alerts*: Cisco Fabric Manager presents real-time and historical performance-monitoring statistics in tabular and graphical formats. Performance-monitoring thresholds and configuration of threshold-based alerts, including Call Home, facilitate rapid response to exception conditions.

- *Historical performance monitoring*: Cisco Fabric Manager provides tabular and graphical reports showing daily, weekly, monthly, and yearly traffic for Interswitch Links (ISLs), host and storage connections, and traffic between specific Fibre Channel sources and destinations. Top 10 and daily summary reports present fabricwide statistics that greatly simplify network hotspot analysis.

- *Powerful configuration analysis*: Cisco Fabric Manager performs zone-merge analysis and configuration checking, simplifying resolution of problems, facilitating successful fabric merges, and resolving configuration inconsistencies automatically.

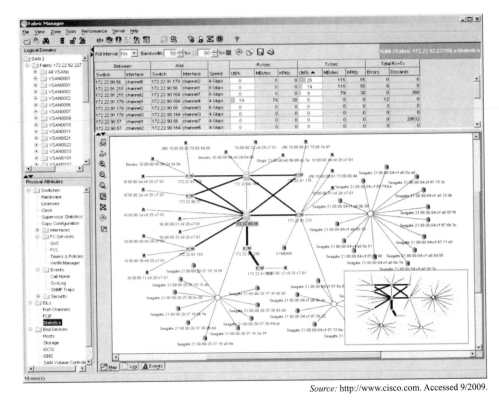

Source: http://www.cisco.com. Accessed 9/2009.

Figure 7-25 Cisco Fabric Manager is a Web-based program to manage Cisco systems in SANs.

- *Network diagnostics*: Cisco Fabric Manager probes network and switch health with Fibre Channel ping and traceroute, allowing administrators to rapidly pinpoint network connectivity and performance problems.

- *Comprehensive network security*: Cisco Fabric Manager protects against unauthorized management access with Simple Network Management Protocol version 3 (SNMPv3), Secure Shell (SSH) protocol, and role-based access control (RBAC).

SANmelody

SANmelody converts standard Intel/AMD servers, blades, or virtual machines (VMs) into fully capable storage servers that virtualize disks and serve them over existing networks to application servers. The program accelerates performance through built-in caching that minimizes delays from slower mechanical drives. The software equitably distributes the available disk space to multiple applications spread across several machines by carving out smaller logical disks from larger physical disks. Ethernet iSCSI host connections and Fibre Channel high-bandwidth ports are supported. Like other powerful Windows-based software, SANmelody runs on a variety of hardware platforms and disk drives on Windows, Linux, UNIX, NetWare, and Mac OS systems.

SANmaestro

SANmaestro is an analysis and decision support tool that monitors, reports, charts, gathers, and analyzes system performance and resource utilization information from multiple networked systems. It generates useful reports and charts, customized to fit the organization's reporting and analysis needs.

SANmaestro software is used to:

- Collect system performance and utilization metrics

- Analyze historical data accumulated over long periods (up to two years)

- Chart, tabulate, and analyze selected metrics with spreadsheets

- Perform hypothetical analyses

- Develop customized reports and charts with SANmaestro's development toolkit

- Export historical data to third-party tools and network management frameworks for further analysis, processing, or audit reporting

HP OpenView Storage Area Manager

HP OpenView Storage Area Manager (SAM) software allows the user to selectively monitor, manage, optimize, and plan storage and storage service availability, performance, usage, cost, and growth. OpenView SAM also enables management and planning for capacity related to Oracle and Microsoft Exchange applications.

The HP OpenView Storage Area Manager software suite consists of five functional modules:

1. *Storage Node Manager*: For device management

2. *Storage Builder*: For capacity management

3. *Storage Optimizer*: For performance management

4. *Storage Allocator*: For storage allocation and virtualized access control

5. *Storage Accountant*: For usage metering and billing

Each component functions either individually or together to enable integrated storage resource, application capacity, and infrastructure management. It integrates with third-party reporting tools and enterprise management tools, and supports Storage Management Initiative Specification (SMI-S)–based devices.

IBM SAN Volume Controller

IBM SAN Volume Controller (SVC) is a block-storage virtualization appliance. It implements an indirection, or virtualization, layer in a Fibre Channel SAN. It is shown in Figure 7-26 and is designed to:

- Combine storage capacity from multiple disk systems into a reservoir of capacity

- Help increase storage utilization by providing host applications with more flexible access

- Help improve productivity of storage administrators

- Support improved application availability by insulating host applications

- Enable a tiered storage environment in which the cost of storage can be better matched to the value of data

- Support advanced copy services from higher- to lower-cost devices

IBM TotalStorage SAN Volume Controller

The IBM TotalStorage SAN Volume Controller enables changes to physical storage with little or no disruption. It simplifies the storage infrastructure by combining the capacity from multiple disk storage systems into a single storage pool, which can be managed from a central point. Its features include the following:

- Manages large storage environments through expanded scalability

- Enables changes to physical storage systems with minimal or no impact to the applications running on the hosts

- Reduces downtime for planned and unplanned outages, maintenance, and backups

- Increases storage capacity utilization, uptime, administrator productivity, and efficiency

- Provides a single set of advanced copy services across multiple heterogeneous storage systems

Figure 7-26   IBM SAN Volume Controller implements
a virtualization layer in a Fibre Channel SAN.

EMC VisualSAN

VisualSAN provides administrators with a single view of all devices across their storage networks and delivers advanced network, performance, and configuration management capabilities. The VisualSAN management suite includes three modules:

1. *VisualSAN Network Manager*: This is the base VisualSAN application for monitoring independent SAN devices. It serves as a common interface for other modules.

2. *VisualSAN Configuration Manager*: This module allows administrators to capture the state of a SAN configuration at a point in time for comparison, historical reference, change management, asset management, and replication of a specific SAN topology.

3. *VisualSAN Performance Manager*: The performance manager provides live and historical analysis of link statistics across a SAN.

EMC VisualSRM

VisualSRM is open management software that offers file-level reporting and centralized storage resource management across all of an organization's major storage and server platforms. It supports a wide range of applications, including Microsoft Exchange, Oracle, Sybase, and SQL Server databases. It also integrates with other storage management applications from backup and framework vendors such as IBM, Veritas, HP, CA, and BMC.

VisualSRM helps administrators to:

- Track system and individual storage consumption and enforce capacity utilization thresholds, ensuring capacity is available when and where needed

- Set policies for moving, deleting, compressing, and archiving files based on the age of the information, the time since the file was last accessed, and predefined capacity thresholds

- Categorize data and define category-based storage management policies that match the most appropriate and cost-effective storage media to the information stored on it

EMC Invista

EMC Invista is a network-based storage virtualization solution. It reduces the downtime associated with the movement of data across storage tiers in support of information lifecycle management (ILM) strategies. It can be used to copy, move, and migrate data across multiple tiers of heterogeneous storage arrays.

MetaSAN

MetaSAN is a high-speed file sharing SAN management software that is designed for cross-platform workgroup collaboration. It allows users of Windows, Linux, and Mac OS X to share files with one another. MetaSAN is shown in Figure 7-27.

Veritas CommandCentral Storage

Veritas CommandCentral Storage is a storage resource management solution providing centralized visibility and control across physical and virtual heterogeneous storage environments. It is shown in Figure 7-28, and its features include the following:

- Identifies current state of the storage infrastructure

- Implements prudent storage capacity management practices

- Transforms storage operations based on predefined policies

- Aligns storage operations with business objectives

DataPlow SAN File System

SAN File System (SFS) is DataPlow's flagship product that runs on devices ranging from consumer electronics to supercomputers. Its features include the following:

- Provides application compatibility

- Heterogeneous file sharing

- Highly available

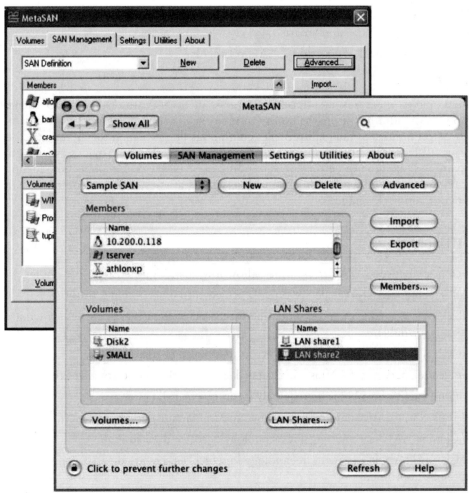

Source: http://www.tiger-technology.com/article.php?story=MetaSAN. Accessed 9/2009.

Figure 7-27 MetaSAN allows users of different operating systems to share files with one another.

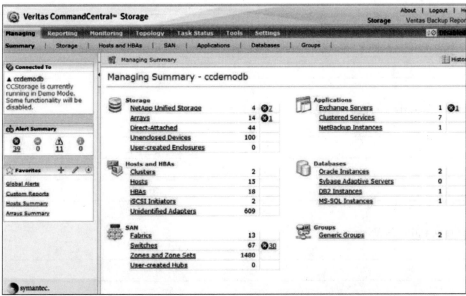

Source: http://www.symantec.com/business/products/screenshots.jsp?pcid=pcat_business_cont&pvid=19_1. Accessed 9/2009.

Figure 7-28 Veritas CommandCentral Storage provides centralized visibility and control across physical and virtual heterogeneous storage environments.

- Fine-grained tuning for optimal performance
- Supports Window, Linux, and Solaris
- Supports Fibre Channel, iSCSI, and Z-SAN protocols

NetWisdom

NetWisdom monitors, measures, and optimizes large-scale SANs with instrumentation and management software. It allows SAN administrators the ability to monitor distributed SANs for performance slowdowns and immediately detect failures or faults. It provides continuous line-rate monitoring that calculates statistics based on monitoring all Fibre Channel frames traveling through the SAN. It provides event recording and line-rate capture capabilities, along with performance trending of SAN device components to identify hardware degradation. It can also gather in-depth Fibre Channel network statistics, such as pending exchanges, to tune queue depths for maximum performance.

Chapter Summary

- NAS commonly uses SATA drives, which allow low-cost, high-density NAS storage.
- A DAS is a computer storage device directly attached to one computer or server.
- Scalable NAS is capable of accommodating file-based content that is always growing and must be pervasively available.
- Scalable NAS can be easily managed when compared to DAS and SAN.
- A storage area network (SAN) is a high-speed subnetwork used to transfer large amounts of data.
- The main benefit of a SAN is how quickly it can transfer data.
- iSCSI is used to transfer data on an intranet and to manage data storage over long distances.
- Fibre Channel SAN is a multigigabit technology used for data storage.
- Fibre Channel SAN is a network technology in which servers are directly connected to storage devices using the SCSI protocol.

Review Questions

1. Explain the NAS architecture.

_____

_____

_____

_____

2. What are the advantages of NAS?

_____

_____

_____

_____

3. What is scalable NAS?

_____

_____

_____

_____

4. What are the differences between NAS and DAS?

_____

_____

_____

_____

5. How is FreeNAS installed?

_____

_____

_____

_____

6. What is SAN?

_____

_____

_____

_____

7. What are the protocols used with SAN?

_____

_____

_____

_____

8. What are the components of Xsan?

_____

_____

_____

_____

9. What are the differences between SAN and NAS?

_____

_____

_____

_____

10. What is Fibre Channel SAN?

_____

_____

_____

_____

Hands-On Projects

1. Read about the differences between DAS, NAS, and SAN.

   ▪ Navigate to Chapter 7 of the Student Resource Center.

   ▪ Open DAS, NAS or SAN Choosing the Right Storage.pdf and read the content.

2. Read about IMB's NAS services.

   ▪ Navigate to Chapter 7 of the Student Resource Center.

   ▪ Open IBM Implementation Services for Network Attached Storage systems.pdf and read the content.

3. Read about massively scalable NAS.

   ▪ Navigate to Chapter 7 of the Student Resource Center.

   ▪ Open Massively Scalable NAS.pdf and read the content.

4. Read about using NAS for disaster recovery.

   ▪ Navigate to Chapter 7 of the Student Resource Center.

   ▪ Open Securing Data in Backup and Disaster Recovery.pdf and read the content.

5. Read about the evolution of SAN.

   ▪ Navigate to Chapter 7 of the Student Resource Center.

   ▪ Open SAN Evolution.pdf and read the content.

6. Read about SAN security.

   ▪ Navigate to Chapter 7 of the Student Resource Center.

   ▪ Open Security for SAN.pdf and read the content.

7. Read about using SAN for disaster recovery.

   ▪ Navigate to Chapter 7 of the Student Resource Center.

   ▪ Open iSCSI-based Storage Area Networks for Disaster Recovery.pdf and read the content.

8. Read more about SAN security.

   ▪ Navigate to Chapter 7 of the Student Resource Center.

   ▪ Open The Growing Need for Security in Storage Area Networks.pdf and read the content.

Chapter 8

Disaster Recovery Services and Tools

Objectives

After completing this chapter, you should be able to:

- Understand the importance of backing up data
- Understand computer backup practices
- Implement several backup techniques
- Use data backup and recovery tools
- Implement off-site backup
- Use enterprise backup tools

Key Terms

Job a backup, restore, or utility operation

Introduction to Disaster Recovery Services and Tools

An organization's data can be even more critical and valuable than its physical assets. If anything happens to those data, be it by accident, attack, or any other disaster, the effects can be devastating. A good backup policy can reduce or even eliminate the damage caused by data loss, but far too many organizations rely on manual backups, which can be unreliable. This chapter teaches you how to implement effective and efficient data backup procedures.

Why Back Up Data?

The main purpose of data backup is to keep secondary copies of data in case the original data are lost. Data can be lost due to any number of reasons, including:

- Hardware failure
- Theft

- Data corruption
- Malicious attack
- Power outage
- Fire
- Flooding
- Virus or worm
- Human error

Backups can be used to access older versions of files, in case changes to files cause undesired effects. Backups can also reduce the amount of IT resources required to maintain an application, if the organization decides to archive older records and only work with current ones.

Preventing Data Loss

Organizations should take the following steps to protect data against loss:

1. *Back up often and wisely*: The most effective thing to do is back up data on a daily basis, but this can be costly and time-consuming. For the average business, the percentage of data that changes daily is between 2% and 5%, so it can save significant time by only backing up those changes.

2. *Prioritize data for disaster recovery*: An organization should prioritize each system and its related data, including e-mail, telephones, databases, file servers, and Web servers. Typically, systems are prioritized into three categories: redundant (required immediately), highly available (minutes to hours), and backed up (four hours to days).

3. *Archive important data for the long term*: Depending on federal and state regulations, data must be retained for between seven and 17 years. Older data should be stored in a separate physical storage location. Some businesses will choose a full-service company that picks up, stores, and delivers the data when it is needed.

4. *Store data cost-effectively*: Most small-to-midsize businesses do not have available IT resources to set up and manage a storage solution. These businesses may wish to purchase an integrated solution. The up-front cost may be a bit more, but in the long run, the time, money, and effort spent on a custom solution will be far greater.

Developing an Effective Data Backup Strategy

While developing a good backup strategy, the organization must first determine what data backup platform (hardware) is best for protecting the data. Tape backup systems are least expensive and are commonly used to back up large amounts of data. This technology only requires user intervention to physically change tapes; there are some technologies to automatically rotate tapes, allowing little chance of human error.

Organizations must next determine how much data must be protected and then choose a backup device suited for that amount. DDS (Digital Data Storage) tape backup systems are normally used in small organizations with less than 10 GB of data to protect. These systems are also best suited for small/home offices because they are economical and considered reliable. On the other hand, DLT (Digital Linear Tape) systems are best suited for larger businesses because they contain great data storage capacity. These systems contain automatic rotation systems to spread data across multiple high-capacity tapes.

The next step is to determine the best backup methodology. Many backup systems provide these options:

- *Full*: Stores a copy of all data to a tape backup, regardless of whether the data have been modified since the last backup was performed. This changes the archive property bit of the file from 1 to 0, indicating that the file has been backed up.

- *Differential*: Backs up every file on the drive that has been added or changed since the last full backup. This does not change the archive property bit of the file from 1 to 0, indicating that the file has changed since the last full backup. Thus, the file will be backed up each time a differential backup is performed. Compared to an incremental backup, it takes more time to run each differential backup and requires more space for each one, but a full restore operation requires only the last full backup and the last differential backup.

- *Incremental*: Backs up files that have been modified since the last backup operation. This changes the archive property bit of the file from 1 to 0, indicating that the file has now been backed up and will not be backed up on the next incremental backup. Compared to a differential backup, it takes less time to run each incremental backup and requires less space for each backup operation, but would require more time to restore the system, as the last full backup and each sequential incremental backup must be used.

The final step is to develop a rotation scheme and decide where to store the backup media. Many organizations store the physical backup media within about three feet of the server. This means that, should a disaster strike the server, it is likely to affect the backups as well. The best course of action is to place the physical media off-site, but still close enough to access it when needed.

Many organizations forget to secure backup data, which makes backups a common target for attackers. Off-site storage must be sufficiently secure. Organizations must always encrypt backup tapes.

A successful backup strategy should meet the following criteria:

- Off-site backup
- Scheduled backup
- Daily notifications
- Sufficient space
- Data availability at all times
- Adequate security
- Guarantee from provider
- Tested regularly

Backup Techniques

Disk Mirroring

Disk mirroring involves creating an exact bit-by-bit copy of all data on a physical disk drive. The mirrored disks are stored off-site and kept synchronized. This way, if the primary disk fails, important data can be accessed from the other disk. Disk mirroring can be done in two ways:

1. *Synchronous mirroring*: The disk is updated on every write request, which can affect application performance.

2. *Asynchronous mirroring*: Multiple changes to the primary disks are reflected in the secondary mirrored disk at predetermined intervals, which does not require an uninterrupted high-bandwidth connection.

Disk mirroring has a few drawbacks. If a file is deleted from the primary disk, it is also deleted from the secondary disk. Also, any effects from viruses or data theft will be synchronized. Establishing a disk mirroring infrastructure may require additional resources and continuous maintenance.

Snapshots

A storage snapshot contains a set of reference markers that point to data stored on a disk drive, on a tape, or in a storage area network (SAN). It streamlines access to stored data and hastens the data recovery process. There are two main types of snapshots:

1. *Copy-on-write snapshot*: Creates a snapshot of changes or modifications to stored data each time new data are entered or existing data are updated

2. *Split-mirror snapshot*: Physically clones a storage entity at a regular interval, allowing offline access and making it simple to recover data

Continuous Data Protection (CDP)

CDP, also known as continuous backup or synchronous mirroring, involves backing up data by automatically saving a copy of every change made to those data. This creates an electronic record of storage snapshots, with one storage snapshot for every instant that data modification occurs, allowing the administrator to restore data to any point in time.

Parity Protection

Parity protection involves creating a parity disk from all the available disks in the array. If any disk in the array fails, the parity disk can be used to recover the data from the failed disk. Parity protection represents a low-cost and low-maintenance mirroring infrastructure, but if two drives fail simultaneously, then the data will be lost completely. Also, any threat that affects one disk could also affect the parity disk.

Backup Schedules

The following are two backup schedules:

1. *Intraday data protection*: In an intraday data protection system, data are backed up several times during the day. The data can be copied onto the same disk or onto a remote disk. Backup strategies using intraday data protection include:
   - Snapshots
   - Application dumps (where application data are backed up every few hours)
   - Continuous data protection
2. *Weekend and nightly backups*: There are three types of weekend and nightly backups, as previously mentioned:
   - Full backups
   - Differential backups
   - Incremental backups

Removable Backup Media

Some types of removable backup media are:

- CD-ROM
- DVD-ROM
- Tape drive
- USB drive
- External hard drive

One of the main disadvantages of using removable backup media is that it requires the user to perform data backup and take the media off-site, which may increase the risk of data loss. Removable backup media contains limited storage space, and there is a risk of media damage.

Disks Versus Tapes

Tape backups have the following features:

- Cheap method for archiving data
- Slow, cumbersome, labor intensive and expensive
- Takes more time to restore the data after the disaster event
- Used when deep archiving is required, such as maintaining important financial documents for tax or other purposes
- Require the user to intervene only when a tape change is needed
- Little chance of human error because tape is not changed daily
- Minimum number of tapes required for fully restoring

Disks have the following features:

- More reliable than tape backup
- Provide faster backup and faster restores by sending multiple backup streams to a disk target
- Shelf life of disks is far longer than that of tapes

- Less prone to errors and corruption
- Used to access data quickly in the event of a disaster
- Provide higher speed and higher storage capacity than tapes
- Provide greater access to information
- Reduce costs due to increased automation

Potential Risks

There are several risks in the backup and retrieval process. For instance, data backed up at a remote location can be a target for thieves and attackers, so the data should be encrypted. Other risks include the following:

- Storage media may be stolen from the delivery vehicle.
- Storage media on the return trip from the centralized storage site may be delivered to the wrong customer.
- The tape system could be destroyed.

The following steps can help manage these risks:

1. Carefully scrutinize contracts with the off-site backup provider.
2. Use locked containers to transport tapes.
3. Encrypt all data prior to writing to backup tapes, or selectively encrypt only sensitive data.
4. Include backup procedures in the corporate strategy.

Challenges in Backup and Recovery

Some of the challenges include the following:

- Increased complexity and burden
- Limited capabilities of conventional solutions
- Time requirements
- Reliability
- Size of data
- Expensive new technologies
- Lack of a simple disaster recovery process
- Maintenance

Backup and Recovery Checklist

The following is a backup and recovery checklist:

- Keep the backup plan as simple as possible.
- Establish reliability through automation. Minimize the potential for human error.
- Implement immediate, granular recovery options.
- Allow users to securely recover individual files.
- Make disaster recovery plans flexible.

When purchasing a third-party data backup solution, organizations should keep the following considerations in mind:

- Does it meet the organization's recovery objectives, including RTO and RPO?
- How easy and reliable is data restoration?
- Does it store data off-site in case of a disaster?

Item	Yes	No	Applicable	Not Applicable	Comments
Select the purpose of the test. What aspects of the plan are being evaluated?					
Describe the objectives of the test. How will you measure successful achievement of the objectives?					
Meet with management and explain the test and objectives. Gain their agreement and support.					
Have management announce the test and the expected completion time.					
Collect test results at the end of the test period.					
Evaluate results. Was recovery successful? Why or why not?					
Determine the implications of the test results. Does successful recovery in a simple case imply successful recovery for all critical jobs in the tolerable outage period?					
Make recommendations for changes. Call for responses by a given date.					
Notify other areas of results. Include users and auditors.					
Change the disaster recovery plan manual as necessary.					

Figure 8-1   This template can be used to conduct a data recovery test.

- Does it comply with the organization's existing disaster recovery plan?
- Are the data secure and encrypted?
- What is the labor and maintenance requirement?
- When will the data be backed up?
- How much does the solution cost, including labor, maintenance, and support?

Testing Data Recovery

It is important to regularly test the backup and recovery solution, perhaps as often as every month. Organizations can use the template in Figure 8-1 to conduct a data recovery test.

Data Backup and Recovery Tools

Norton Ghost

Norton Ghost is a comprehensive disk imaging solution. It is shown in Figure 8-2 and includes the following features:

- Full system backup (disk image)
- File and folder backup
- FTP backup
- Off-site backup
- Remote management over LAN
- Google Desktop integration
- Advanced compression and encryption

Norton Online Backup

Norton Online Backup delivers automatic file backup over the Internet using a secure Web portal. It stores files on separate storage arrays at the data center for added file safety. It is shown in Figure 8-3, and its features include the following:

- Automatically backs up files to one central, secured location
- Quickly recovers data in case of hard drive crashes, file system damage, or natural disasters
- Allows access and file restoration from any Web-connected PC

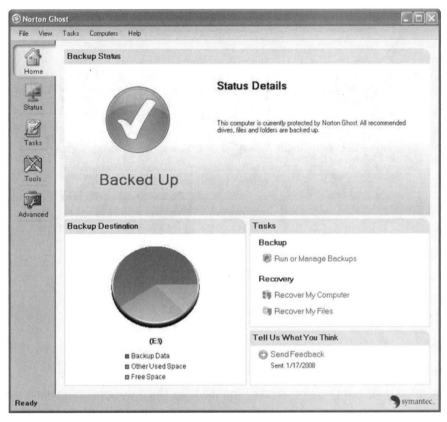

Figure 8-2   Norton Ghost uses Drive Image to make accurate backups.

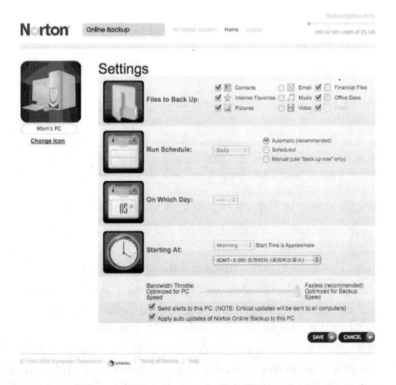

Figure 8-3   Norton Online Backup allows file access from any
Web browser.

Figure 8-4 Syncplicity is an online, real-time backup solution.

- Backs up as many as five PCs with one account
- Automatically compresses files before backing them up and only uploads changes made since previous backups
- Uses 256-bit government-grade encryption
- Eliminates relying on external backup drives and memory cards

Syncplicity

Syncplicity, shown in Figure 8-4, is an online backup solution with the following features:

- Real-time backup
- Share any folder with anyone
- Access anytime, anywhere
- Uses 128-bit SSL

Handy Backup Server

Handy Backup Server for Windows performs automatic backup, restoration, and synchronization of multiple servers and workstations. All workstation backup tasks are managed by a central server and require no user intervention. It supports image backup for both servers and workstations on CD/DVD, external USB and Firewire drives, FTP, SFTP, LAN, and more.

Handy Backup Server is shown in Figure 8-5, and its features include the following:

- Centralized backup, operated from a single server and invisible for users on remote workstations (running as a Windows service)
- Full and incremental backup of workstations and the central server
- Backs up ODBC databases (MySQL, Microsoft SQL, Oracle, FoxPro, Microsoft Access, etc.)
- Plug-ins that save Microsoft Exchange Server, Oracle, Microsoft SQL, DB2, and Lotus Notes/Domino data during remote workstation backup and local server backup
- Minimal consumption of system resources, allowing workstation backup tasks during working hours
- Image backup of server and workstations (backing up of the entire hard drive including all primary, logical, and extended partitions, as well as system and boot records)
- Backs up Microsoft Word documents, Excel files, PowerPoint files, etc. (using file filtering)

Source: http://www.handybackup.net/backup-screenshots/ftp1.shtml. Accessed 9/2009.

Figure 8-5   Handy Backup Server performs automatic backup on Windows machines.

- Excludes temporal, system, and other files from backup (using file filtering)
- Bidirectional synchronization of network computers
- Allows task scheduling and launching other applications before or after backup tasks
- Verifies images
- E-mail notification after backing up remote workstations
- Remote task management by a central server
- Direct backing up to the central server, requiring no disk space on client computers for backup files

NovaBACKUP

NovaBACKUP is designed for small offices running an SQL and/or Exchange Server. It works with Microsoft's Volume Shadow Copy Service (also known as VSS) in order to back up open files online. It is shown in Figure 8-6, and its features include the following:

- Free and premium off-site backups
- Users can backup and recover data anywhere
- Disk imaging
- Microsoft SQL 2008 and Exchange 2007 support
- Flexible scheduler
- E-mail reporting
- Virus protection and updates

BackupAssist

BackupAssist performs automatic scheduled backups of Windows servers. It is able to back up everything from individual files to complete servers (including Active Directory, Exchange, and SQL). It is shown in Figure 8-7, and its features include the following:

- Simple restoration of individual e-mails, calendars, tasks, notes, contacts, or entire mailboxes
- Automatically backs up Exchange mailboxes

Figure 8-6 NovaBACKUP uses VSS to back up open files.

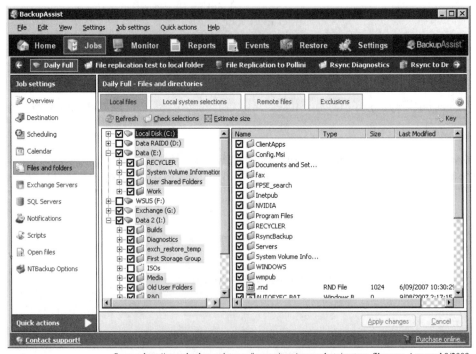

Figure 8-7 BackupAssist automatically backs up Windows servers.

- Live, online backups of SQL Server databases
- Backs up open files using an open-file manager
- Straightforward restore wizard for individual databases and complete servers
- Allows user to restore data from different points in time

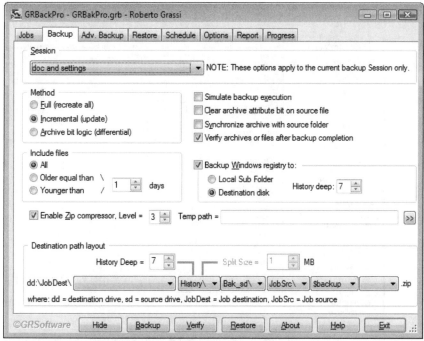

Figure 8-8   GRBackPro creates backups in Zip files.

GRBackPro

GRBackPro can run as a service while the user is logged off and has an integrated scheduler to plan backups. It supports standard Zip compression to save disk space and allow backups with any Zip-compatible software. The program supports network shares, hard drives, CDs, DVDs, and other removable storage.

GRBackPro is shown in Figure 8-8, and its features include the following:

- Supports network UNC names
- Can run as a Windows 2008/Vista/2003/XP/2000/NT service process
- Can span across multiple removable media
- Supports PKZIP 2.0 standard password protection scheme
- Allows user to copy files or compress them into a single archive or one archive per folder
- Re-creates source directory structure
- Synchronizes user backup archives with source files and folders
- Runs in the background and can be run from the system tray

Genie Backup Manager Pro

Genie Backup Manager Pro backs up an entire system to a secure location, and recovers it instantly. It supports 256-bit encryption and can be set up to run automatically at preset time intervals and rotate various backup types. Genie Backup Manager Pro is shown in Figure 8-9.

Veritas NetBackup

Symantec's Veritas NetBackup is a data backup solution for UNIX, Windows, Linux, and NetWare environments. It is shown in Figure 8-10, and its features include the following:

- Advanced disk-based data protection features that include data deduplication, virtual tape library (VTL) controls, support for third-party disk appliances, and snapshot capabilities
- Integrated data protection and recovery for virtual environments, critical applications, databases, and servers
- Single platform to manage, protect, and recover data across storage tiers, locations, and operating systems

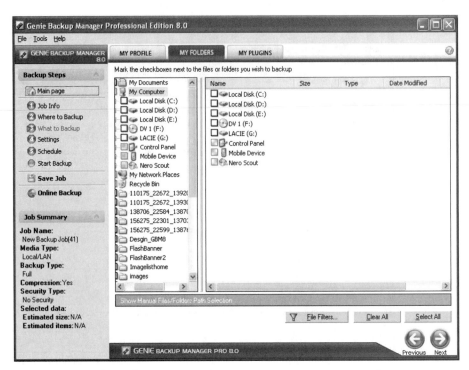

Figure 8-9 Genie Backup Manager Pro supports government-grade 256-bit encryption.

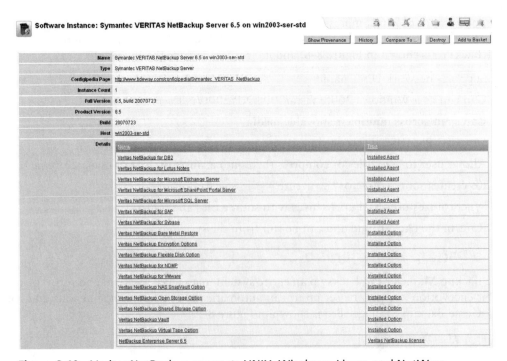

Figure 8-10 Veritas NetBackup supports UNIX, Windows, Linux, and NetWare.

- Automate and manage snapshots for VMware virtual machines from host-based and array-based providers
- Provides desktop, remote office, and data center protection across the entire enterprise
- Advanced protection for VMWare environments, e-mail applications such as Microsoft Exchange Server 2007, and large databases

Off-Site Data Backup

Off-site backup involves storing backup data at a separate, secure location, so that if any disaster occurs at the primary site, the backup data will remain safe. Data can either be physically moved to the secondary site using storage media, such as DVDs or backup tapes, or it can be transmitted using a network such as the Internet.

Figure 8-11 shows how off-site data backup over the Internet works.

Advantages of Off-Site Data Backup

Some advantages of backing up data off-site include:

- Protects data in the event of a disaster
- Automatically performs the backup operation
- Encrypts data
- Eliminates the necessity of tapes
- Protects data from damages such as hardware failure, database corruption, and natural disasters
- Can be cheaper than tape alternatives
- Convenient
- Dependable
- Efficient
- Data can be accessed from other remote systems

FTP Backup

File Transfer Protocol (FTP) is typically used to reliably transfer large files over the Internet. Data can be accessed on an FTP server from a backup program, a special FTP client, or a standard Web browser. Private FTP servers require authentication, which provides a layer of security.

Advantages of using FTP servers for backup include the following:

- Users can view the files stored on the FTP server any time using any FTP client or Web browser.
- Mobile users can back up data from anywhere in the world with an Internet connection.
- FTP backup is less expensive than a specialized remote backup service.

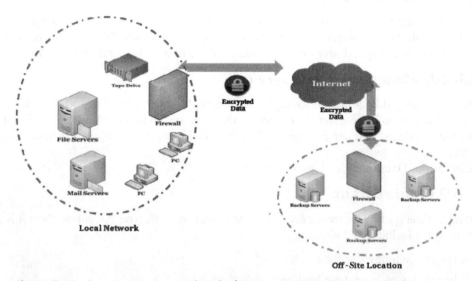

Figure 8-11 Be sure to encrypt data before transmitting it over an open network like the Internet.

Figure 8-12   EMC Remote Office Backup catches duplicate data before it is transferred.

The main disadvantage in this method is data security. FTP is not a secure protocol, and anyone who discovers a legitimate user's username and password can easily access files. Data must be manually encrypted before transferring it to the FTP server, or else it could be intercepted and viewed.

One option is to store data in a standard password-protected Zip archive. The data can then be extracted using any Zip client, many of which use strong encryption algorithms, such as AES or Blowfish.

Off-Site Backup Services

EMC Remote Office Backup

EMC Remote Office Backup uses EMC Avamar software, which catches duplicate data before they are moved across the enterprise network, reducing bandwidth demand. It includes Mozy Enterprise software, which backs up data over the Internet with a monthly subscription. EMC Remote Office Backup is shown in Figure 8-12.

Egnyte Online File Storage

Egnyte is designed for easy upload and storage of large files and data. It provides an online file server, which supports any number of folders and subfolders with set permissions. Files can be securely accessed using either a Web browser or a mapped network drive and easily searched. It is shown in Figure 8-13.

DataReady Managed Backup Service

DataReady Managed Backup Service supports features like direct-to-disk and data deduplication, which allow full server backups to be completed in minutes. Data are automatically transferred off-site every night to secure data storage facilities, and can be recovered using a Web portal. For faster restoration, a client-side program is available.

A diagram of DataReady is shown in Figure 8-14.

DriveHQ Online Backup

DriveHQ Online Backup delivers a secure, reliable, and cost-effective backup service. It is shown in Figure 8-15, and its features include the following:

- Runs as a Windows service
- Scheduled weekly or daily backups
- Real-time backups as change occurs

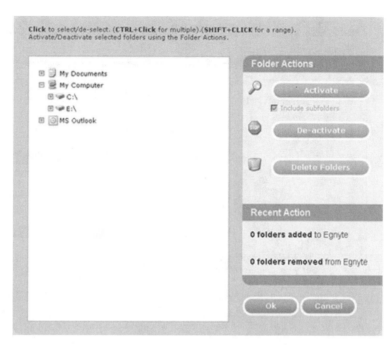

Figure 8-13   Egnyte Online File Storage is designed to handle large files.

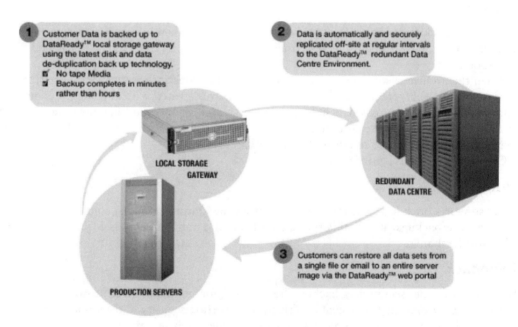

Figure 8-14   DataReady backs up servers in minutes.

- Incremental backups, saving time and storage space
- Easy and reliable restore through Web, DriveHQ Online Backup, or FileManager
- Quick launch from Windows Explorer through right-click menu
- Encryption of backup data
- Secure data transfer through HTTPS/SSL

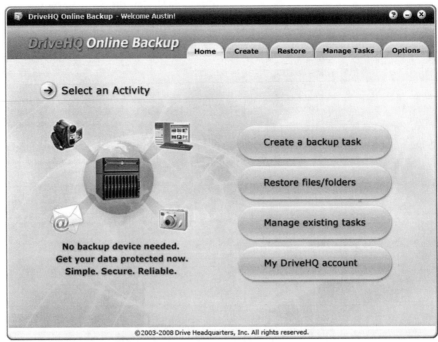

Source: http://www.drivehq.com/Downloads/OnlineBackupScreenshots/main.htm. Accessed 9/2009.

Figure 8-15   DriveHQ Online Backup backs up data to a remote server.

Offsiter

Offsiter is a backup utility that compresses files and sends them as encrypted attachments to off-site e-mail accounts. Files can be stored using any e-mail account, including free accounts provided by Yahoo!, Microsoft, and Google.

When the archive is sent to an e-mail account, it is divided into separate e-mail attachments. Each attachment is strongly encrypted. The program can use archives created with any compression application; however, Offsiter's own Zip compression includes the option to archive only files that have changed since the last backup. To recover an archive, a user simply downloads the attachments from the e-mail account and uses Offsiter to decrypt and merge them to re-create the original archive.

Offsiter is shown in Figure 8-16.

Ahsay

Ahsay supports brick-level Exchange backup (including Outlook e-mails, contacts, and calendars) for Internet-based remote backups. It contains specialized backup databases such as Microsoft SQL Server, Oracle, and Microsoft Exchange.

Rhinoback

Rhinoback provides secure data backup and recovery for small and medium-sized businesses. It stores data in a professionally managed data center with state-of-the-art security and redundancy. It can perform backups automatically every day, and data can be restored immediately at any time.

Rhinoback is shown in Figure 8-17, and its features include the following:

- User-configurable incremental backup mode
- Offline backup mode and logout backup reminder
- Customizable backup schedule
- Compresses and encrypts data automatically
- Incremental backup strategy
- Supports both full and incremental backups
- Runs on Windows, Mac OS X, Linux, NetWare, UNIX, and all other platforms supporting a Java 2 Runtime Environment

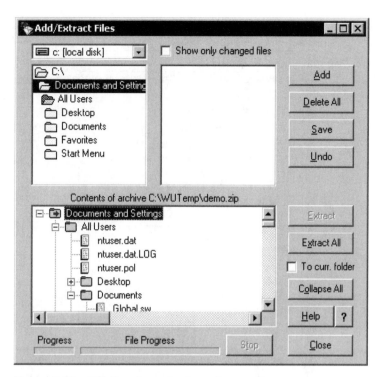

Figure 8-16   Offsiter stores backups in e-mail accounts.

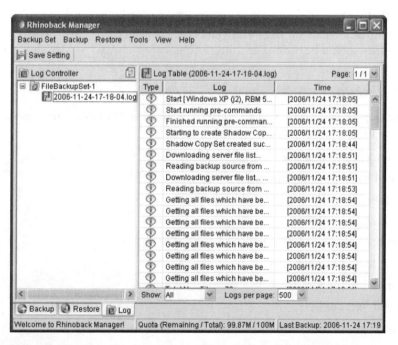

Figure 8-17   Rhinoback is designed for small and medium-sized businesses.

Figure 8-18   Cucku backs up data and sends them to a trusted friend.

Cucku Backup

Cucku automatically backs up data and sends an encrypted copy to a trusted friend or family member. It chooses what files should be backed up and continuously archives them, even if they are in use. Cucku is shown in Figure 8-18.

Safe Data Backup

Safe Data Backup backs up data to a CD, DVD, local drive, USB drive, or network drive. It is shown in Figure 8-19, and its features include the following:

- Windows Vista compatible
- Unlimited backup configurations
- Uncompressed or Zip-compressed backups
- Backup to CD or DVD
- Remote backup via FTP or e-mail
- Backs up locked or open files
- Network drive support
- Scheduled backups
- Saves revisions of modified files
- Saves deleted files

Backup Platinum

Backup Platinum creates backups on any type of storage media: hard drive, CD, DVD, Blu-ray disc, or FTP server. It provides 128-bit encryption with Blowfish and Zip compression on the fly. A built-in CD/DVD engine allows for erasing a rewritable disk before burning and automatically splitting large backups into several parts using disk spanning.

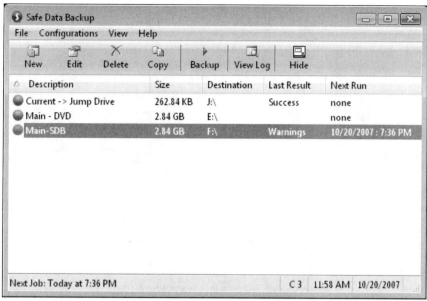

Source: http://www.beiley.com/data_backup/images/Safe-Data-Backup-Window.gif. Accessed 9/2009.

Figure 8-19   Safe Data Backup works with network drives.

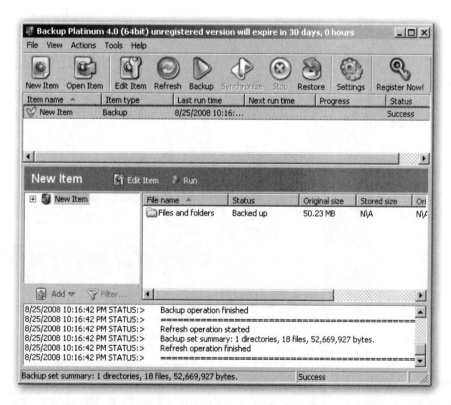

Figure 8-20   Backup Platinum can perform backup tasks in Windows service mode.

Backup Platinum is designed for Windows. The program comes with a flexible scheduler to provide automatic backups and can run in service mode under Windows NT/2000/XP/2003 to execute scheduled tasks even when no one is logged in.

It creates detailed logs of all operations and can back up open files. Restoring files is as easy as clicking a button. Backup Platinum is shown in Figure 8-20.

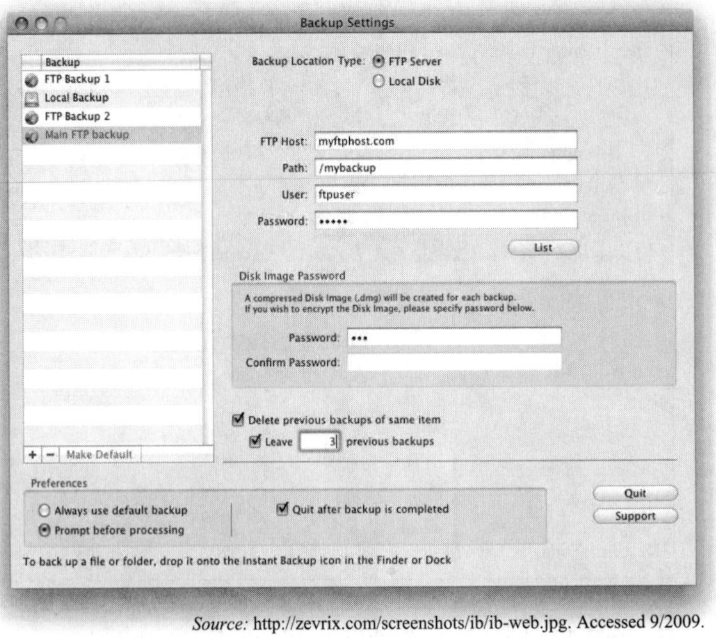

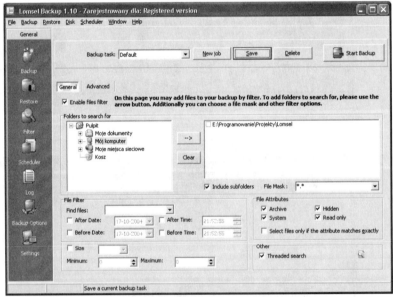

Source: http://zevrix.com/screenshots/ib/ib-web.jpg. Accessed 9/2009.

Figure 8-21   Instant Backup is a simple FTP backup utility.

Source: http://www.lomsel.net/index.php?action=shotspl&lng=en&progid=1. Accessed 9/2009.

Figure 8-22   Lomsel Backup uses Windows Scheduler to automate backups.

Instant Backup

Instant Backup is a simple solution to back up and archive important and sensitive files to a password-protected FTP site. It is not a replacement for complete backup systems; its main draws are its ease of use and flexibility. Instant Backup is shown in Figure 8-21.

Lomsel Backup

Lomsel Backup works with Windows Scheduler to automate backup processes. It is shown in Figure 8-22, and its features include the following:

- Simple and intuitive interface
- Fast access to the most important options

- Shell integration
- Backup settings adjustment
- Backs up open files
- Registry backup
- Windows shell backup
- Incremental backup
- Backup password protection
- Export/import backup job settings
- Wizards for backup and restore
- Spanned backup files
- Strong 256-bit encryption

Enterprise Backup Tools

Symantec Backup Exec System Recovery

Backup Exec System Recovery is a complete disk-based system recovery solution for Windows-based servers, desktops, and laptops. It captures a recovery point of the entire live Windows system, including the operating system, applications, databases, all files, device drivers, profiles, settings, and registry, without disrupting the user. A recovery point can be saved to various media or storage devices such as SAN, NAS, DAS, RAID, and Blu-ray disc/DVD/CD.

Backup Exec System Recovery can be managed remotely either by a licensed copy of Backup Exec System Recovery or Backup Exec System Recovery Manager. Backup Exec System Recovery Manager can be used to centrally deploy, modify, and maintain recovery activities, jobs, and policies for local and remote systems. It can be used to constantly monitor and resolve problems. Backup Exec System Recovery works together with Google Desktop and Backup Exec Retrieve to recover end-user files without IT support. The Symantec Backup Exec System Recovery Granular Restore option can be used to restore an individual's Microsoft Exchange e-mails, folders, and mailboxes.

Figure 8-23 shows the steps of running Symantec Backup Exec System Recovery.

Key Features and Benefits

Benefits of Symantec Backup Exec System Recovery include:

- Rapid and reliable recovery, even with dissimilar hardware or virtual environments
- Flexible off-site protection and enhanced recovery capabilities
- Integration with other leading technologies

It also includes the following features:

- Flexible restoration options
- Enhanced virtual support
- Easy remote system recovery
- Enhanced Exchange, SharePoint, and file/folder recovery
- Scalable, centralized management

Symantec Backup Exec for Window Servers

Symantec Backup Exec for Windows Servers delivers disk-to-tape backup and fast, efficient recovery. In Backup Exec, backup, restore, and utility operations are known as *jobs*. These jobs are performed through the administration console. Administrators run the administration console from the media server or a remote computer. Once jobs are created, the Backup Exec server components begin backup, restore, and utility operations on the media server.

Figure 8-24 shows a diagram of Symantec Backup Exec.

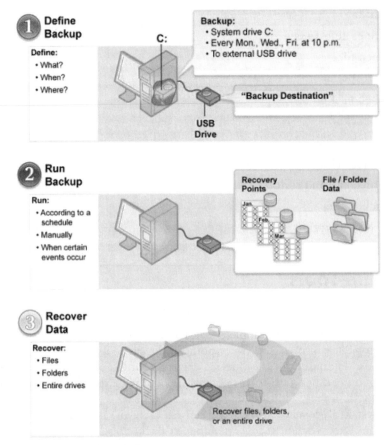

Figure 8-23 Symantec Backup Exec System Recovery captures a live recovery point of the entire Windows system.

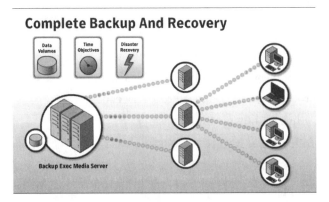

Figure 8-24 Symantec Backup Exec provides fast, efficient recovery.

Key Features and Benefits

Key features of Symantec Backup Exec include:

- Comprehensive data protection for VMware Infrastructures and Microsoft Virtual Servers
- Data protection for Microsoft Windows 2008 Server
- Expanded granular recovery benefits for SharePoint Server

- Backup Exec infrastructure manager
- Enhanced protection for NDMP-enabled NAS devices
- Acts as a remote media server agent for Linux servers
- Complete data and system protection for Windows environments
- Protects data for physical and virtual server environments
- Granular Recovery Technology (GRT) recovers critical Microsoft application data in seconds
- Centralized three-tier setup, reporting, and patch management
- Scalable heterogeneous support through remote agents and options
- Continuous data protection for Exchange, SQL, and file servers
- Multiproduct integration
- Online storage

Benefits include:

- Fast and reliable
- Eliminates backup windows
- Enables faster backups
- Recovers individual files, Exchange messages/mailboxes, and SharePoint documents within seconds
- Provides file retrieval for the end user without any IT intervention
- Provides complete disk- and tape-based data protection
- Increases Windows application availability
- Offers simple, scalable, and centralized management
- Provides certified compatibility across Microsoft Windows 2000 and Windows Server 2003 environments
- Provides complete data and system protection
- Provides granular recovery and continuous protection

AmeriVault-AV

AmeriVault-AV is an online data backup service that delivers automated, one-step online backup and off-site storage. It is shown in Figure 8-25, and its key features include the following:

- Continuous data protection (CDP)
- Total automation
- Point-and-click restores
- Centralized management
- Redundant storage
- End-to-end encryption
- Compliant processing
- Integrity verification
- Supports Windows, UNIX, Linux, Mac, VMware, System i, Novell NetWare, and Sun/HP UX/AIX
- Automatic upgrades

MozyPro

MozyPro is a simple Internet backup system, shown in Figure 8-26, containing the following features:

- 128-bit SSL encryption using AES and Blowfish
- Automatically detects and backs up new and changed files
- Provides automatic or scheduled backups

Source: www.amerivault.com. Accessed 9/2009.

Figure 8-25 AmeriVault-AV is a one-step online backup service.

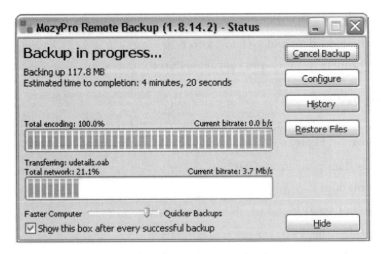

Figure 8-26 MozyPro is a simple Internet backup system.

- Provides block-level incremental backups
- Supports SQL, Exchange, network drives, Windows, and Mac

PC Backup Pro

Migo PC Backup Pro is an image-based backup and recovery tool. It backs up open files and scans the backups for viruses. PC Backup Pro is shown in Figure 8-27.

Auto Backup

Auto Backup can automatically or manually back up critical data to a local disk, network drive, or remote FTP server. It allows full, incremental, and differential backups on Windows systems with 256-bit encryption. Auto Backup is shown in Figure 8-28.

Source: http://www.dtransfer.com/products/data-backup/pc-backup-pro/. Accessed 9/2009.

Figure 8-27   PC Backup Pro can scan backups for viruses.

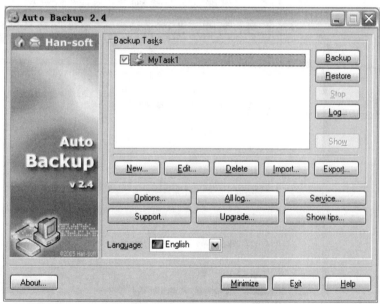

Source: http://www.han-soft.com/habt.php#screen. Accessed 9/2009.

Figure 8-28   Auto Backup allows full, incremental, and differential backups.

SyncBackPro

SyncBackPro can be used for backing up and synchronizing files on local drives, network drives, removable drives, or FTP servers. It supports backups spanning multiple CDs or DVDs, and can synchronize files with an e-mail server. Users can even write their own scripts to control the program. SyncBackPro is shown in Figure 8-29.

Kabooza

Kabooza is an online backup service that automatically backs up files and photos without user interaction. It encrypts files before transfer and stores multiple copies of files in several geographical locations to ensure protection. It also maintains a file's history for 30 days to restore accidentally deleted or damaged files. Kabooza is shown in Figure 8-30.

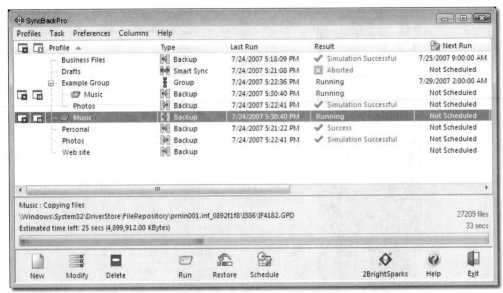

Source: http://www.2brightsparks.com/syncback/sbpro-screenshots.html. Accessed 9/2009.

Figure 8-29 Users can write their own SyncBackPro scripts.

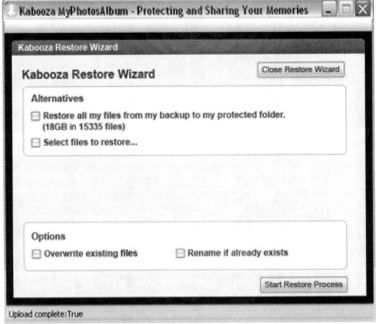

Source: http://www.kabooza.com/images/kabooza_restore_wizard.jpg. Accessed 9/2009.

Figure 8-30 Kabooza keeps a file's history for 30 days.

iStorage

iStorage features unlimited storage space for photos, files, and critical data. It features redundant data storage with 256-bit encryption and stores large files using the included WhaleMail tool. iStorage is shown in Figure 8-31.

SOS Online Backup

SOS Online Backup backs up files to a global network of SOS datacenters. Data are compressed using proprietary delta compression. It is shown in Figure 8-32, and its features include the following:

- Continuous data protection
- Integrated local backup

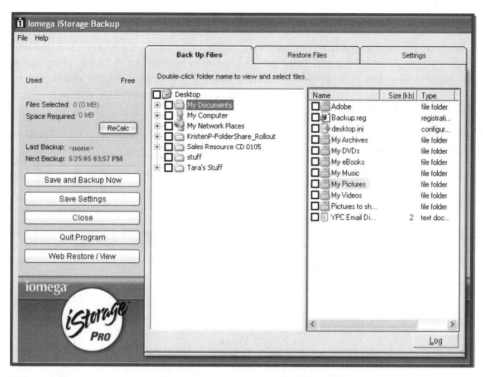

Figure 8-31   iStorage provides unlimited storage space.

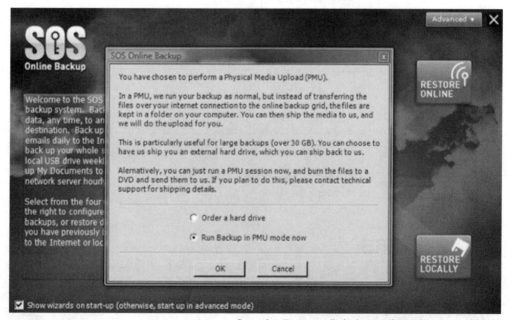

Source: http://www.sosonlinebackup.com/features.htm. Accessed 9/2009.

Figure 8-32   SOS Online Backup stores files on a global network of datacenters.

- Complete privacy protection
- Allows 20 to 30 GB of data
- Supports multiple computers
- Intelligent file filters
- Powerful recovery
- Scheduled backups

SiteShelter

SiteShelter is an automated utility that backs up, mirrors, monitors, and even repairs Web sites and FTP sites. It is particularly useful for Web site developers who want to provide an online backup service for their client's Web sites. It supports all types of servers—Windows, UNIX, Linux, and others. SiteShelter is shown in Figure 8-33.

EVault Backup Software

EVault Backup Software is a disk-to-disk backup and recovery solution. It is shown in Figure 8-34, and its features include the following:

- Ensures data availability and recoverability
- Scalable and efficient

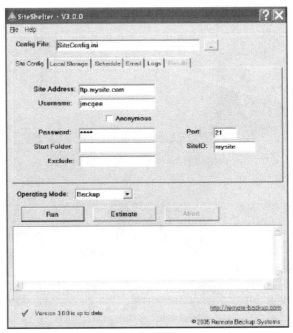

Source: http://www.remote-backup.com/siteshelter/docs/siteshelterwt.htm.
Accessed 9/2009.

Figure 8-33   SiteShelter is useful for Web site developers.

Source: http://www.evault.com/site. Accessed 9/2009.

Figure 8-34   EVault is a disk-to-disk backup program.

- Encrypts the data before and during over-the-wire transmission
- Web-based centralized management for distributed environments
- Compliance with industry and corporate governance requirements
- Broad platform support

IDrive

IDrive online backup provides automated protection for critical data. It can restore data from either its desktop client or its Web client. Users can drag and drop files to restore from the online drive to the local system. IDrive Pro is shown in Figure 8-35, and its features include the following:

- Allows access to files anywhere, anytime
- Supports multiple systems
- Encrypted backups
- Retains 30 individual versions of the backed-up data
- Drag-and-drop restore using the optional IDrive Explorer interface in addition to IDrive Classic options

Backup2net

Backup2net is an automated backup program, shown in Figure 8-36, that has the following features:

- Local and remote secure server backup
- Easy-to-use interface
- Easy file and folder selection
- Built-in task scheduler
- Intuitive backup and restore
- Secure shell data transfer

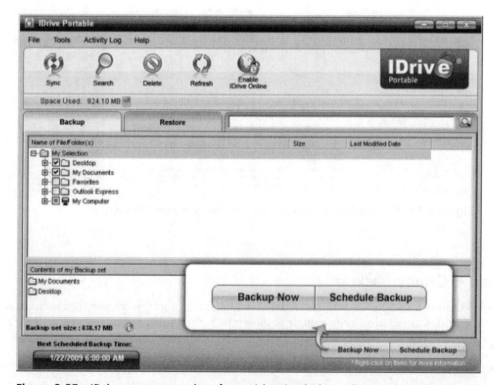

Figure 8-35   IDrive can restore data from either its desktop client or its Web client.

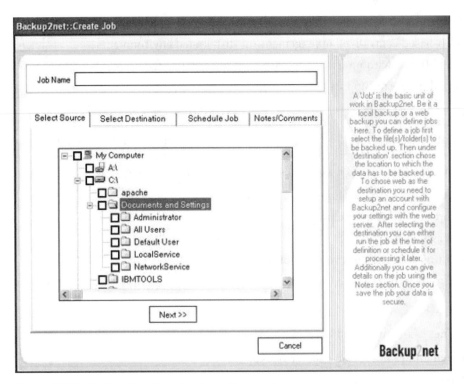

Figure 8-36 Backup2net is a simple online backup and restore program.

Figure 8-37 Quad-B Online Backup requires minimal user interaction.

Quad-B Online Backup

Quad-B Online Backup is an automated data backup and restoration system that requires no human interaction after the initial installation and setup. It is shown in Figure 8-37, and its features include the following:

- Easily scheduled online backups
- Low bandwidth requirements and adjustable bandwidth settings
- Flexible version control to define which versions to store

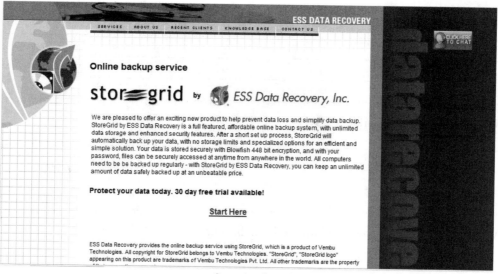

Figure 8-38 StoreGrid provides unlimited data storage and enhanced security.

- High encryption and security
- Backs up individual files or entire directories
- All data are compressed and encrypted locally before being sent to the server
- All data on the server are stored in a compressed and encrypted format
- Supports the backup of local files, network files, and open databases (VSS compatible)

StoreGrid

StoreGrid is an online backup system with unlimited data storage and enhanced security features. It stores data securely using Blowfish 448-bit encryption, and it allows the user to access files securely anywhere in the world. StoreGrid is shown in Figure 8-38.

Chapter Summary

- It is extremely important to regularly back up data.
- Backups can be done to a local tape drive, but it is safer to use off-site storage.
- Use encryption on backups.
- Disk backup is used to recover data quickly in the event of a disaster.
- Removable media backup refers to the use of CDs, DVDs, tape drives, USB drives, and external hard drives.
- Most online backup solutions are highly reliable.
- Files can be backed up online using File Transfer Protocol (FTP) servers.

Review Questions

1. What is disk mirroring?

_____

_____

_____

_____

2. What are some challenges faced in maintaining backups and recovering data?

_____

_____

_____

_____

3. What are some causes of data loss?

_____

_____

_____

_____

4. What are some risks involved in maintaining backups?

_____

_____

_____

_____

5. Why is it necessary to secure backups with encryption?

_____

_____

_____

_____

6. What is off-site backup?

_____

_____

_____

_____

7. What are the advantages of off-site backup?

_____

_____

_____

_____

8. What is online backup?

_____

_____

_____

_____

9. What is a disadvantage of using FTP for backup?

_____

_____

_____

_____

10. What are some services that provide online backup?

_____

_____

_____

_____

Hands-On Projects

1. Use Norton Ghost to back up files and folders.

   - Navigate to Chapter 8 of the Student Resource Center.
   - Install and launch the Norton Ghost program.
   - Select **Back up selected files or folders** and click the **Next** button.
   - Select the files and folders to back up and click the **Next** button.
   - Select a destination folder and click the **Next** button.
   - Select a schedule option and click the **Next** button.
   - Select **Run Backup Now** and click the **Finish** button to run the backup.

2. Use Norton Online Backup to back up files online.

   - Navigate to Chapter 8 of the Student Resource Center.
   - Install and launch the Norton Online Backup program.
   - Enter the name of the computer in the **Display Name** field and click **OK**.
   - Add files and folders for backup, and create a schedule to run the backup.
   - Click **Back up Now** to back up immediately.
   - Click **Restore** to recover the files.
   - Check the activity log by clicking **View Log**.

3. Use BackupAssist to manage backups.

   - Navigate to Chapter 8 of the Student Resource Center.
   - Install and launch the BackupAssist program.
   - Select the type of backup and click the **Next** button.
   - Select the destination backup directory and click the **Next** button.
   - Select the files and folders to back up and click the **Next** button.
   - Enter a name for this job and click the **Finish** button.
   - Go to the **Jobs** menu, select the job that was just created, and click the **Run** button.
   - Click the **Events** tab and view the events that have occurred.
   - Click the **Restore** tab and click on **Restore using NTBackup**.
   - Click **Recent job reports** to view reports.

4. Use Genie Backup Manager Pro to back up data.

   - Navigate to Chapter 8 of the Student Resource Center.
   - Install and launch the Genie Backup Manager Pro program.
   - Click **Backup** to create a new backup job.
   - Select the backup media and location for the backup, and click the **Next** button.
   - Select the files to back up and click the **Next** button.
   - Select the settings for backup and click the **Next** button.

- View the report.
- Click **Restore** to recover the backup files.
- Select the files to recover and click the **Next** button.
- View the report.

5. Use Handy Backup to schedule data backups.

- Navigate to Chapter 8 of the Student Resource Center.
- Install and launch the Handy Backup program.
- Select the task type and click the **Next** button.
- Choose the files to back up and click the **Next** button.
- Select the backup location and click the **Next** button.
- Enter the backup name and click the **Finish** button.
- Check the settings and click the **OK** button.
- Click the **View** tab and click **Save Log** to save the log.
- Select **Restore task** and click the **Next** button.
- Select the restore location and click the **Next** button.
- Click the **Finish** button to recover the files.

Chapter 9

Certification and Accreditation of Information Systems

Objectives

After completing this chapter, you should be able to:

- Understand certification and accreditation
- Enumerate the guidelines for certification and accreditation
- Understand the role of risk assessment in the certification and accreditation process
- Compare different certification and accreditation processes
- Implement physical security requirements
- Understand how threat and vulnerability analysis applies to the certification and accreditation process

Key Terms

Accreditation   the official approval to operate an information system for a specific period of time

Approval to operate   an official permission granted by a designated approving authority (DAA) to operate automated information systems (AIS) or networks in a particular security mode

Certification   the process of assessing whether the technical and nontechnical safety features of an IS satisfy the minimum security requirements

Introduction to Certification and Accreditation of Information Systems

Certification and accreditation are important aspects of maintaining and strengthening the security of an information system. This chapter introduces you to the concepts of certification and accreditation. It covers what is involved in the process and how other processes contribute to the certification and accreditation process. The chapter also covers how threats and vulnerabilities are related to the certification and accreditation process.

Certification and Accreditation

The risk involved with operating an information system (IS) can never be completely eliminated, but it can be reduced using a risk management approach. Certification and accreditation authorities are appointed to effectively manage the risk associated with operating an information system.

Certification

Certification is the process of assessing whether the technical and nontechnical safety features of an IS satisfy the minimum security requirements. Security certifications for information systems provide an assurance to their various stakeholders that the system is operating under acceptable risk limits and proper controls are implemented to handle and respond to an information security incident.

Certification should:

- Validate that the security measures meet the minimum security requirements of an IS
- Test the security safeguards
- Evaluate the technical security measures in terms of functionality and assurance

The certification process supports the risk management process in the information system's security program. This certification process is divided into two tasks: security control assessment and security certification documentation.

Security control implementation deals with the implementation of the security requirements in an organization. The objectives of the security requirements implementation are to:

- Prepare for the security assessment
- Conduct the security assessment
- Document the results

Preparation for security assessment involves generating and gathering appropriate planning and supporting materials such as system requirements and design documentation, security control implementation evidence, and results from previous security assessments, security reviews, or audits.

System certifiers and accreditors are the individuals responsible for providing security certifications or assessing management.

Accreditation

Accreditation represents the official approval to operate an information system for a specific period of time. It is the official declaration by a responsible senior manager that an automated system is permitted to process information up to a maximum sensitivity level, under specified controls and operating procedures. It signifies senior management's official approval of the residual risk.

Procedures and Controls to Detect or Prevent Unauthorized Access

Table 9-1 describes procedures and controls for detecting or preventing unauthorized access to information systems.

Certification and Accreditation Guidelines

An organization should follow these guidelines to pass the certification and accreditation process and get certified. These guidelines provide an overview of measures to achieve certification and accreditation.

The guidelines are as follows:

- Apply consistent, comparable, and repeatable evaluations of the security controls to information systems.
- Understand and recognize the mission risks resulting from the operation of information systems.
- Create more complete, reliable, and trustworthy information for the authorizing officials.
- Achieve secure information systems.
- Create a documentation policy and document all the procedures and controls implemented in the organization in a clear, concise manner.

Procedures and Controls	Focus On
Information Security Policies	Definition of the appropriate security controls
	Assessment of the current security controls
	Guidelines to report, assess, respond to, and handle organizational security incidents
	Recommendations for the appropriate controls to safeguard sensitive information
Awareness and Training	Development of the required skills in security teams
	Creating awareness among end users regarding roles and responsibilities related to the system and information access
Access Controls	Use of relevant logical and physical security controls such as identification and authentication, and privilege assignments
	Creating user groups and granting differentiated permissions according to their roles and duties in the organization
	Password protection of all access points
	Installation of physical security controls such as biometric scanners and smart-card readers
	Deployment of security personnel, fencing, and surveillance
Disaster Preparedness	Development of procedures to protect information systems from unlawful destruction and accidental loss
	Preparedness to overcome natural disasters and environmental hazards
Information Encryption	Encrypting information in all its states, i.e., during collection, processing, and transmission
	Encrypting all communication channels
Use of Automated Tools	Automated tools to manage access to information systems and resources
Evaluation and Audits	Audit of all the access control measures to ensure their effectiveness
	Evaluation and audits lead to certification and accreditation of information systems

Table 9-1 These are procedures and controls for detecting or preventing unauthorized access to information systems

Certification and Accreditation Documentation

Organizations should maintain documents that contain information about the corrective and security measures applied in the organization to achieve certification and accreditation. The set of documents should also include the result of applying the controls and the extent to which the desired outcome has been achieved.

The documentation should include the following:

- System categorization statement document
- System description document
- Network diagram and data flows
- Software and hardware inventory
- Business risk assessment
- System risk assessment
- Contingency plan
- Self-assessment document
- System security plan

Organizational Certification and Accreditation Process

A typical organizational security certification and accreditation process consists of four phases:

1. *Initiation phase*: This phase ensures that an organization's information security manager is in agreement with the contents of the information system security plan. This phase consists of three tasks:
   - Preparation
   - Notification and resource identification
   - Information system security plan analysis, update, and acceptance

2. *Security certification phase*: This phase ensures that security controls in the information system are implemented correctly and produce the desired outcome. This phase consists of two tasks:
   - Security control assessment
   - Security certification documentation

3. *Security accreditation phase*: The purpose of this phase is to find out if the remaining known vulnerabilities in the information system pose an acceptable level of risk to the organization's operations, the organization's assets, or individuals. This phase consists of two tasks:
   - Security accreditation decision
   - Security accreditation documentation

4. *Continuous monitoring phase*: The purpose of this phase is to provide complete information system security monitoring on an ongoing basis and to inform the organization's information security manager when any changes occur in the information system. This phase consists of:
   - Configuration management and control
   - Security control monitoring
   - Status reporting and documentation

Role of Risk Assessment in the Certification and Accreditation Process

Risk assessment is an important activity in an organization. An information security program supports security accreditation and is needed by the security certification and accreditation authority. Information security policies and procedures based on risk assessment help to reduce security risks. Thus, risk assessment is important to the certification and accreditation process. Risk assessment cost-effectively reduces the information security risks to an acceptable level and ensures that information security is addressed throughout the life cycle of each agency information system. It enables more consistent, comparable, and repeatable assessments of the security controls in an information system.

Comparison of Different Certification and Accreditation Processes

The following are three methodologies used for certification and accreditation initiatives:

1. Defense Information Technology Security Certification and Accreditation Process (DITSCAP)
2. National Information Assurance Certification and Accreditation Process (NIACAP)
3. National Institute of Standards and Technology (NIST)

Defense agencies primarily use DITSCAP, though civilian agencies may also use it. It is based on a process published by the National Security Telecommunications and Information System Security Instruction (NSTISSI). Most civilian agencies instead use the NIST methodology.

NIST and NIACAP establish a framework to provide certification and accreditation to an organization. NIST and NIACAP both stipulate definitions and requirements for a system's characterization, risk assessment, verification and validation of the security controls, and testing.

All certification and accreditation processes consider the entire system, network, and application life cycle from a security standpoint. The certification and accreditation process is a manual audit of policies, procedures, controls, and contingency planning. NIST is designed for unclassified information.

The following are the four phases of the NIST model:

1. Initiation
2. Certification

3. Accreditation

4. Continuous monitoring

The following are the four phases of the NIACAP model:

1. Definition

2. Verification

3. Validation

4. Postaccreditation

DITSCAP also involves the same four phases as NIACAP. Though there is a difference in the nomenclature of phases in the certifications listed and accreditation methodologies, the underlying basic principles are the same. They all evaluate the security controls implemented in an organization.

Monitoring the Certification and Accreditation Process for Vulnerabilities

The certification and accreditation process determines the security of an information system; it suggests the means to protect information from vulnerabilities. The security of information can be protected by implementing countermeasures that are selected according to the possible threats and the importance of the data. Threat analysis is performed during the certification and accreditation process, and the sources of any vulnerabilities are continuously monitored. An effective continuous monitoring program requires the following:

- Configuration management and configuration control processes
- Security impact analysis on changes in the information system
- Assessment of selected security controls in the information system

Vulnerability detection can be carried out at any phase in the system development life cycle. The vulnerability detection process can be performed through various means such as questionnaires, interviews, document reviews, and automated scanning tools.

Vulnerability sources can be located in the following places:

- Previous risk assessment reports
- Audit log reports
- System anomaly reports
- Vulnerability scans and penetration-testing reports
- Security testing and evaluation reports
- Hardware/software security analyses

Relationship Between Vulnerabilities, Risks, and Attacks

Vulnerabilities, risks, and attacks on an information system are interrelated. Risks are compounded by vulnerabilities in the system and in controls implemented to overcome attacks. Attacks often involve the exploitation of system vulnerabilities. The risk of attack increases with the presence of vulnerabilities in a system.

Approval to Operate (ATO)

Approval to operate is an official permission granted by a designated approving authority (DAA) to operate automated information systems (AISs) or networks in a particular security mode. Before granting permission, the DAA verifies an accreditation statement to make sure that the residual risk is within the acceptable limits. The DAA ensures that each AIS fulfills the AIS security requirements, as reported by the information systems security officer (ISSO). Responsibilities of an ISSO include the following:

- Establish and manage security for systems operated by an agency, contractors, and command personnel
- Appoint the person who will directly report to the DAA
- Assign levels of classification required for applications operating in a network environment
- Verify the accreditation plan and sign the accreditation statement for the network and AIS
- Verify the documentation for AIS security requirements, which are defined in the AIS network security program

Security

Security Laws

The following are some of the security laws that regulate and are referred to by certification and accreditation authorities:

- *Federal Information Security Management Act (FISMA)*: It sets guidelines for conducting annual reviews of an agency's information security program and reporting the results.
- *Health Insurance Portability and Accountability Act (HIPAA)*: It sets strict guidelines to ensure the integrity and confidentiality of individually identifiable health information and helps protect information against reasonably anticipated threats and unauthorized disclosure.
- *Sarbanes-Oxley Act (SOX)*: It provides guidelines to improve the accuracy and reliability of corporate disclosures.
- *Gramm-Leach-Bliley Act (GLBA)*: It sets guidelines for the security and confidentiality of a customer's financial information.

Physical Security Requirements

The physical security of systems and data is important in an organization. It includes measures to protect personnel, critical assets, and systems against deliberate attacks and accidents. The intent of physical security is to prevent the unauthorized access of information and other assets of a company. It can be achieved by means of securing data and systems through physical access controls and restricted entry to the server and data storage rooms. The first and foremost security measures to be implemented in an organization are the physical security measures.

The following are some physical security measures organizations typically implement:

- *Lock up the server room*: Management implements policies to keep the server room locked and to allow only authorized personnel to open the lock and enter the server room.
- *Set up surveillance*: There may be the chance of misuse of authority by an authorized person, so a logbook should be maintained to keep track of who goes in and out and when. Surveillance equipment should also be installed in areas containing highly sensitive information.
- *Place valuable devices in a locker*: All network devices and important data disks should be kept in a locker; this protects the devices and helps prevent theft.
- *Use rack-mount servers*: Rack-mount servers are small and easy to secure.
- *Protect portable devices*: The physical security of portable devices is important, as they can be easily stolen by anyone.
- *Pack up backups*: Backup tapes, disks, or discs can be stolen and used by outsiders; backups should be kept off-site in a secured place.
- *Disable drives and ports*: Information can be stolen with the help of removable media. When the organization is not using them for business purposes, it is advisable to disable or remove floppy drives, USB ports, and other means by which external drives can be connected.
- *Protect printers*: Printers store information concerning recently printed documents in memory. It is important to protect printers, as they may lead to important information leakage if not protected properly.

Physical security measures vary according to needs and circumstances and depend on the cost of what is being protected. A prudent mix of physical, technical, and operational measures helps ensure sufficient physical security.

Security Inspections Covered During the Certification and Accreditation Process

The objective of the security inspections conducted during the certification and accreditation process is to determine the risk to organizational operations, organizational assets, or individuals and to determine if the organization-level risk is acceptable. During this process, the planned or completed corrective actions to reduce or eliminate vulnerabilities are checked. The final risk to the organization and the acceptability of that risk is determined during this security inspection process.

The security inspection process can be divided into the following phases:

- Preparing for the security assessment
- Conducting the assessment of the security controls
- Preparing the final security assessment report

Security Policies and Procedures Implemented During the Risk Analysis/Assessment Process

The following are some of the security policies and procedures implemented during the risk analysis/ assessment process:

- Identifying threats that harm and affect vital information security operations and assets
- Estimating the likelihood that such threats will occur, based on past information
- Identifying and ranking the value of operations and assets
- Estimating the cost for potential losses, damage, and recovery
- Identifying cost-effective actions to reduce potential risk
- Documenting the results and developing an action plan

Vulnerabilities Associated with Security Processing Modes

The security processing mode of an information system is determined based on the classification of data, clearances, access approval, and need-to-know of the users of the information system. Only authorized persons are allowed to access information and make changes to that information. Management is responsible for deciding who is allowed to access and modify which information.

Depending on management policies, security processing is differentiated into the following modes:

- *Dedicated security mode*: In this mode, all users must have the required security clearance, formal access approval, and a need-to-know for all information processed by the system. All users can access all information on the system, which could lead to information leakage.
- *System high-security mode*: In this mode, all users must have the required security clearance and formal access approval, but they do not need to have a need-to-know for all information processed by the system. Users only have to have a need-to-know for some of the information. This could lead to a user accessing or modifying information he or she should not access.
- *Compartmented security mode*: In this mode, all users must have the required security clearance. However, all users do not need to have formal access approval and a need-to-know for all information processed by the system, just for some of the information.
- *Multilevel security mode*: In this mode, all users do not need to have the required security clearance, formal access approval, and need-to-know for all information processed by the system, just for some of the information. This is the most secured mode.

Threat and Vulnerability Analysis Input to the Certification and Accreditation Process

An organization prepares a system security plan for the certification and accreditation process that contains complete information about the information system, security categories, potential threats, and vulnerabilities.

Threat analysis input to the certification and accreditation process includes:

- List of all potential threats that affect the information system
- Threat information such as capabilities, intentions, and resources of potential adversaries
- Threat detection information that is documented in the risk assessment process

Vulnerability analysis input to the certification and accreditation process includes:

- Flaws or weaknesses in an information system
- Vulnerability identification information that is documented in the risk assessment process
- Vulnerability information associated with the information system and common security controls

How Certification and Accreditation Provide Assurance That Controls Are Functioning Effectively

The certification and accreditation process considers the vulnerabilities, processes, and solutions to deal with the vulnerabilities. The certification and accreditation authorities check the suggested and implemented solutions in an organization to overcome vulnerabilities and counter attacks.

The process of security control assessment consists of three phases:

- *Phase I*:
  - Prepare for the assessment of security controls.
  - In the first phase, proper planning and collection of supporting material takes place, after which methods and procedures are developed for assessing security controls.

- *Phase II*:
  - Assess the security controls.
  - In the second phase, the developed methods are implemented for the assessment of solutions that are suggested and implemented in the organization.

- *Phase III*:
  - Document the final results of the assessment.
  - This is the assessment phase in which the assessment of the results of the control measures takes place; the outcome is compared with the expected result documents and corrections, if any, are suggested for better results.

Protections Offered by Security Features in Specific Configurations

Depending on the organization's policies and the security measures applied to the system, the protection provided to the system is divided into the following four categories:

1. *High*: This system profile is recommended for systems that contain sensitive data and are accessed by many users. All networking services are disabled for this type of system. Only the transfer of information to other systems is allowed, and receiving data is not allowed.

2. *Improved*: This system profile is recommended for systems accessed by groups of users who can share information. User IDs can be reused as desired. Only limited networking services are enabled.

3. *Traditional*: This system profile is recommended for compatibility with other systems. Passwords are necessary to access the system, but they are not configured to expire. All networking services are enabled.

4. *Low*: This system profile is recommended only for systems that are not publicly accessible. It is also implemented in systems having a small number of cooperating users.

Threat/Risk Assessment Methodology Appropriate for Use with System Undergoing Accreditation

The threat/risk assessment methodology used for a system undergoing accreditation focuses on the following:

- *Prioritization of risk*: Risks anticipated by an organization need to be prioritized according to their seriousness. The more serious and potentially damaging risks are attended to first and given higher priority. The countermeasures applied to counter the risks are dependent on the expected damage caused by the risks and the impact of the damage on the organization.

- *Categorization of recommended safeguards*: The countermeasures to be applied are categorized according to their urgency and cost effectiveness.

- *Feasibility of implementation of solutions*: It is the responsibility of the organization to use the most appropriate means to safeguard against damage caused by a threat. Appropriate and useful countermeasures should be selected to effectively control an attack.

- *Other risk mitigation processes*: Often, lessons learned from previous risk management are used to implement countermeasures. Lessons learned from previous mistakes are taken into consideration when designing new countermeasures.

Information Technology Security Evaluation Criteria

The Information Technology Security Evaluation Criteria (ITSEC) is a UK scheme in which security features of IT systems and products are tested independently of suppliers to identify logical vulnerabilities.
ITSEC defines the following security criteria:

- A security target and informal architectural design must be produced.
- An informal detailed design and test documentation must be produced.
- Source code or hardware drawings should be produced.
- A formal model of security and semiformal specification of security-enforcing functions, architecture, and detailed design should be produced.
- Architectural design explains the interrelationship between security-enforcing components.
- A formal description of the architecture and security-enforcing functions should be produced.

Questions Asked by the Certifier During the Certification and Accreditation Process

Authorizing officials must consider the suitable factors and decide to either permit or reject the risk to their respective agencies. The following are some of the questions asked during the certification and accreditation process:

- Are the security controls in the information system effective at maintaining the preferred level of protection?
- What actions have been planned to correct any deficiencies in the security controls for the information system?
- Could any of the modifications to the information system affect the existing, known vulnerabilities in the system?
- Have the resources needed to effectively complete the security certification and accreditation of the information system been recognized and allocated?
- To what extent are information system security controls implemented?

Chapter Summary

- Certifiers are responsible for conducting a comprehensive assessment of an information system.
- Accreditation represents official approval to operate an information system for a specific period of time.
- The certification process supports the risk management process in the information system's security program.
- Risk assessment policies and procedures reduce security risks to an acceptable level.

Review Questions

1. Explain certification and accreditation.

_____

_____

_____

_____

2. List the procedures for detecting and preventing unauthorized access.

_____

_____

_____

_____

3. List the guidelines for certification and accreditation.

_____

_____

_____

_____

4. What are the documents required to prepare certification and accreditation documentation?

_____

_____

_____

_____

5. Describe what happens during the initiation phase.

_____

_____

_____

_____

6. Describe the importance of the security certification phase.

_____

_____

_____

_____

7. What is the role of risk assessment in the certification and accreditation process?

_____

_____

_____

_____

8. Compare the different organizational certification and accreditation processes.

_____

_____

_____

_____

9. List the security policies and procedures implemented during the risk analysis and assessment process.

_____

_____

_____

_____

Hands-On Projects

1. Navigate to Chapter 9 of the Student Resource Center. Open Accreditation+guidelines.pdf. Read the following sections:

   ▪ Becoming Accredited

   ▪ Accreditation standards for all PCIA accredited programs

   ▪ Technical Accreditation Standards

2. Navigate to Chapter 9 of the Student Resource Center. Open taxonomy.pdf. Read the article.

3. Navigate to Chapter 9 of the Student Resource Center. Open CNSSP-6.pdf. Read the following sections:

   ▪ National Policy on Certification and Accreditation of National Security Systems

   ▪ Section II - Definitions

Index